WE SHALL MARCH AGAIN

Gerhard Kramer

WE SHALL MARCH AGAIN

Translated from the German by
ANTHONY G. POWELL

G. P. PUTNAM'S SONS

NEW YORK

TRANSLATOR'S NOTE

POSSIBLY out of a desire to preserve the "exclusive" character of the German officer corps, the armed forces of the Third Reich did not normally grant commissioned rank to specialists called up for auxiliary duties on wartime formation staffs. Men in this category received the temporary officer status of a *Sonderführer* (literally "special leader") and were always liable to be returned to the ranks when their particular qualifications were no longer required. A *Sonderführer* messed with the officers, was saluted by the non-commissioned ranks and wore officer's uniform with distinctive epaulettes. There were three grades—*Sonderführer B, Sonderführer K* and *Sonderführer Z,* equivalent to major, captain and lieutenant respectively.

This book is about a German who began the war as a *Sonderführer* because of his command of foreign languages but who subsequently reverted to the rank of private.

Part One

CHAPTER I

I T WAS the ground plan of a fortress in the Dutch frontier defenses around Amersfoort, cleanly executed in Indian ink. It showed the fire power and location of each firing point—a medium machine-gun here, a light one there. It showed the position of every rifleman and the layout of the magazine, ration depot and troops' sleeping quarters. It was all the handiwork of the Dutch agent V.27 —one of those people known in German military jargon as V-men. V.27 had also supplied the plan of a little town in the Grebbeberg area where an infantry regiment was stationed. It was a neat piece of fifth-column work showing not only the position and structure of the barracks and the distribution of the supplies, but even the billets of the officers from the commander on down. It told one, for example, that Second Lieutenant de Jong, a platoon commander, lodged with a widow called Classen at 4 Rheender Street and that his telephone number was 279.

Velten translated the accompanying Dutch text into German. He often got such jobs nowadays. A short time ago it had been an exact diagram of the telephone network in a Dutch frontier district, with explanatory notes couched in a wealth of technical detail. He had not found it easy to render the unfamiliar terminology.

"Do you still think we're going to leave Holland in peace?" he asked, tossing the drawing across the table to a squarely built man in his forties, who, wearing a pair of earphones, sat turning the knobs of an army radio set.

Ever since their appointment the two *Sonderführers* had been intrigued by the German high command's intense interest in the Dutch and Belgian defenses. It was the winter of 1939-40, and the adversaries of World War II still faced each other expectantly from

3

behind their own frontiers, crouching like mighty beasts of prey on opposite banks of the Rhine. Neither side made any move to attack, but watched unwaveringly for the merest hint of the other's intentions. It was war without bloodshed—a unique, phony war which the French, to reassure themselves, facetiously dubbed *une drôle de guerre*. Sandwiched between the static battle-fronts were the neutral states of Holland, Belgium and Luxemburg—the unknown quantity in an equation of hostile powers. Neutral territory had been suddenly overrun once before; and at the present time, as was abundantly clear from monitoring reports, the enemy was busy trying to guess whether German armies would again thrust westwards across the Rhine and the neutral countries beyond.

While Dr. Schwierig was wrinkling his brow over the sketch of the Dutch fortress instead of answering Velten's question, the latter reminded him with ill-concealed agitation of a whole series of things which had repeatedly struck them as peculiar. Hadn't they been cautioned to pay particular attention to the Belgian radio's daily forecasts of weather conditions and winter sports prospects in Ardennes resorts like St. Vith, Bastogne and Houffalize? What could all this possibly mean but invasion?

But Schwierig would admit nothing. A secondary-school teacher hailing from a small town in Brandenburg, he took his Government at its word. Had not the Führer pledged immediately after the outbreak of hostilities that "We shall naturally respect the neutrality of the small states in the West"?

"You know perfectly well," he said peevishly, "that we've just picked up news of British and French troop concentrations on the Belgian frontier. Even their railway engines were supposed to have steam up. Certainly everything's ready for an invasion—but from the other side!"

"Yes," Velten retorted, "but they don't happen to have marched in yet. And the reason they gave for their movements was news of *German* invasion preparations!"

"There," said Schwierig pedantically, "we have the German national vice—always allowing ourselves to be influenced by what other people are doing. We go on justifying their actions until we're swallowed up by our own objectivity."

He had switched on the large receiver, and as if to confirm his

4

words it blared forth a lively march and a chorus of lusty male voices:

> We'll hang out our washing on the Siegfried Line
> If the Siegfried Line's still there. . . .

Schwierig triumphantly bared his somewhat crooked teeth.

"Well," he inquired, "who built the Siegfried Line for the defense of Germany? And who wants to destroy it and hang their washing on it?"

"The BBC timed that to suit you just nicely," said Velten. "But I can't help it . . . If you're only supposed to be defending the *Westwall* you don't need to know all about roads and flood-lines in Belgium and Holland."

He lit a cigarette, got up and went to the window and stared pensively into the clear winter air outside.

"You're a member of the scholastic caste, Schwierig," he went on with a slight smile. "It may interest you to know what I learned in my history lessons in the sixth form at school . . . 'Make my right wing strong!' is what old Schlieffen is supposed to have said. According to my history tutor that meant the Kaiser's biggest mistake in 1914 was to treat only *Belgium's* neutrality as a scrap of paper! He ought to have gone through Holland too! Success would have justified him!

"And that is why," he added, pointing to the sketch of the Grebbeberg on the table, "our General finds the Dutch flood-lines so much more interesting than the whole of the Siegfried Line."

Schwierig snapped off the loudspeaker, and the strains of the Siegfried Line died away.

"If you'd only stop your everlasting political chatter!" he replied sharply. "Our job's to listen to the radio and do translations. I studied languages and I'm an interpreter. What's it got to do with me how the war is conducted?"

"Of course," Velten retorted violently, "our celebrated German specialist again! Proud to be able to put his knowledge at the State's disposal. Doesn't care a damn about the outcome!"

"You don't do anything more about it yourself, Velten, however much you belly-ache. We're all doing our duty, after all. Where we're told to do it."

5

Velten was spared a reply. There was a sharp knock at the door of the ground-floor room in the small requisitioned villa where they worked, and the burly figure of Padre Bemmel ambled in. He was a frequent guest of the interpreters. Since the genuine military types on the staff did not take their intellectual complement entirely seriously, a spontaneous association had developed among those fulfilling the less soldierly functions.

Bemmel was a clergyman who took a sympathetic interest in every aspect of temporal life. He was a robust, vital man whose Saxon intonation and lively disposition made him not unlike his historic exemplar Martin Luther. He, too, was a great preacher. With uncommon courage and something more than discreet innuendos he would attack everything in Wehrmacht and State which incurred his displeasure. Whenever he was in the pulpit his little church was packed to the last seat. "They like to hear me slate the Nazis," he would say. "But I doubt whether they draw any practical conclusions."

Bemmel got a lot of fun out of the interpreters. At this very moment he was looking from one to the other with a quizzical smile: "I wonder what God was thinking of," he mused, "when he stuck three ill-assorted characters like you together?"

The interpreters were certainly a queer trio. Reliability and staunch respectability were the blond, thick-set Schwierig's most obvious attributes, though he was also notable for his perpetual willingness to submit to regimentation and a tendency to acknowledge anything simply because it existed.

Then there was Velten. Dark-haired, highly strung, quick and haphazard in his actions. Easily provoked and always ready to contradict. In the last analysis, however, he, too, was prepared to submit to the inevitable, even if he had mental reservations where others acquiesced. In such situations he benefited by his essentially technical approach to things—a faculty whose undoubted practical value still did not prevent him in his better moments from reproaching himself as a cynical opportunist.

The third element in this extraordinary mixture of personalities was Lieutenant Hagestein, an entirely uninhibited man who reached out to take life's pleasures as they came and remained quite unperturbed by the course of events or the problems of his time.

6

"Yes," Velten agreed as he locked up his papers in the desk, "we're a motley bunch. But Schwierig was just saying that we've one thing in common all the same—our devotion to duty."

"In which respect," Bemmel interjected ironically, "our Mr. Hagestein sets a particularly good example."

Velten took him up on the allusion. "How do you mean?" he inquired in mock surprise. "The Herr Oberleutnant was put in charge of the department by the head of GSI. After all, the responsibility must ultimately be borne by a military officer. . . ."

"And he's got so much responsibility to bear," Bemmel observed with relish, "that the two quasi-soldiers have to do all the duty between them . . . from 0001 to 2359 hours, in two shifts."

Velten was about to point out that this was not so, in view of the interval observed by all transmitters between two and six o'clock in the morning, when Schwierig sulkily asked what the padre meant by "quasi-soldiers," seeing that he himself had served in World War I. "Our old soldier Dr. Schwierig," Hagestein would say whenever he wanted to load him with any extra work.

"Quasi-soldier!" Velten laughed. "For Schwierig an insult, for me a flattering exaggeration! I'm a civilian disguised in field-gray. And that's what I shall stay—for the whole of this *drôle de guerre*."

"Fine sort of attitude," growled Schwierig, but Bemmel smiled to himself.

"It's even recognized by my superior officers," Velten retorted. "The Chief-of-Staff was recently gracious enough to draw me into conversation in the mess. And when I had sufficiently shocked him with my civilian views, he slapped his thigh and roared with laughter. 'Velten,' he said, 'I'd give a lot to see your memoirs—war reminiscences of a civilian in disguise!' "

Schwierig maintained an offended silence. He didn't like the Chief-of-Staff. When Schwierig, at the beginning of his attachment, had named his town of origin, his superior had laughed uproariously: "*Landsberg-on-Warthe*—what a hole! God, I wouldn't want to be buried there!" Schwierig regarded such belittlement of his native town as a personal affront.

"At all events the Chief is something of a character," said Velten. "I can form no opinion of the Army Group Commander. He seems to hover over everything like a demi-god. Even the highest staff officers get scared when they get too near him." He laughed. "The other day Major Wiesner from the transport section gave me a terrific bawling out for cutting in front of him to help the Chief into his overcoat. Not that I had any military ideas in my head when I did so. I just thought 'He's an old man—help him on with his coat.' "

"An old man!" said Bemmel, raising his index finger admonishingly. "A colonel-general of the Wehrmacht is never an old man, particularly when he commands an army group!"

"He can prove it first," said Velten disrespectfully. "The only people who impress me in the whole inflated set-up are those I can see doing something. You can count them on ten fingers. First the Chief. Then the G1 (Ops), Colonel Herder, and our G1 (I), Mattersen. And then the four or five officers each of these two has got round him. You can tell by the look of them that *they* work. When they open their mouths, something sensible comes out. The others are merely lightweights. They're only there to increase the splendor of a senior staff by their numbers and officiousness."

Velten scornfully puffed out his cheeks. "Only yesterday Lieutenant Bellman gave me some tips on military formalities. From captain upwards, he informed me, one addresses an officer in the third person . . . 'Has the Captain, would the Major' and so on."

"The Führer abolished all that long ago," Schwierig interrupted irritably.

"In that case, Schwierig," Velten laughed, "you'd better tell Bellmann. He's an inspector in the Ministry of Justice—an authority very close to the people! If he hears about that he'll soon have the whole headquarters addressing each other as 'Citizen.' "

Schwierig made no reply. Instead he shuffled his papers preparatory to monitoring the BBC's evening news bulletin. Velten put his coat on.

"I've never in my life owned a gun," he remarked as he put on his belt and pistol holster. "In spite of which they whisked me out of my lawyer's practice in Berlin and stuck me into this comic uniform. Just because they found my name on the court list of accredited interpreters."

Schwierig glanced up involuntarily: "Do you mean you weren't . . . ?"

8

"No," said Velten with a grimace, "I wasn't. Never worn a uniform in my life—brown, black or gray!"

He clattered to the door in his heavy shoes and turned towards the others. "It was only four weeks ago that I first heard the row my feet make with army shoes on. As I came out of the barracks where they'd disguised me in field-gray, the two sentries came to attention with a terrific crash when they spotted the silver clothes-line on my cap. I rocked right back on my heals—with fright!" He smiled maliciously, fully aware that Schwierig took a proud delight in accepting the troops' salutes. Bemmel grinned, but Schwierig's face was expressionless.

Velten decided he must soothe his colleague. "Don't upset yourself, Schwicrig," he said in a conciliatory tone, "it's just my bad luck to belong to the grumblers. I've been like that ever since the beginning of the Thousand-Year Reich. In my profession one sees too much of the other side of the medal. It's the same as with our padre there. When I think that nowadays I'm not only permitted to listen to foreign stations but actually have to! And the poor devils I defended for doing the same thing got at least three or four years' hard labor. . . ."

The look he gave Bemmel carried a mock threat, for he knew that the padre had only come to hear what Schwierig monitored. "Doing that without official approval," was his parting shot, "can cost you five years and an ignominious discharge."

CHAPTER II

"TELL ME, Count," said Velten to the tall major wearing the Iron Cross of World War I, "do you really have to be back in uniform at your age and"—pointing to his stiff right arm—"with that trouble?" The two of them were sitting on the terrace of the Rhine Hotel, which Army Group Headquarters used as an officers' mess. It was the biggest building in the locality, though that occupied by the Commander-in-Chief was more famous. In the days when Adolf Schicklgruber had still seemed capable of European statesmanship it had served him as a headquarters for his negotiations with the tired old gentleman of umbrella fame who came over daily on the ferry from the suburb on the opposite side of the Rhine. The other bank was visible from the glass-covered terrace of their hotel, and above the little town they could see the hill with the castle on top. The Rhine was free of ice again, and a motor-barge chugged northwards on the tide, the red, white and blue colors of the Netherlands fluttering from its stern.

Instead of answering Velten's question, the major pointed to the craft. "I don't suppose the old *Geusen* flag will be seen in these parts much longer."

"The *Geusen* flag was slightly different," Velten remarked. "It was *orange,* white and blue. As orange as hell-fire, the papists used to say when they cursed the Prince of Orange. Or blue as the eyes of a Flanders maid, as the *Geusen* put it when they saw the tricolor flying from the masts of their privateers . . . That war lasted eighty years. They were quite different men then from the comfortable mijnheers of today. I wonder whether *they* could resist Adolf for eighty years?"

"Perhaps, if he lasts that long."

The two men so entirely different in character and outlook—one a grand seigneur from east of the Elbe who ranked as uncrowned king of the district where his estates lay, and the other a Berlin lawyer—had become acquainted through a trial. The same event was the source of their mutual regard and the trust which allowed them to speak openly to one another in spite of the difference in rank.

When National Socialism took over in 1933, all hell had broken loose in the rural district where the Count resided. *Kreisleiter* Fritze, the local Nazi leader, had tyrannized the entire area. He had mobilized the Brownshirts against the so-called unreliables. There had been boycotts, blackmailing threats and nocturnal raids. Eventually, at the Count's instigation, the most harassed elements of the population had resorted to a somewhat reprehensible solution: with a view to reducing the visitations and financial victimization to a bearable minimum, they had floated a fund to which every land-

10

owner had to contribute according to his means. The trustee was a gentleman-farmer called Wohle, and it was his job to receive the *Kreisleiter's* demands and beat him down to the best of his ability. As a result, private individuals were left in peace and Fritze obtained the requisite funds for his luxurious existence. "Regulated corruption" had been Velten's ironic definition of the arrangement. When the District Leader's turbulent mode of life finally prompted the public prosecutor to intervene, the whole story came to light— the extravagant orgies of eating and drinking, the hush-money paid out to rape victims, the honoraria for illegal operations, and similar scandals. The Wohle fund was discovered to be the source of the money. What the State now needed was a smart prosecutor who, by putting Wohle in the dock, could obliterate the Party's disgrace and simultaneously show up the reactionary landowning class in a bad light. It was impossible to implicate him in any of Fritze's infamous doings, as he had obviously had no idea to what use the money was put. A charge of bribery was no good either because District Leader Fritze was not a member of the civil service. At length they found a way. Had not the treasurer of the NSDAP, Schwarz, forbidden Party branches to open "black" accounts? Any money Fritze accepted from Wohle automatically belonged to the Party, and when Fritze drank, feasted and whored it away he had been guilty of defrauding the Party. By supplying the money, Wohle had been guilty of aiding and abetting.

Wohle duly found himself in court with Fritze. The latter got several years' penal servitude. Wohle, who did not belong to the Party and could hardly be expected to know its internal rules, was given a prison sentence. The Supreme Court annulled this impossible verdict, and in the subsequent retrial at the assizes, at which Fritze, his sentence already confirmed, appeared shaven-headed in the unbecoming black attire of a convict, Velten finally succeeded in getting Wohle acquitted. That was how Velten came into contact with a branch of society hitherto outside his circle. At the solemn celebration held after the acquittal he quoted from Heine, permitting himself a somewhat drastic amendment:

> You seldom understood my folk
> And I seldom understood yours:

11

> Only when (brown) mire engulfed us both
> Did our two worlds join hands.

"Yes," said the Major in reply to Velten's question, "Wohle's back with his cavalry regiment as a captain."

Other officers had joined them in the meantime. Thanks to a well-cut uniform, Velten had become fully acceptable in an officers' mess, despite his "narrow gauge" *Sonderführer's* epaulettes. The fact that he sat with the Count at meals seemed to have completely secured his social status.

The face of one Capt. Norden, who had only recently attained the scarlet trouser-stripes of the General Staff, was crimson with indignation as he told of an affair particularly repugnant to him as a pastor's son. The Reichsführer SS, Heinrich Himmler, had issued an edict reminding all members of the Black Guard of their duty to compensate, regardless of obsolete bourgeois conceptions of morality, for the biological gaps likely to be caused by the war. The whole document had read like a summons to the racially pure men of the SS to commit adultery with the wives of men in the field.

"It makes one damn sick!" Norden exclaimed. "We're expected to send men to their death when back at home a pack of pig-dogs are being set on their wives."

"Perhaps dying's easier when you know your family's going to the dogs," remarked Capt. von Schlichten of GSI(b), a quiet man who read Rilke and Baudelaire.

"Oh rot!" interjected Baron von Genzfeld. "It's just that we're too darned slack. After all, *we* hold the cards. *We* control the weapons."

This was the signal for yet another of those conversations which had been taking place for some years now whenever men with a little imagination and intelligence fell into talking about the state of the country—the lawlessness and lack of freedom, the domination by all that was vulgar and mean. And then this war. Irresponsibly unleashed and inadequately prepared. Ration cards a whole week before it broke out. U-boat production not properly started. Admittedly the Luftwaffe was said to be all right, but where was the gasoline to come from? And all the other urgently needed raw materials? Then there was the spiritual condition of the country. Thousands upon thousands in the concentration camps. The State in conflict with the Church.

12

"Can one possibly fight a war after the confusion of a revolution like that?" asked Norden.

"Of course you can," Schlichten told him. "The French won all their invasion campaigns after *their* Revolution and finally conquered Europe. The Russians fought victoriously against the Entente and the Poles."

At last Velten became provocative. "You must explain one thing to me, gentlemen," he said, glancing round the circle of faces. "All of you are against it. You know how unjust this war is and with what questionable methods and bad faith it was brought about. You stress how badly prepared it was and what dangers it brings. Why don't you actually do something? You, who have all the cards in your hands, as somebody said a few minutes ago?"

Glances of astonishment were cast in his direction. The silence was embarrassing.

"My dear sir," said Genzfeld at length, the very form of address emphasizing the gap he felt between himself and the non-soldier, "four generations of my family have been soldiers in the service of Prussia. I have sworn an oath."

Just when the assembled company had agreed that, since there happened to be a war on, everyone had to do his duty, damn it, an orderly appeared to inform the Count that the General wished to speak to him. The others enlightened Velten: "There's something up. We're shifting to Düsseldorf tomorrow."

CHAPTER III

MEANWHILE the preparations for the big push had made further headway. It was no longer a secret at Army Group Headquarters that the Low Countries were to be overrun. Major Mattersen, the G1(I), had been to Holland several times in civilian clothes to issue instructions to agents in Venlo and already boasted how smoothly things were working out.

A new officer, 2nd-Lieut. Waldmann, had recently joined the staff. Velten's instincts told him the other was genuine, and a cordial friendship swiftly developed between the two men. Waldmann had been commissioned in the Great War and, in addition to the Iron Cross First and Second Class, held a high decoration for outstanding bravery awarded by one of the smaller German principalities. He was now in his middle forties. A child of the Rhineland and a wine merchant by trade, he had lived in Holland for seventeen years and, like Velten, spoke Dutch just as well as his mother tongue. He was at present working under the AQMG and had been sent to study the work of the headquarters' interpreters for a few days. Shortly afterwards he approached Velten with a request.

"Look, Velten," he said in the guttural language of Germany's little neighbor, a tongue in which they were wont to converse because of its cosy associations, "I need your help. I've got to examine about eighty interpreters in Dutch."

"What," Velten exclaimed, "eighty? What's all that in aid of?"

"It means," Waldmann replied, "that they are to be assigned to town major's offices. Hilversum and Enschede. And Doetinghem and Soesdijk and everywhere else where there's a Dutch teapot on the stove and a cauldron of pea soup and pork simmering on the fire." He sighed. "God save our poor old Holland when the locusts are let loose on her."

From then on things moved rapidly. On April 9th Norway's and Denmark's turn came. The operation had been kept so dark that not even the General or the Chief-of-Staff had previous knowledge of it.

On the eve of May 10th Waldmann was duty officer. At nine o'clock in the evening the G1(Ops) looked in to tell him to keep his wits about him in case of "anything special." One hour later it was the Chief-of-Staff: "Ring me up if anything happens." At about two in the morning the General appeared in person. "Waldmann," he said, "I want particular vigilance tonight. Put a call straight through to my quarters if there's any unusual occurrence." My God, the balloon's going up, thought Waldmann, putting his head in his hands. It was the very first time the Chief had ever shown himself to a duty officer.

At four in the morning the skies were black with aircraft. The

14

droning of their engines enveloped the Rhineland town in a blanket of sound. A hail of bombs annihilated the troop concentrations on the Franco-Belgian frontier and the airfields in France, Belgium and Holland, as the Stukas came howling down at them. Enormous bird-like shapes floated into view over the Belgian frontier fortifications along the Albert Canal—gliders which, having been uncoupled from their parent aircraft far out of hearing of the frontier posts, slid gently to earth beside the concrete emplacements. They disgorged crews of men who, trained for months in sealed camps, now crawled up to fortresses of which enterprising spies in the Belgian Defence Ministry had long ago purloined the plans. They pushed Bangalore torpedoes into the embrasures and their flame-throwers hissed viciously with long, white-hot jets. In next to no time Fort Eben Emaël, the pride of Belgium's defense system, had been smoked out.

In the interior of Holland paratroopers fell on Rotterdam, Arnhem and Nijmegen. Taken unawares, the Netherlanders opened their dikes and sluices to inundate Groningen and Drenthe. But though massed armor bore the assault forward in other frontier regions, a prescient planning staff had made due allowance for the Dutch flood-lines, and a cavalry division from Oldenburg duly moved into the affected area. Where tanks and self-propelled guns would have been bound to fail in the knee-deep mud and water, horseflesh was eminently successful.

A kind of frenzy seized everyone in any way connected with the operations. Every member of the headquarters was imbued with a sense of relief now that the tension was over, happy to see the war machine finally in operation after being held in readiness for so long. And how well it operated! What certainties of further victories these first successes created!

A few days after the start of the offensive Velten was ordered to go as the mess officer's interpreter on a trip into newly occupied territory. Just as Quickloot and Grabber in Goethe's *Faust* follow in the footsteps of the war-lord to get their greedy claws on enemy possessions, so now did a corps of administrative units, foragers and "procurement men" move in behind the German armies. The troops began to live from the land even before the country was fully occupied. The headquarters paymaster had a copious supply of the

15

newly printed scrip on a par with the currency of the conquered country. So when 2nd-Lieut. Schloyka, the mess officer, drew out sufficient to cover his purchases, Velten, too, converted a portion of his cash.

When their open touring car drew up at the Dutch-German frontier somewhere near Venlo, they found the road barred by a turnpike just as in the most balmy days of peace. But German soldiers and customs officials watched over it; and on the other side the Dutch frontier guards were missing. The countryside lay at peace in the sunlight, the lush green of the meadows, alternating with the silvery gray of the cornfields. The houses in the villages and hamlets through which they passed shone prosperously in the cleanliness of their neat red bricks and white window-frames. Except for an occasional road-block one could drive unimpeded along the smooth well-kept highways of this rich little country. Only columns of prisoners slowed them down from time to time—tired, listless men in Belgian and French uniforms. Dutch prisoners were less frequently encountered, having already been marshaled on municipal sports grounds behind hastily erected barbed-wire entanglements. In the first flush of victory they were being magnanimously treated. Before long they were to regain full liberty.

Schloyka, who had already been in Holland the day before, was telling Velten of the treats to come at a café in the town where he had to make purchases for the mess kitchen.

They were not disappointed. If one ignored the slight restlessness of a people usually so stolid, there was an entirely peace-time atmosphere about the little place. All the businesses and shops were open, and German soldiers and Dutch civilians mingled indiscriminately. When they sat down on the sunny terrace of the café and Schloyka ordered *Bohnenkaffee,* the waiter grinned and inquired what other kind of coffee they imagined there was. During the first months of the war it was not easy to make the citizens of this prosperous colonial power understand that in a country where the slogan "Guns instead of Butter" was a mark of heroism rather than an imposition, the word coffee could signify a brew of malt and dried turnips.

As they walked through the town after their sumptuous repast, Velten noticed how Dutch women watched the German soldiers buying half a dozen or a dozen pairs of artificial silk stockings at a

16

time, as well as shirts, neckties and underclothing. "They're hoarding, you know, hoarding!" he heard them whisper to each other excitedly.

Shortly afterwards Velten found himself in the narrow office of the wholesale dealer on whom they had called to buy coffee and cocoa at 80 cents per kilo. The sacks and cartons were already being loaded into the car outside. The dealer was a well-fed man with a thick gold watch-chain across his comfortable paunch. When Velten, having calculated what he owed in marks at the official rate of exchange, laid a roll of German scrip on the table, the Dutchman gazed at the notes in astonishment and suspicion.

"What's the matter with you," said Velten, "that's good money. If we win the war, you'll be glad to have it. And," he added hesitatingly, "if we lose, we shall still have to pay up." At that a broad smile spread over the man's round face. "If you poor devils lose this war," he said good-naturedly in his heavy Limburg dialect, "I don't believe you'll be able to pay a single pfennig." Then he pocketed the notes without counting them and gave Velten the change in clinking silver guilders and those dainty little ten-cent pieces called *dubbeltjes* which are also made of silver.

Velten lost no time in leaving.

CHAPTER IV

THE WAR went on. In their hectic pursuit of information about the enemy Velten and Schwierig hardly found time to taste the unusual fascination of being able to observe and check the movements of their own armies in the mirror of the other side's radio transmissions. The element of surprise in the Germans' strategy proved momentous. Like Velten's history teacher, the enemy had based his counter-measures on the traditional strategic theory that the Germans would deliver their main thrust on the right wing, particularly

17

as the marvel of the Maginot fortifications seemed to render any possibility of an attack in the south illusory. Counting on this appreciation, the German military command had planned precisely the opposite and, what was more, had succeeded in keeping its preparations secret. In reality it was not the right wing which delivered the main punch. Only twenty-eight divisions attacked in Army Group B's sector in Holland and Belgium, whereas Army Group A, which was storming through undefended Luxemburg farther to the south, had a strength of forty-four divisions and was able to force a break-through between Mézières and Sedan.

Only a few days before, the English radio had reported on the morale of the Parisians. In the silvery, mellow light of Paris in springtime, a commentator had declared, people were sitting in front of their cafés and restaurants and viewing the future with equanimity, so confident were they in their Government and the protection of the Maginot Line. Now, in contrast to this, panic and dismay seemed to reign. The streets were jammed with the cars of fleeing inhabitants, and the stations serving rail traffic to the south and west, the Gare de Lyon and the Gare d'Orléans, were besieged with refugees. Things were now moving so fast that German information staffs were hardly able to keep up with the battle. Holland was already completely in German hands. Soon after the Queen's departure by ship the capitulation had been declared.

Velten's staff had been transferred to Brussels. The headquarters' vehicles drove along the main city axis to the railway station and, swinging into the boulevard Adolphe Max, pulled up on the place Brouckère facing the high gray façade of the Hôtel Métropole. The familiar double guard was already standing with sloped arms outside the constantly revolving door of the entrance lobby.

The Belgian hotel staff had been left in their jobs and were now working alongside German orderlies and quartering officers behind the long reception desk in the big foyer.

Army Group Headquarters had requisitioned this big luxury hotel both as living accommodation and offices. Hagestein, Velten and Schwierig each had a room with a bath, and for their office a room with an additional bathroom leading off it. Radio monitoring was once again their most important function. Their main commitment consisted in looking for signs of fatigue at the enemy's weakest point

—the sector occupied by the Belgian Army—now that Holland had collapsed and the French front was penetrated. As Hagestein's availability for duty was being taxed even more heavily than usual by the diversions of the Belgian capital, Velten and Schwierig were compelled to divide up the shifts between them and resist their own urge to join in the rapidly blossoming life around them. Nevertheless, Velten cashed in unblushingly on the zeal and conscientiousness of his colleague Schwierig.

Brussels was a tempting sight. Its shops and big stores were stacked full of goods. The newspapers published under the supervision of propaganda officers made a particular point of noting the good behavior of the troops, who shopped on a grand scale and paid in cash. The restaurants had re-opened. In the night-club district and the porte de Namur the snug little bars and discreetly luxurious hotels with their *chambres à l'heure* plied a busy trade. The fascination of the foreign male was already having its effect, and it was not only girls of easy virtue who found their way to a field-gray breast.

During this phase of the war Velten felt like a tourist traveling abroad at the State's expense. He obtained an advance from the paymaster and, feeling he would enjoy himself better when free of the constraint of uniform, acquired a blue civilian suit from a shop in the rue Neuve. As no one could leave the hotel in civilian clothes, he had to hide it in a suitcase and spend his leisure hours wandering through the busy streets and enjoying the absurd but delightful sensation of being one of the victors in a conquered land . . . All were drunk with the success from which further successes spring.

Already a fresh stroke was pending. The army commanded by the King of the Belgians was finding it increasingly difficult to withstand the pressure on its flanks. There could be no question of effective relief, and at the enemy's General Headquarters there was whispered talk of sacrificing Belgium's forces to gain time to establish a new front. Would the King sacrifice his army and allow it to be pounded into annihilation, or would he capitulate? Though the tough, self-sacrificing resistance of the Belgian troops still held the front together, events were bound to take a decisive turn at almost any moment now.

*   *   *

19

One Sunday afternoon Jacqueline Bevermans sprang out of bed in a room of the Hôtel Royal du Nord, jarred into wakefulness by the din outside. Naked as God had made her and displaying all the sensuous splendor of her twenty-five years, she gazed through the slits of the Venetian blind at the strange drama being enacted in the sunlit street below. Belgian troops—a clattering, hooting procession of tanks, artillery, trucks, cars and motorcycles—were moving in impeccable order along the broad avenue, escorted by German military police. The clamor of the thousands of Belgian civilians who had packed the pavements to see their troops march into captivity heightened the uproar. Something had happened— something which made her bowels contract and tears well up in her eyes. Without so much as a glance at the man who, naked like herself, lay stretched on the bed, she snatched up her scattered clothes and dressed at lightning speed. "Let me go!" she gasped, evading the arms which sought to stop her. She wanted to go somewhere where she could cry her eyes out. Not even deigning to look at him, she disappeared without a word and rushed wildly downstairs to run the gauntlet of the soldiers standing around in the hall below. In another instant she was lost to sight in the crowd.

With an air of consternation Lieut. Merrem of the Signal Corps put on his uniform and awkwardly descended the stairs. Outside, his eyes were stung by the dazzling glare of the afternoon sun. He found difficulty in making his way through the crowd, and waited some time before he was able to get into the Boulevard Adolphe Max through a gap in the endless stream of prisoners.

On entering the Rôtisserie Ardennaise, he found Velten and Bemmel taking an *apéritif* at one of the tables. He dropped heavily into the third chair and ordered a vermouth and soda.

"Well, and who spit in your soup on this wonderful day of triumph?" asked Bemmel.

"She was such a nice girl," Merrem replied sadly in his friendly Rhineland dialect.

He had met her in a shop a few days before, it appeared. She had taken him round the city and shown him the Grand Place, the Manneken Pis and the Edith Cavell memorial. They had been to the market and seen the fat, slovenly basket-women hawking their wares in their extraordinary-sounding French. They had talked about each other—she of her dreary life with a morose and ageing father. Her mother had died young leaving her no brothers or sisters. Some unhappy love affair, of which she had said very little, seemed to darken her past. Despite their caution they had soon fallen in love, and he found it quite natural that she should have given in to his pleas and followed him to the hotel.

"And now she has got a particularly dangerous kind of hang-over," said Velten. "Not just the ordinary moral one, but the special patriotic variety. And it's particularly violent in this case because it doesn't come from national exultation but from the despair of defeat."

"Professionally speaking," Bemmel added, rubbing his hands together and smiling, "I can only feel gratified at your return from the path of sin, my son!"

"And if you hadn't shown such unconscionable perseverance in skipping your duties," Velten went on, "you would already have known that the King of the Belgians has capitulated. The front's being cleared at this very moment. I don't suppose," he added with a regretful glance at the sumptuous cold buffet in the background, "that we shall be here much longer."

The news made little impression on Merrem in his self-pity. "I can't understand it," he grumbled, "she always talked about her hair being cut off and being made to stand naked on the Place de la Bourse if we ever got pushed out of here as we were in 1918. I can't see what she's got to worry about now the Belgians are capitulating."

"God bless my soul," snapped Bemmel, rapping sharply on the table. "It's about time you stopped your grizzling. And now"—turning to Velten—"perhaps you'll order something appetizing and let us celebrate the victory."

"And while doing so," laughed Velten, "we'll leave it undecided whether we are celebrating the victory over feminine sensuality or the one over the King of the Belgians."

He beckoned to the *maître d'hôtel,* with whom he proceeded to have a brief but pregnant discussion. They were served with canta-loups into whose hollow centers they poured heavy port. Then came fat Roman snails, braised in deliciously fresh butter and served with finely chopped herbs and a suggestion of garlic. With this they

21

drank a pale Meursault of the most delicate sweetness. As the *pièce de résistance* they had the inevitable Brussels *poularde* and the delicious fresh vegetables of the country.

By the time they reached the cheese course Merrem had forgotten his troubles. When he ordered the second Armagnac with his coffee, he was already laughing at Velten's description of the inimitable skill with which Belgian troops had been easing their way out of the marching columns of prisoners. Once among their compatriots on the pavements, they had thrown away their caps, taken off their uniforms and disappeared through the front doors of the houses. "At any rate there'll be plenty of parties in Brussels this evening to which our padre can't possibly object," Velten observed with a smile.

When they went out into the street just before curfew and turned in the direction of the place Brouckère, the boulevards were still full of excited crowds. Just outside the Hôtel Plaza the cheery wine-bibbing face of Waldmann bobbed up in front of them. He had come over from Holland to find accommodation for the staff of the general who was to take over as Military Governor of Belgium. The job in Holland was finished, he told them. A civil administration was being set up. When decreeing this, the Führer had had a particular brain wave: In grateful memory of the Dutch relief to the starving children of Vienna after the Great War he had decided that the administration of Holland should have an Austrian flavor. A Viennese had already been appointed Reichskommissar. "A somewhat novel form of expressing his thanks," remarked Waldmann.

"Let us hope," added Bemmel, "that it doesn't turn out to be the thanks of the House of Hapsburg."

When Velten tried to order an egg for breakfast some days later, the mess waiter informed him that there were no more to be had. "What's wrong?" Velten asked his neighbor. "Don't tell me we've got to put on another act of Prussian frugality for the benefit of a visiting brass-hat!"

When the headquarters had moved into Brussels the mess had taken a turn for the better. A French chef had been immediately engaged, and thanks to his skill the monotonous, inadequate meals

22

had given way to a variety of choice dishes. The waiter explained that the ban on one egg for breakfast had been issued, without any obvious reason, by the Army Group Commander himself, who was reported to take the view that his headquarters staff was beginning to live too well.

"He's in a bad mood," said Schlichten, who was sitting opposite. "The King of the Belgians is to blame."

"How's that?" asked Velten, "He's nowhere near here." It was known that the captive King was in Bruges and had been bitterly resisting all attempts to make him return to the capital.

"The General is in an absolutely vile temper," Schlichten explained, "and he's venting it on us. To begin with, the King didn't offer him his hand when the General went to see him in Bruges, and behaved very condescendingly all round. Then he stepped badly on the General's corns by refusing to accept his brother, Colonel von Stumm, as a personal aide. He sent him straight back with a message that he had no use for an officer who didn't speak French."

"As a result of which," Velten observed, "we have no eggs for breakfast. World History seen in kitchen-boy perspective."

Meanwhile the Battle of Flanders and Artois—to quote the official name given to it in the war diaries—was drawing to a close. The news that German armor had reached Abbeville on the Somme estuary meant that the Anglo-French forces in the north were surrounded. It meant, too, that for both friend and foe the name Dunkirk was soon to become a symbol of fateful decision.

One night Major Mattersen sent for Velten. An indefatigable worker, he was sitting behind an ostentatious imitation of a Renaissance writing-desk piled high with plans, maps and order-of-battle schedules.

"Now I want you comical half-soldiers to get on your toes," he said. "They're getting ready to embark off the Dunkirk beaches and one of them may spill something over the air. God," he went on, his wide-awake little eyes gleaming at the thought, "what a thing it would be if they cleared out now and we could get straight across behind them! You know yourself what bad shape they're in over there. They've got nothing more than a few rusty cannon, and their Home Guard's practicing with broomsticks. If we put all our weight

23

in at one go, we ought to get into the ports. No Home Fleet would be any help to them then. Velten, you could be Gauleiter of England the day after tomorrow!"

Velten modestly suggested that the Führer probably had worthier men in mind for so elevated a post, and reminded the major that an economic staff for England was already being set up under a colonel from the War Ministry. Then he returned to the office to put Schwierig in the picture, since it was quite possible that news of the start of the British embarkation would filter over some neutral transmitter. Very soon they picked up the report of a speech by the British Prime Minister in the House of Commons. He had appeared on behalf of H.M. Government to inform Parliament of the hazardous situation which had developed. His pronouncement had carried a grim foreboding of disaster yet to be told, for he had asked the House not to insist on a Governmental statement that day. One could clearly imagine that massive bulldog skull sinking down between his shoulders and the thick lower lip jutting forth when he added the fateful words: "Meanwhile the House may prepare itself for hard and heavy tidings!"

Only a few days after that the Battle of Dunkirk had already become history. The man responsible for British war policy announced the defeat with pitiless candor and warned the nation of the blood, sweat and tears to come. Though the British Expeditionary Force had managed to escape, all equipment down to the last button had had to be sacrificed, and the Dunkirk beaches were now littered with weapons and material of every conceivable description. Immediately after the battle German technical units got down to the job of sifting all this booty, which was of incalculable value.

But one thing had failed to materialize—the landing in England. Germany had missed a unique opportunity of overrunning the unarmed country at a time when its own troops were streaming back in confusion. A mischievous utterance by the Chief-of-Staff went the round of Army Group Headquarters:

"Dunkirk was the Battle of the Marne of the Second World War."

CHAPTER V

THE HEADQUARTERS' vehicles were drawn up on the place Brouckère ready to leave for the new location. There was talk of Army Group Headquarters being nearer the front this time—only a few kilometers behind the Somme. The General commanding one of the armies in the Group had recently moved close up to the front line; and because of some longstanding petty jealousy the Commander-in-Chief had resolved, if possible, to go one better than his rival.

Once again the move was made in small columns of at most seven vehicles. Only one of the officers in the front car knew their destination. The journey took them through the valley of the Senne, past the dusty, smoky city of Mons into the Borinage—that dirty, wretched coal-mining area on which Vincent van Gogh had once turned his back to seek the brilliant light of Arles.

The presence of war became gradually more apparent as they drove through country on which it had left a sharper and more durable imprint. No longer did one see merely the fleeting hoof-marks of the Riders of the Apocalypse: here war in its full fury had eaten into the landscape like a corrosive acid, leaving their route marked with festering sores and open wounds. While the villages on the Belgian side of the frontier were still—or once again—passably populated, those in France were without exception empty and dead.

Two endless streams of traffic surged towards each other along the dead-straight, poplar-lined highway. The one coming from the front moved in a deafening roar of tanks, guns, empty munition trucks and heavily laden ambulances. The other, of which they were part, was made up of supplies and reinforcements. Above all the din and bustle stretched the steel-blue dome of a glaring sky whose blazing sun drowned everything below in an unbearable heat. Everyone suffered in that scorching glow—attacker no less than defender,

25

but worst of all the legions of refugees. Men and women dragged themselves forward with their last reserves of strength, clinging to one another for support. Others lay motionless in the ditches or fields—asleep, unconscious or dead.

Shortly afterwards they turned off the main road into a lane. It led to a village over the roofs of which rose the ramparted towers of a château: Havrincourt, their new headquarters.

The château was a monstrosity in imitation Tudor, with an incredible number of turrets and chimneys decorating its roof. It was built entirely of red brick, and the mortar in between showed up just as white as the wood of the window-frames. The total effect was utterly prosaic, as if the place had been prefabricated. For that matter, the whole village made the same impression—mass-produced, cheerless and completely lacking in human warmth.

Subsequent conversations with the villagers confirmed that the Great War had laid the whole locality, including the church and château, in rubble and ashes. Even the trees in the park and the orchards had been destroyed by the time the German retreat started. Several years had passed before the village, château, church and park were restored, and now they stood self-conscious and forlorn amid the bare and unattractive landscape.

Shortly afterwards Hagestein reappeared in boisterous mood. He had found them good quarters with office accommodation attached. Old soldiers always believed in keeping as far away from trouble as possible when in enemy country, he said, and in their case this meant getting as far away as they could from the watchful eye of authority. He had therefore made a point of convincing Major Mattersen that his interpreters should in no circumstances be accommodated in the château, since the noise of their monitoring sets would disturb the work of the operations staff. They were to draw their rations independently, too. Everybody else would be supplied by the field kitchen of the headquarters' defense company. "That does not mean," said their organizing genius with a knowing smile, "that we need yearn for the fleshpots of Brussels. You gentlemen will understand that I shall be less concerned with operational matters than with procuring those commodities necessary for the maintenance of our fighting spirit."

"I never doubted for one moment that you would again take the heaviest burden on your own shoulders," said Velten, giving Schwierig a discreet nudge.

"My young friend," Hagestein grinned, "I shall give every satisfaction. Just watch me produce the goods."

The house which was to be their home for the immediate future lay in the middle of the village and had clearly come through the first world conflagration intact. Instead of being tediously new it was, to the opposite degree, tediously old. It must have been built about 1880, probably on the site of some earlier war ruin. Though the plaster of the façade was gray with age and damaged in a number of places, the building as a whole conveyed a certain impression of stiff bourgeois prosperity.

On the wooden door of the courtyard Hagestein had chalked AG/GSI/INTERP. in large letters, and underneath "Hagestein, Lieut." That secured the billet for them. The house had doors opening off both sides of its gloomy hall, and as they entered the farthest on the right opened.

"Look," Velten exclaimed in some surprise, "the place is occupied."

"Obviously," said Hagestein indulgently. "The only kind of place I move into is one where there's a housewife to look after me."

A simply dressed woman of about thirty appeared, faded and toil-worn as working-class women of every nation tend to be by that age. Hagestein introduced the newcomers, and as he did so Velten realized with a smile that in the few short hours this skilled psychologist had spent in the house a bond of trust had sprung up between the two.

Mme Delgastre was not the owner of the house, as she herself was at pains to point out. It belonged to Mme Picot, whose late husband had been a tenant of the present owner of the château and estate. Like the marquis, she had chosen to go south when the invaders had approached, taking care to place the house in Mme Delgastre's charge before leaving. The gravity of her task prompted Mme Delgastre to inform them, half-pleadingly and half-threateningly, that she was responsible for seeing that nothing got disturbed or lost. Her husband was a cobbler and they had closed down the shop when he was called up. He was in the Maginot Line and now —Mme Delgastre pursed her lips at this juncture—no further news could be expected from him. "Even the Maginot Line was no help," she complained, "when you came round from the side."

However, she was once again politeness itself when a shy little girl of about nine appeared to be presented as Adrienne, her elder daughter. Adrienne was induced to shake hands with Velten and Schwierig and say "Bonjour, M'sieur" with a dainty curtsy.

"We'd better introduce the whole family while we're about it," said Hagestein jovially and pushed open the kitchen door. Crawling around on the floor was a plump one-year-old infant who showed two rosy little buttocks as she bent down. There was something blissfully familiar about little Angèle's species of griminess, in contrast to which the elder child was scrubbed so clean that one could smell the carbolic soap.

Apart from Angèle there was a crone of great age squatting by the range. They were unable to discover whether she was Mme Delgastre's mother-in-law or her mother-in-law's mother—her grandmother-in-law, as it were. She told them she had repeatedly had the pleasure of company from the other side of the Rhine—the first time as quite a little girl and the second as a very much older woman. When imparting this information she closed one rheumy eye in an unpleasant wink and grinningly bared the yellowed front tooth which bored into her flabby lower lip.

Velten and Schwierig were kept more than busy in the days that followed, for Hagestein, true to his promise, drove out into the countryside every morning. He always brought back a large supply of provisions, and no one ever inquired after their origin. To Mme Delgastre's delight he never failed to deposit something or other in the cellar of the house—a few sacks of potatoes, vegetables, cereals or sugar. They particularly appreciated the cases of fresh eggs he brought; and they got so many fresh vegetables to eat that they hardly needed to draw on the defense company. Mme Delgastre arranged their menu with a housewife's skill, ensuring at the same time that her own family did not go short.

One day Hagestein appeared with a car load of wines and liquor. It was a selection of the best varieties—red and white burgundy, bordeaux, champagne and an abundance of liqueurs. The news soon got around that the biggest and best choice of drinks was to be found at the "interpreters' bar," and many an officer—first and foremost the redoubtable Bemmel—became regular guests at the modest drinking parties which took place on moonlit nights in Mme Picot's garden.

But the interpreters worked hard, too, and occasionally at jobs which did not belong to their normal run of duties. One evening an orderly appeared with an enormous sack bearing a red, white and blue stripe and obviously weighing little despite its bulk. A covering note in Mattersen's almost illegible scribble told them it contained French army mail captured at Dunkirk which he required them to sort and report on.

"Hagestein'll have to do his share this time, though," Schwierig remarked, "if Mattersen's to get his report by tomorrow morning." Fortunately Hagestein was there, having nothing to "organize" for the moment, so all three of them got down to the job. At intervals one of them would break the silence to read out some particularly striking passage.

The letters afforded a dramatic insight into the state of mind of the enemy troops just before their embarkation and Dunkirk's capture by the Germans. The picture of demoralization they painted was startling. All told of the defenders' utter helplessness in the face of the German air attacks hammering unremittingly on the ruined town. They were living like rats in cellars and holes in the ground, they said, as there was no trace whatever of anti-aircraft defense. No one saw any chance of escaping from this hell.

"There you have it," said Hagestein, "air superiority is what does it. We lost the first war because the others were stronger in the air. We'll win the second because we're the masters."

There were letters from men who had learned to pray again. Letters begging parents, wives and children to forgive all the sorrow and wrong the writer felt he had inflicted on them. Farmer boys invoked the Mother of God and made vows of what they would do if ever released from this agony.

Schwierig burst out laughing. "There seem to have been a few Hagesteins among them," he said spitefully, and proceeded to read out a letter in which a soldier complained bitterly to his wife that there were people in this hell-on-earth who only thought of stuffing

29

their bellies and lining their pockets. Some of his comrades had been taking advantage of every pause between artillery bombardments and air attacks to crawl out of their slit trenches and ransack the abandoned houses for food and valuables. Though face to face with death and surrounded by piles of corpses which could not be buried, they were systematically equipping themselves for a life of plenty.

"Don't exaggerate too much with your comparisons," Hagestein told him. "In any case I'm glad to see there are cold-blooded men in every nation."

A letter written by a British soldier had strayed into the French mail. With all the cool composure of his insular temperament he informed his wife that he was already prepared for the worst, since it would be a rare stroke of luck if he and his comrades ever got aboard a ship. Unlike the French he made no mention of his discomforts and hardships. His only ambition, he added, was to enjoy a hot bath "and then lie with you in a soft white bed."

"That's a race for you," said Hagestein. "A thousand pities we have to fight on different sides." And he went on to tell of some British prisoners he had seen among a crowd of captured French, striding along like aristocrats beside the lamentable figures of their allies—heads high, eyes to the front and knapsacks slung over their shoulders. The German guards had looked like a herd of flunkeys trotting alongside.

"You mustn't forget," Velten interjected, "that the call-up groups the British have sent over are quite different from what the French can muster in this sector. What a lot of sorry-looking old men and half-trained boys we've seen among the French troops. The English, on the other hand, have sent a corps of young, sturdy, first-line soldiers across the Channel."

While they were discussing their evening's work and knocking out a report, Velten remarked that it was like groping around in the entrails of a wounded animal.

"The quarry's already killed," Hagestein told him. "France will never recover from this defeat. After the blood-letting of the first war they weren't ever in a position to oppose us. Now that the English have left them in the lurch they can only give in. France is finished."

30

In the meantime an incredible mass of reinforcements had rolled up to the front: day and night tanks, self-propelled guns and mobile infantry had been passing through the village. The enemy did not make the slightest attempt to interfere with the German build-up, and only slight air reconnaissance was reported. He seemed to be staring in fascination at the preparations for his own *coup de grâce,* just like a rabbit under the hypnotizing gaze of a snake.

Soon afterwards, in the upper reaches of the Somme around St. Quentin, the struggle broke loose which was to go down in history as the Battle of France. Borne on the clear summer air, the thunder of the artillery preparations and the Luftwaffe's hammer-blows on the enemy positions was clearly audible and told of the calamity to come. The women's lips went white and their eyes dark. The house took on an oppressive atmosphere which the three Germans could not fail to sense.

Consequently, when Bemmel came round early one morning to ask whether Velten would like to go on a trip up to the front, the latter was glad to accept. The Commander-in-Chief had given the padre permission to visit his son, who was serving in an infantry brigade in the Péronne area near to their own location. Bemmel had had no difficulty in finding this out, an obliging operations officer having made the necessary inquiries for him through Army, Corps and Division.

"I'm in a terrible state of mind," said Bemmel. "The kid's only nineteen and he's in action for the first time. I can't get rid of the feeling that something's happened to him. It's a horrible presentiment."

Velten got permission from Mattersen to accompany Bemmel. In the opinion of the G1(I) it could do a comic soldier-civilian like him no harm to smell a bit of powder. So off they went. As they drove out of Roye, the place near which young Bemmel's Battalion Headquarters was supposed to be, close-support aircraft passed overhead, flying west. The white blobs of shell-bursts could just be seen against the blue sky. The intermittent chatter of machine-guns reached their ears from the edge of a nearby wood. Bemmel's agitation increased. There was still no sign of German troops as they drove along the deserted highway. "There!" the driver cried at last, pointing to a track branching off towards the west. It led to a farm house nestling in a copse some two hundred yards from the main road. In front were a *Kübelwagen,* the German equivalent of the jeep, and a dispatch-rider leaning against his machine.

"All right!" Bemmel shouted. "That must be them!"

They turned off and drove across country to the farm. Under a great lime tree near the well two officers were sitting on canvas chairs at a table. Several soldiers squatted on the farmhouse steps in the background. By the wall of the courtyard a man was looking through a pair of periscopic field-glasses.

Bemmel got out and presented himself to the senior officer, a sun-tanned major in his thirties, and stated his request. The battalion commander looked up in astonishment and appraised his unusual visitor with angry eyes.

"You've got rather a nerve, haven't you?" he shouted hoarsely. "D'you think we're a rest-home? The new positions we took over this morning are only six hundred yards from here. We're attacking in two hours. I suppose you think you're going to take afternoon tea with your offspring? You'll get straight back, of course. This is no place for sight-seers."

Bemmel pulled out his passes, as well as a personal chit from the Army Group Commander. Shaking his head disapprovingly, the major consulted with his adjutant. Finally he asked: "What company is your son in?"

"Number four," Bemmel replied.

"I'd like to know what we have field post numbers for when fathers are so well informed about the order of battle! Your son is going to have a little trouble explaining that."

"But he was already in No. 4 Company of this battalion at the depot," Bemmel replied quietly. "I used to visit him there."

"All right," said the major, glancing covertly at the Chief's chit, "as far as I'm concerned you can see what they know at Company Headquarters. But you're not to go a step farther. I'll have a runner take you there with a note for the company commander."

He scribbled something on a pad, tore off the sheet and handed it to a heel-clicking soldier with instructions to guide the gentlemen from Army Group to Company Four's Headquarters. "You can take your vehicle as far as the bend in the track, but after that you must go on foot. And," he added with a fierce glare at Bemmel's

32

waistline, "I trust you'll have to crawl the last bit as you can be seen by the enemy from there."

Things did not turn out as the major had hoped. After they had followed the track about one hundred yards to the west, the runner pointed to a group of men making their way across country towards a wood.

"No. 4 Company's ration party," he said. It might almost have been a scene from a peacetime maneuver—a steaming field kitchen drawn by two horses and escorted by five or six soldiers on foot.

"The sergeant-major should be there too, in that case," said Bemmel.

"So he is," said the runner, pointing to the tall man with a machine-pistol and map-case on his shoulder who was bringing up the rear.

They jumped out of the car and ran after the group. Bemmel was there first.

"It's the Herr Pastor!" the sergeant-major exclaimed. He knew Bemmel from the days when he had visited his son as a recruit.

"How are you, Siebert?" asked Bemmel. "Everything all right?"

"Why, certainly, sir. We're advancing damned fast."

"And my Gottfried's with you, of course?"

"No," came the hesitating reply, "he's not with us any longer."

"What?" cried Bemmel. "He's dead? Out with it, man!"

"No, sir, he was wounded this morning at five o'clock in the first attack on Hill 308"—here the sergeant-major made a vague gesture to their rear—"and then evacuated. He's supposed to have caught it in the stomach. But that doesn't have to be very bad."

"In the stomach!" Bemmel groaned. "Dear God, how are we to know that they haven't already buried him."

"But, sir, there're belly-wounds and belly-wounds, you know."

"Where can he be?" asked Bemmel.

"We took him to the main dressing station, but that's been moved forward in the meantime, of course. He'll be in the field hospital by now."

"That's in Albert," interposed one of the medical orderlies.

"In Albert?" Bemmel ripped out his map. "That isn't so far away. Let's go."

The drive was a torment for both of them. Half the time Bemmel

33

talked unceasingly; the other half he stared vacantly in front of him.

"We shall see. He's dead. Shot through the stomach at five o'clock this morning, and now it's two."

After a pause: "Damn the war. My only son. Damn this crazy war."

At last they reached Albert. It was as quiet as the grave. By following a few ambulances they found the way to a small château whose red cross identified it from afar as a hospital. Bemmel sprang out and ran towards a nursing sister who was just coming out of the right wing of the building. Having exchanged a few words with her, he vanished through the doorway.

In one corner of the courtyard Velten found an unguarded party of twenty or thirty French prisoners, some standing around in groups and some sitting on the ground, talking and smoking. He learned from a corporal among them that they had been captured that morning in the first assault. How had that come about, Velten wanted to know. "Did you fight hard?"

"Merde," the corporal grinned showing a row of perfect white teeth beneath his blond mustache. "Try fighting yourself when those damned Stukas are coming down at you! We simply waited for your boys to turn up and then threw away our arms and shoved our hands up."

"Don't act the fool," said Velten and gave him a cigarette. "You don't need to flatter me—I'm not from the *deuxième bureau* and not here on duty, either. I'm talking to you as man to man and want to know what it was really like."

"Mon capitaine," said the Frenchman, assuming from Velten's *Sonderführer K* insignia that that was his rank, "I swear to you on the head of my five-year-old child that we didn't fight. They'd told us you would come in cardboard tanks, and we felt safe behind the Maginot Line. Then you suddenly came at us from the flank in real tanks and turned the heavens black with your aircraft. Did we simple folk have to let ourselves get slaughtered for the damned politics we didn't make? The English have cleared out and left us to face the whole of your power alone. It's sheer madness to resist. If only you send us home soon you'll have the whole of France on your side."

34

Velten was left no time to answer the arguments which the other put forward with true Gallic sprightliness, earning nods of approval from his comrades. For Bemmel reappeared in the same agitated state as before and reported that no order had been established in the hospital so far. The day's arrivals had not yet been listed, and no one in the orderly room had been able to say whether his Gottfried was among them or not. They suggested he should go over to the empty conservatory and see if he could find his son there.

Velten followed the trembling Bemmel. The conservatory was a fairly long room, and the wounded were lying on soft bundles of straw on the ground, Frenchmen intermingled with Germans, exactly as they had arrived. There was a smell of blood, human excrement and disinfectant in this slaughterhouse of war. Most of the men lay motionless on their straw. Only one or two were groaning gently.

Bemmel gave a sudden cry. He had discovered his Gottfried among a group of wounded who were chatting quietly in the far corner. He had been dozing on his straw, and stared wide-eyed as his father plunged towards him. Velten followed more slowly. For an abdominal wound, he thought, the boy looked pretty fresh and rosy.

"Stomach wounds?" he heard Gottfried say as he drew near. "I keep on hearing about my stomach. Look!" He lifted the blanket and pulled up his shirt to show his young manhood and an un-harmed belly. There was a thick bandage round his left thigh. "Thigh wound," he said. "It went straight through like a knife through butter. Didn't touch the bone at all. A nice wound. Bet I get four weeks' leave."

Without a word Bemmel went into a corner, turned his face to the wall and folded his hands. His shoulders shook with silent sobbing. Gottfried grinned with embarrassment, feeling a little ashamed in the presence of his comrades. Velten could not restrain an inward smile. Now the man was actually offering thanks to the God he imagined had nothing else to do but protect Bemmel junior's belly! At the same time it was impossible not to feel envious. How delightfully uncomplicated life could be when one had such faith as this!

35

Bemmel had sufficient self-discipline not to disturb the others by carrying on a long conversation with his son. He sped back to the car to get an imposing parcel of chocolate, cigarettes and cigars which he handed over to the sister on duty with a special request that she distribute its contents regardless of nationality. They were told that Gottfried would be in the next party of less seriously wounded cases to be taken down to base and would probably leave that day.

After brief farewells they left. "How happy I am to know," said Bemmel, "that my wife will be seeing the boy again soon." Then, becoming thoughtful, he added in an undertone so that the driver did not hear: "What useful purpose can this damned war be serving? If only the fiends who instigated it had to tremble for a son as I've done today."

They found a noisy party going on in Mme Picot's garden on arriving back at Havrincourt that evening. Hagestein was drinking schnapps with Captain Kelsen and Lieutenants Dr. Schwertfeger and Blüthner. Schwierig, who was on monitoring duty in the veranda, had just passed his glass through the window to Hagestein for replenishment.

"They certainly go well together," Velten murmured to his companion as they made their way towards the revelers.

Dr. Schwertfeger, in civil life an editor on a big daily paper, was the staff press officer. Blüthner, a Saxon manufacturer, commanded the defense company. The chief was wont to have the company changed at the slightest irregularity, particularly any lack of smartness, and Blüthner was already the third officer to have filled the job in Velten's time. Most of the officers on the headquarters gave Kelsen a wide berth. He was propaganda officer and in charge of all welfare in the Army Group area. In other words he belonged to the species who were later to earn such a doubtful reputation as National Socialist Leadership Officers. Nobody ever discovered exactly what he did in civilian life. All that was known was that he was a party member and an SS officer.

The two men were greeted with a loud hello which rose to a triumphant shout when Bemmel recounted the happy ending of his adventure with Gottfried.

"That calls for a celebration," said Hagestein. He disappeared

36

into the cellar to return with a magnum of Mumm extra dry. Velten went into the kitchen to make sandwiches for his and Bemmel's supper. When he got back an animated conversation was in progress.

"Are you starting your eternal belly-aching all over again?" screeched Kelsen, by now obviously well lit. Apparently even conquest had a gradually dulling effect once it became a matter of routine, and the period of inactivity behind the front had again led to discussions about the war and to doubts regarding its necessity and outcome. It was plain that either Bemmel or Blüthner had enraged the inveterate Nazi in Kelsen by some remark or other.

"I tell you," Kelsen cried, "the Führer is no longer concerned with the course of the war. He's leaving it to his generals to clear up in France. What he's doing now is to work on his plans for the new European order after the war. Every nation will get its task. Even the French. We, of course, shall have the leadership."

"The master race fights the wars and the slave peoples work for it," observed Schwertfeger. Velten glanced at him suspiciously out of the corner of his eye. One never knew whether the man was being sardonic or really believed in his own newspaper slogans.

"There's just one thing I don't understand," said Bemmel reflectively, "must a new order be born with so much violence and injustice?"

"Revolutions are always violent." Kelsen's voice rose. "Do you think you can change the world with prayers? Of course there are always innocent victims. Of course the birth of a new era is marked by violence and broken laws. We're living at a turning point in history. This isn't any ordinary war. We're fighting for our Weltanschauung. We're changing Europe and we're going to change the world."

"I believe there must be an ethical basis to our world order." The more heated the other became, the quieter was Bemmel's own voice. "You know that as a practicing Christian I cannot be a convinced supporter of your doctrine. But tell me, what moral values would you substitute for our conceptions?"

Kelsen did not answer. Turning suddenly to Velten, he asked: "What about you, you remote intellectual, do you believe in God?"

Was the fool trying to sound him out? Velten wondered. "I feel

37

no link with God as conceived by the Christian denominations," he replied, "or with any other form of deism. But I do believe the world is regulated by something else besides the laws of force and matter. I am convinced that there is a spiritual will behind physical phenomena. And even if there is no absolute Spirit, our own spiritual existence compels us to act as if there were."

"If that is so," said Kelsen triumphantly, "we must foster the phenomena which nature, expressing the will of the Spirit, places before us as tasks to be accomplished. Those of Folk and Race, for example, neither of which can be fulfilled without land and living space and purity of blood. But, according to the eternal laws of nature, living space can only be acquired by the strong through displacement of the weak. Such is the will of nature."

"That is the most barren materialism," Bemmel murmured to himself. Kelsen was drunk now, and he did not want to provoke him unnecessarily.

"As we're just in the act of seeing the strong displace the weak," said Schwertfeger inscrutably, "we may assume that this is not only the will of the Führer but is also due to a natural law and the power of the Spirit, if there happens to be one."

"Which is about the best way of settling the argument," said Hagestein as he poured out the second magnum. "I don't see why all that Kelsen says can't still hold good without all that high-falutin' philosophical twaddle. World history swings to and fro like a pendulum. Before we were underneath and now we're on top. And I find it very gratifying to be on top. It suits me down to the ground."

"Apart from which," said Blüthner, "we're all pretty high and should find something to talk about which doesn't get us all hot under the collar." And he proceeded to tell a more than usually juicy story from the time of their stay in Brussels.

Meanwhile an almost full moon had risen. The night was peaceful and there was no gunfire to disturb the stillness. It was difficult to believe that the front was so near. Soon they heard the "duty pilot," the name they gave to an enemy aircraft which came with monotonous regularity every night to circle over the neighborhood. Nothing ever happened. No bombs were ever dropped. The few anti-aircraft guns at the edge of the village did not fire. The marquis, people said, had good friends on the French General Staff who had promised that his château at Havrincourt would not be exposed to any danger. Malicious tongues maintained, moreover, that the German Intelligence Service had long been aware of the fact and that this was the reason why the Commander-in-Chief had decided to set up his headquarters there.

The offensive was carried farther westward over the Somme. The Oise and Aisne were crossed. The Marne was reached. At every river the enemy tried to set up a new defense line. But in vain.

The French Government moved from Paris to Bordeaux. Paul Reynaud, the Prime Minister, spoke to the French people over the radio. Velten listened to it with Mme Delgastre, whom he was in the habit of calling onto the veranda whenever he was on duty alone. The two others were opposed to this, their view being that the French civil population in German-occupied territory were just as much affected as German civilians at home by the ban on listening to enemy broadcasts. But Velten thought it cruel to deprive her of every source of news except what she heard from the Germans quartered with her. With a fine sense of tact she had grasped the position and always remained in the doorway of the living room, ready to disappear immediately anyone approached.

What she heard today, however, was hardly likely to inflame her will to resist. The speech was desperately grave and contained not a glimmer of hope. When Reynaud closed with the words: "Je crois à la France: je crois au miracle," she buried her face in her hands: Monsieur Reynaud believed in miracles! That seemed to her the best possible proof that France was really finished.

Shortly after that Velten and Schwierig sat at their sets together. Everything now depended on their remaining constantly at their posts, for any moment might bring some critical decision. It was not long before Velten grabbed the field telephone and demanded to be put through to the G1(I) himself. "Special announcement by the French radio," he cried. "General Hering, Military Governor of Paris, has declared the capital an open city. The troops are pulling out. Public safety is being taken over by the police."

CHAPTER VI

THEY STOOD on a hill near Senlis, gazing towards the southwest where the silhouette of the Eiffel Tower was a thing of silver against the blue of the sky. Velten, von Schlichten and Schwierig were traveling together. Paris had been occupied four days before, and now their headquarters was moving to a new location. They had told their driver to stop while they stretched their legs along the deserted highway.

Velten was again struck by the unreality of this, the strangest of all wars. Paris—the Mecca of earlier journeys when a niggardly currency allowance had generally imposed a severe check on one's stay—stood open before them. This time there was to be no anxious vacillation between one's hunger for adventure and a scanty stock of francs, nor that cautious selection of the most reasonable hotel or the most worth-while luncheon and dinner.

"I feel like a student with an inexhaustible traveling scholarship," he told his companions with a laugh. "I can hardly wait to see old *Paname* again."

"And what's that supposed to mean?" demanded Schwierig, who was in a particularly peevish mood that day. As a born provincial he felt reather uneasy at the prospect of entering a city of the world.

"*Paname,*" Velten replied, "is a word you won't find in your dictionaries. It's the name the loafers on the big boulevards, the butter-and-egg men of the suburbs and all the nice little girls give to their capital. *Paname* is Paris. 'The Paris near Pontoise.' "

Schwierig looked at him uncomprehendingly.

"Ach so," said Velten, "you don't go in for François Villon either. Can you imagine a man making fun of something he loves very dearly?"

He went on to quote the lines:

> Je suis Françoys, dont ce me poise,
> Né de Paris, emprès Pontoise,
> Qui, d'une corde d'une toise
> Sçaura mon col que mon cul poise.

" '. . . dont ce me poise,' " he repeated. "Hasn't it ever depressed you to be German? Oh, yes, I know, in Germany you're the bird which befouls its own nest if you make the slightest attempt to laugh at yourself."

"Oh, rot!" Schlichten interposed. "I'm not feeling very enthusiastic either. After all, what's Paris? Just an accumulation of the masses—a concentration of everything vulgar and mean. One big city's just like another." And with that slight uncertainty in his voice which made him so charming on occasions like this, he quoted from Rilke: "Thy great towns, Lord, are lost to shame, Things merged in misery and maddened. . . ."

"Yes, yes," Velten broke in, " 'Nature shall reign again supreme, Her waters uncheck'd, her vales serene . . .' But you need something more than fine verse to get over the facts of social evolution. Besides, it simply isn't true that beauty and magical language thrive only among 'a race of herdsmen and tillers.' " He recited from Stefan Zweig's stirring translation of Verhaeren's *Visages de la Vie:*

> En ces villes d'ombre et d'ébène
> D'où s'élèvent des feux prodigieux. . . .

Schlichten laughed. "To think those lines were spoken by a man in field-gray with the swastika of mass brutalization on his breast. You should know better than most what the masses are and what they can be turned into."

"Wrongly interpreted Ortega y Gasset," Velten smiled. "The essential contribution of these mass psychologists from Le Bon onwards is that they expose our weakness and incompetence in dealing with the problem of the masses. The masses are only masses when one wants them to be, when one forces them into a shapeless mass for one's purposes—to be misused as an anonymous authority in the attainment of an object. There are just as many characters and personalities with wills of their own among the

41

masses of a big city as in your much-lauded rural community. These masses have a million individual impulses. They are constantly striving"—there was a slightly self-conscious undertone in his voice as he quoted Verhaeren again:

> Avec des milliers de causes qu'on ignore
> A chaque effort vers le futur qu'elle élabore
> Rouge et tragique, à l'horizon.

"Well," Schwierig observed dryly, "we shall presumably have an opportunity before long to see how the masses of Paris get along with authority. *They* can't very well have cleared off too."

"God knows," said Velten, "but it'll feel good to see civilians again." And for one furtive moment he thought of that suit in his case.

They climbed into the car and drove on. Velten thought of Paris. Nothing could damp his spirits now.

"One thing is quite certain," Schlichten laughed, "we and our poetry would never have conquered Paris."

"Perhaps it might have been worth trying to conquer it with something other than squadrons of aircraft and tanks," Velten mused. "This Europe of ours is waiting for a conqueror. Didn't old Napoleon say that though he himself had had to subdue it by force of arms, the man who came after him must unite it by genius? But I suppose guns are cheaper."

As they drove through the villages of the *banlieue,* signs of life began to appear. They met military vehicles and saw sentries outside billets. Civilians wandered around singly or in groups, still staring curiously at the foreign soldiers. They drove past the ruined airfield of Le Bourget. A few German aircraft were already standing alongside the wrecks of French machines, now cleared to one side. The German bombers had done their job with precision. Except for window-panes shattered by blast, not one house on the left of the road was damaged. Only once or twice did the car have to drive cautiously around a bomb crater.

By the time they reached La Villette large numbers of people were out in the streets, many of them lining up to buy vegetables and horse meat.

"Damnation!" said von Schlichten. "Now comes the problem of

feeding the civil population. The entire country's disorganized. There are millions of refugees and the bridges are all blown up. No railways, no road transport. And the British will blockade." The time was not yet ripe for the iniquitous order that, if there were to be hunger in Europe, it wasn't the victors who would starve.

At the Gare de l'Est they turned off to the left into the boulevard de Strasbourg and followed the broad avenues in a westerly direction. In complete contrast to the familiar picture of peacetime, the nearer they got to the center of the city the stiller the streets became. The popular big brasserie Aux Armes de France on the boulevard Montmartre, whose enormous basement bar was normally crammed with a motley assortment of businessmen, messenger boys, petits bourgeois, street girls and various other indefinable figures, was shut. Not far away, in a side street near the Richelieu Drouot underground station, was Papa Ziegelmeyer's cosy little establishment. Ziegelmeyer was a native of Lorraine with a paunch and a pale yellow, waxed mustache. He catered for local baptisms, first communions and weddings, and in his almost primitively furnished restaurant maintained an excellent cuisine and an astonishingly large cellar ranging from refreshing Moselle to the Entre Deux Mers of the western coast.

Velten recalled with melancholy longing the splendid leg of lamb and haricot beans which had been one of Papa Ziegelmeyer's specialities in earlier days—crisp and brown round the outside, then a creamy white layer of tenderest fat, and finally the firm flesh itself.

Velten debated for a second or two: ought they to stop at Ziegelmeyer's? Perhaps they could eat there and avoid the dreary fare of the mess? But he rejected the thought immediately. Neither of his companions would fit into that environment, the aesthetic Schlichten no better than the pedantic Schwierig.

They finally stopped on the place de l'Opéra. It was past twelve and it seemed a good idea to have a meal in Paris before they showed up at their new location. The police were on duty in groups, and two of them—wearing the elegant blue uniform with coquettish cape, white gloves, and képi and carrying white batons—supplied the requisite information. Here, in the center of the peacetime

43

tourist quarter, everything was still closed. But on the Left Bank, the other side of the river from where they now stood, they could be sure of finding some place open.

They drove down the empty boulevard des Capucines. All the businesses here and in the rue Royale had their shutters down. Maxim's was shut. On the place de la Concorde there were only field-gray uniforms, sentries outside the hotels and military vehicles driving busily hither and thither. They went over the bridge, past the Chamber of Deputies and into the boulevard St. Germain. It was just as deserted as the boulevard Raspail which came after it. The big Hôtel Lutetia was devoid of life. No one could have guessed then the clandestine role it was destined to play as the headquarters of the counter-espionage service—the Abwehr—in the life of occupied France.

Now they turned into the sun-bathed boulevard Montparnasse. The Café du Dôme, rendezvous of émigrés from Hitler's Germany, was shut. The awnings were raised and the shutters down. But on the left-hand side there was actually a restaurant open.

"Bonjour, Monsieur Pierre," Velten greeted the *maître d'hôtel* who stepped to meet them, correctly attired in dinner jacket and winged collar. The man stared at him in amazement. Velten left him to work it out and glanced quickly round the room: perfectly polished nickel above red leather upholstery, clean mirrors. All the bar accessories gleaming with cleanliness. "Well," he said, removing his cap, "everything here's the same as before. But where's the *patron?*"

"Mon Dieu, Monsieur Victor," the manager cried, "ça alors—you, of all people, our first guest in field-gray." Repeatedly interrupting himself with little exclamations of astonishment and with much shaking of the head, he explained that the proprietor, an Italian, had fled and that he himself was carrying on alone in his absence. It went without saying that the kitchen was operating and that the gentlemen would be served in the manner to which Velten had been accustomed, "en ce temps-là."

He piloted the three of them to a corner table from which they had a comfortable view of the whole room. There were only a few customers, all of whom did their best to appear oblivious of the foreign uniforms. A paralyzing silence descended on the place. An atmosphere of constraint hampered every movement. Although the meal produced by Monsieur Pierre was in the circumstances appetizing and satisfying, they were happy to pay their bill and leave. With a professional smile the manager bade them good day and expressed the hope that they would come again before very long.

They drove back the way they had come. At the place de la Concorde they turned left into the avenue des Champs-Élysées and at the Rond Point came upon two or three of the Army Group cars. Bemmel and Paymaster Knorr were standing by them.

"Who does the big car belong to?" inquired Velten, pointing to a long-drawn-out two-seater sports model with a drop head. It emerged that the wonder vehicle had borne Knorr to Paris.

When the first carefully censored newspaper came out some days later, the vigilance of the censors was eluded, in a report on the triumphal entry of the German troops, by a reference to the victors' transport. It was pointed out with thinly disguised malice that one could identify the course of Germany's victories from the vehicles taking part in the parade. Apart from the military transport, the press remarked, there had been magnificent civil models of various makes bearing the registration numbers of all the countries through which the exponents of lightning war had passed.

The paymaster's car belonged to this category of booty. After traveling from Aachen to Brussels in a modest baby Opel, he had indignantly protested to the motor transport officer against the implied slight. Thereupon a 12-cylinder Lincoln Zephyr had been placed at his disposal—a thing of bright green body-work and gleaming metal fittings. Its dashboard was a confusing maze of ivory buttons and levers. The registration number began with the letters HZ, and the car bore a plate marked NL. So it was in Holland that the dream-car had found its way onto the staff.

They made their way to the Arc de Triomphe on foot. Among the instructions on deportment issued to them before their departure was a directive that all ranks would salute at the tomb of the Unknown Soldier. Having reached the stone slab, therefore, they lined up and raised their right hands to their peaks, remaining in this position for some minutes. They must have been a most picturesque sight, these uncommonly martial figures, as they stood before the eternal flame in the shadow of the archway and the gray-white walls inscribed with the names of the battles won by Napoleon I, from Marengo and Lodi to Jena and Auerstädt. But whoever was stage-managing the performance of "German Soldiers in Conquered Paris" was well versed in mass psychology, for the uniformed visitors had great success with their salute. A few elderly people sitting on the benches below the monument smiled at the Germans with a certain trust and at the same time with the utmost respect.

After that, they got into the cars which had followed them up. The destination was now known. Versailles. They were to be quartered in the Hôtel Trianon, close to the entrance to the big park.

Velten was pleased to find that his room had its own bath. Down in the dining room there was a further pleasant surprise: Drinks were being supplied free of charge from the hotel cellars. This ill-considered liberality was soon to have very unpleasant consequences. Night after night certain members of the headquarters —primarily those older gentlemen who had no idea what else to do—sat drinking champagne. Only the very best brands—Rœderer, Cliquot, Irroy or Bollinger—cascaded down their throats.

At the new location the offices were separate from the quarters. The interpreters were accommodated with the operations staff in the prefecture, which was situated in a broad avenue only a short distance from the baroque castle. For their offices Hagestein had taken over the sub-prefect's dwelling on the ground floor in the right wing of the building, the official naturally having left with his family. The suite, which included kitchen and bathroom, was equipped with every modern convenience. Trooper Rudolf Altenkirch, a native of Gardelegen who had been allotted to them as an orderly because, though only twenty years old, he was suffering from some rupture trouble or other, slept in these rooms at night. For that matter, he did the same thing in the daytime whenever he had the chance.

And Germany was still at war with France. The armistice conditions, though announced, had not yet been accepted. Paris was under curfew from 9 p.m. onwards. About this time the brisk little policemen would blow piercing notes on their whistles and shout out their long-drawn-out warnings: "Concierges, fermez les portes!

46

Éteignez les lumières!" The blackout operated despite the absence of enemy air activity.

About four o'clock one morning Velten was frightened out of his slumbers by the shrill jangle of the telephone. It was Lieutenant Merrem of the Signal regiment to say that he had picked up a radio message in French. As it appeared to be an important governmental communication he was sending it over for translation. A dispatch-rider brought the text almost immediately, typed out on the usual blue WT form. "Le Maréchal Philippe Pétain au Chancelier Adolf Hitler"—a personal message from one Head of State to another!

"L'avancement rapide des forces allemandes," it ran, "risque d'obliger le Gouvernement Français . . ." What elegant verbal construction, Velten thought. Difficult to put into good German. He began writing. "The rapid advance of the German forces is liable to oblige the French Government"—how ponderous German seemed compared with the clearness and flexibility of the Latin tongues!—"to take the weighty decisions imposed on it" (the French wording "décisions graves qui lui sont imposées" conveyed a far greater sense of burden than his German rendering, "die schweren Entscheidungen, die ihr auferlegt sind") "in the presence of German arms." "La résistance héroique des armées françaises m'autorise à une demande!"—Velten went on translating: "The heroic resistance of the French armies gives me the right" (That wasn't much good—perhaps "empowers me" was better? But no, it sounded so bureaucratic and colorless!) "to make an appeal," (he searched in vain for a German word somewhere between *Bitte* and *Forderung*—something meaning too proud to beg and too polite to demand!), "namely, to be able to consult quite freely with my ministers."

If only the house-painter from Braunau could understand French! If only he had been granted the gift of sensing another people's spirit, culture and history through the medium of its language— would this war ever have come about? But no, that was nonsense when one considered how many of his henchmen had a command of other peoples' tongues and only used this faculty to increase the effectiveness of German arms. No, intimate insight into the soul

47

of a neighboring people did not supply the key to fraternal understanding. It merely guided the dagger into the soft parts of the enemy's body.

Nevertheless, heed was paid to Pétain's appeal. Bordeaux was not occupied before the conclusion of the armistice. When Velten arrived there some weeks later the city still seemed to enjoy a special status, despite the fact that the French Government had already moved to Clermont-Ferrand and thence to Vichy. The Tricolor fluttered over the Mairie, and there was no curfew. Refugees and local inhabitants alike populated the streets until the early hours.

CHAPTER VII

THE WORST THING of all was the silence. It hung over the scene like a black cloud in the brooding heat of the summer afternoon. Velten was standing in the ticket office of Orléans station—or rather he had just managed to push his way through the entrance and step a few paces inside. It was impossible to get any farther. The stone floor of the glass-covered, vaulted space was carpeted with human bodies. Men, women and children were jammed together indiscriminately. Refugees. This simple generic term now applied to every one of them. Ragged, filthy and half-starved, they lay just where they had crawled together, struck down by the hand of that egalitarian destiny which turns professors and locksmiths into conquerors and writers, and cobblers and businessmen into tramps. They were crammed so tightly together in their hollow-eyed, pale-faced misery that not one of them could budge without moving somebody else. They all had to lie on their right or left sides simultaneously, and if anyone wanted to turn over the whole row had to follow suit.

Over in one corner, by the ticket window, a woman was lying

on some straw. She owed this luxury to the fact that she had given birth to a child the night before. Naturally it was dead. The pathetic remains had already been buried somewhere or other. In another corner an old man had breathed his last just before dawn. He was still lying there, and those near by were at pains to maintain some sort of gap between themselves and the withered corpse. Every time they touched the cold limbs they started up in alarm.

The few people who noticed Velten's field-gray uniform wearily raised their heads.

"Monsieur," someone asked, "when is there a train to Paris?"

"How am I to know?" he replied. "Aren't there any railway people around?"

His question was pointless, for so far no communications had been restored. There was still a state of war, no armistice having yet been signed. Velten had wandered into the station building quite by chance. The job which had brought him to Orléans was finished and he had taken the opportunity to have a look round the town. Here, on the northern bank of the Loire, was where the flow of refugees had come to a standstill. The destruction of the bridges in the face of Germany's advancing legions had left them isolated in their tens of thousands on this side of the river. Millions of them were believed to be stranded in districts south of the Loire. They had got away earlier and were now unable to return. The few pontoon bridges in existence were required exclusively for the supply of the field-gray armies.

"What a crime it is to blow all the bridges sky-high like this!" Dr. Goebel, the Luftwaffe judge to whom Velten was attached that day, had kept saying during the drive to Orléans. Every time they had to cross an emergency bridge, Goebel had waxed indignant about the "criminal lunacy" of a government which acted quite regardless of the interests of its own population. They had blown every bridge from the Meuse to the Loire, he fumed. As if they hadn't learned that no advance could be held up in this way. Just imagine anyone trying to act like that in Germany! Quite impossible with our people's balanced outlook. What German would tolerate such a thing, and what kind of leader would even dream of such madness!

They had come to Orléans to attend a Luftwaffe court martial

49

convened to try a case of rape involving two members of an anti-aircraft unit stationed in the Army Group area. Both the accused had fully admitted their guilt. Both had been in full possession of their mental faculties. Their smart appearance and obvious remorse had made the best possible impression. There was no psychological explanation for the crime. They had simply succumbed to a sudden urge. Neither of them knew how or why. *What* was it that had turned these ordinary-looking, mediocre men into raging animals? The court refrained from going into the moral and emotional undercurrents of the case. There was, in any case, precious little trace of human feeling in the crude, clumsy phrases which the two accused, avoiding all euphemisms and embellishments, had used to describe every detail of their deed. Apart from asking for a chance to redeem themselves at the front, they had nothing to put forward in their own favor. The Court sentenced them to twelve and fifteen years' hard labor respectively, accepting in mitigation the fact that one man had shot down two enemy aircraft and been recommended for the Iron Cross.

On the way back Goebel and Velten had had an animated discussion. They agreed that crimes of this nature were only sporadic in the German armed forces. War with all its animal atavism had always brought out the sexual brutality in the male. There could be no doubt that were the present situation reversed—such a contingency was quite out of the question, of course—German women would suffer a similar fate on probably a much larger scale. Only a very small number of offenses of this kind had been reported in France. The few cases of rape which had occurred during the campaign in Poland had been mostly linked with the murder of resisting menfolk and had ended in death sentences. Velten shared Goebel's view that the German did not, generally speaking, show any tendency towards sexual acts of violence. The mass murders of the period after the Great War had been merely isolated phenomena.

"The thing that particularly frightened me about the organized violence of the Brown Revolution," Velten reflected, "was the systematic and compliant way all the beatings-up, tortures and murders were carried out. They went about them just as dispassionately as routine official duties and beat men and women unconscious like

50

apathetic robots. That's what I found most horrible of all—the fact that women were clubbed just like men."

What was happening to the German people? How did this talented and industrious nation, normally so deeply averse to individual acts of violence or paroxysms of passion, come to commit unimaginable cruelties merely because organized might and orders from above afforded a semblance of justification? One felt almost grateful to the two condemned ravishers for providing the exception to the rule and acting on their own responsibility.

It was late by the time they got back to the Hôtel Trianon. A banquet was in progress in the big dining room. The armistice was signed and the headquarters staff had met to celebrate. The Army Group Commander and the Chief-of-Staff had toasted the German victory, thanking each other for their mutual support, lavishly extolling one another's professional accomplishments, and making generous use of the lofty epithet "warlord." Decorations had been distributed, from the Knight's Cross down to the *Kriegsverdienstkreuz* Second Class. The Iron Cross, normally only awarded for valor at the front, could now be conferred on the gentlemen of the General Staff, regulations having recently included "the assistants of senior commanders" among those eligible. Thus the Commander-in-Chief's aide, 2nd-Lieut. Count Helmsfeld, had received the Iron Cross Second Class.

When Major Mattersen joined Velten at the table for late-comers in an ante-room, he was wearing his new Iron Cross First Class, the E.K.I. He rather tended to play it down, assuring Velten that in the course of time he, too, would automatically get some ribbon or other.

CHAPTER VIII

FAR BACK in the misty ages, when migrating Teutonic tribes invaded the cultured lands of Italy, Spain and North Africa, when the Mongols overran Eurasia, and the Manchus conquered China, it was invariably the case that the conqueror learned from the gentler customs, higher living standard and more advanced civilization of the conquered. In due course some of the latter were destined to overcome their conquerors by accustoming them slowly but surely to their own way of life, their own moral code, and even their language. By the time the people of the Führer broke out of the plains between the Rhine and Vistula and the lands between the North Sea and the Alps to storm right up to the Pyrenees, the outward tokens of European civilization were more or less common to both conqueror and conquered. Nevertheless great differences soon emerged between the approaches of victor and victim to everyday life. It took even the Führer's officers some time to realize that a well-made-up woman looked better than the one who exposed her face to the sun in the same state as she had raised it from her pillow. They needed just as long to learn that meals should be planned not only for man's sustenance but also his edification. They had to discover the difference between an *apéritif* and a *digestif*. At first they still shouted for brandy before a meal, or drove the waiter almost frantic by calling for "One beer and one cognac."

At the outset the language caused considerable difficulties. Anyone educated in the schools of the Third Reich, with its supreme contempt for erudition, obviously knew hardly anything of the tongue of Germany's neighbor. As for the older ones, they had long forgotten the French learned in earlier days. Fantastic misunderstandings arose. Paymaster Knorr, for example, was firmly convinced that the French for public convenience was Byrrh, having

52

seen the well-known *apéritif* advertised on those numerous sheet-iron rotundas in the Paris streets from which the user's head and feet peep so coyly and which the Parisians call *Vespasiennes* in memory of the Roman emperor who found nothing malodorous about the revenue he derived from such installations.

It was not surprising, therefore, that interpreters suddenly found themselves very much in demand. Hagestein was, unfortunately, seldom available, since he now had a range of commitments so wide as to keep him almost permanently away from the office.

In point of fact, no one had been taking official duties very seriously since the armistice. Velten himself was seldom to be found at work in the sub-prefect's dwelling, for nowadays he was frequently commandeered to act as a guide in Paris. The big stores, shops and restaurants had all re-opened in turn, bewildering the troops from the land of clothing-cards and dockets with the plenitude and quality of what they had to offer. In the Printemps, the Galeries Lafayette and the Samaritaine, German soldiers surged round the counters and literally wrested watches, bracelets and rings, and above all stockings and other silken materials from the assistants' hands. Soon every soldier was adorning himself—strictly against regulations but with the tacit consent of authority—with a more or less fancy silk scarf beneath the open neck of his shirt.

But these were not the only things purchased by the troops. They also invaded the hat, lingerie and shoe shops where they acquired the appropriate articles of clothing for their wives, daughters or sweethearts.

The officers did their shopping at the better houses. Velten took a whole crowd of them to the big fur shop on the corner of the rue la Boétie and rue de Miromesnil where, full of enthusiasm, they looked over a selection of the most elegant models. Many purchases were made. It was a mystery to Velten where the money came from, for it was clearly laid down that no member of the German armed forces could draw more than one month's pay at once, either in scrip or French francs. He never succeeded in solving the secret.

There was one point, however, in which the conquered adapted themselves to the ways of the conquerors. The Paris street girls, who in earlier days would sooner have bitten off their tongues than demand their remuneration before fulfilling their own side of the bargain and who had at most been wont to remind the customer of his subsequent obligations by a discreet "Tu seras gentil, n'est-ce pas?" now did not undo a single blouse button until the sum was agreed on and paid up.

When the first big run on the shops had subsided, a large-scale operation was initiated at Army Group Headquarters. Once everyone had packed his gains into boxes, these were all secured with an official seal and loaded onto trucks. Then, under the direction of the Camp Commandant, a column of "WD property" left for the Rear Headquarters of Army Group right back in Germany. Only thus was it possible to circumvent the customs regulations still in force. At a later stage it was to be decreed that any soldier arriving from occupied territory could import into the Reich "what he could carry on his back."

At the same time, Paris was not immediately accessible to everyone for these shopping expeditions. The many dangers of the metropolis had prompted the commander of the Paris garrison to forbid all members of units located outside the capital to enter it unless on duty and in possession of a special pass. This caused no difficulty as far as the officers of Army Group Headquarters were concerned, as the passes in question were liberally dispensed by the staff clerks.

For Velten, who had furnished himself with one of the permanent red passes for Paris, it was the beginning of a happy interlude. The worthy Schwierig was always ready to stand in for him, however threadbare Velten's pretext, so that he now drove in from Versailles almost daily.

One afternoon Velten was strolling along the Champs-Élysées, which became increasingly populated as the days went by. A streetwalker had attached herself to him at the Rond Point and, in a queer mixture of French and broken German that would not have got her far in social circles, had been promising him all the delights of paradise. She obviously took his silence for bashfulness and persisted in her efforts. As they drew near the big café he suddenly wheeled on her: "Fiche-moi la paix!" he growled with deliberate coarseness. "Tu m'emmerdes!" The tart immediately desisted and remained rooted to the spot with astonishment.

Velten made his way through the rows of chairs in front of the

54

Colisée. The crowded tables were mainly occupied by civilians, only an occasional uniform being visible here and there. Most of the officers sat in pairs over a coffee or some other beverage. At this early stage none of them had female company. Suddenly Velten halted in his tracks, completely thunderstruck. The possibility of meeting any of his Parisian acquaintances again had never occurred to him and now it had happened! She was sitting alone at a table, sucking absent-mindedly at a straw as she gazed at the bustling throng in the street. Her face was unmistakable. The pale complexion, the capricious, slightly over-prominent nose, the narrow-lipped mouth and the determined chin. There could be no doubt about that delicately shaped figure! It was Corinne.

He hesitated, thinking it over. The uniform was an abominable hindrance. Would she even recognize him—would she *want* to recognize him? Then the pleasure of reunion triumphed, and he stepped cautiously up to her table. With a slight bow and without waiting for a reply to his "Permettez, madame," he drew the chair next to hers up to the table. A few of the civilians sitting nearest to them took note of the scene with surprise and disapproval. Then, as well-bred children of the metropolis, they turned away.

He threw her a surreptitious glance. She did not seem to have noticed him. As he was giving the waiter his order she appeared to start faintly at the sound of his voice. He had taken off his cap, and now he turned round towards her and looked her full in the face: "Is that how one treats an old friend, Corinne?"

Dropping the straw, she gazed at him open-mouthed, her mind probing and groping. Then her pale cheeks flushed: "Mon dieu, Victor, vous—dans cette tenue!"

Yes, the uniform, that accursed uniform! She glanced hastily around them. No, no one was paying any attention. Then, quite suddenly, the old light came back into her black, clever eyes. She smiled, showing her little, slightly pointed teeth. With a sudden rush of pleasure she stretched both hands towards him: "But what a wonderful surprise this is! The first gleam of light since the invasion!" And then the questions and exclamations came bubbling forth.

"What have you been doing all these years since 1936? How do you come to be wearing the uniform? Weren't you an anti-militarist?

55

What have you done to our France—the France where you were always so happy?"

He gave her a brief account of his life.

"And you, Corinne, what are you doing these days? How are your friends—our friends?"

"I'm a poor soldier's wife now," Corinne replied with half a smile. "Yes, it may surprise you, Victor, but I married just before war broke out. Partly because I thought I ought to, and partly because I liked him. I'm not getting any younger, and the cabaret didn't turn out as I'd hoped. My husband's a good boy. Earns enough for both of us as a car salesman. He adores me. I've no idea where he is now. The last letter came four weeks ago: he was somewhere in the south then. I imagine he'll have got out all right—he was always 'très débrouillard.' "

"And where do you live now, Corinne?"

"We've got an apartment in the 17th arrondissement." She named a street near the Porte de Champerret.

"Why," said Velten, raising an eyebrow, "that's in *Putainville*." Whoretown was the name the Parisians gave to a part of the district between the boulevards Péreire and Gouvion St. Cyr because of the many kept women who occupied more or less luxurious flats in the area.

"Don't advertise your local geography," she retorted. "You ought to be well aware that there are a lot of hard-working people living there too. With our housing shortage and high rents you can't always pick the quarter which suits your taste. Anyway, my moral standards were never exactly monastic."

"Now it's you who are bragging, Corinne! Are you trying to make a name for yourself as a model of licentiousness!—Sale prétentieuse!" They both laughed.

Corinne was a girl with a keen sense of the need for a well-arranged emotional life. She was one of those diligent women whose existence as cabaret artistes in the French capital is far more bourgeois than the foreigner—who takes the gay exterior for reality—can possibly suspect. Corinne's speciality was literary cabaret. Though her voice was only of moderate strength and always slightly husky, it had a peculiarly captivating quality, and she used to sing and recite those airs and ballads which owed their provocative

56

flavor to the dismal social background of the great cities and modern society as a whole. "Dans les prisons de France il y a des voleurs"—thieves and murderers, the bugbear of the well-fed citizen! That had been one of her most successful numbers, with its radiant and yet ominous ending: "Dans les jardins du monde un jour nous danserons. . . ."

She was not a singer of any great talent. Her *genre* was more effectively expounded by that insignificant-looking woman with the dreamy gaze who had emerged from Paris's thickly populated east end and whom the Parisians had already given the tender and adoring nickname of Môme.

La môme Piaf was to bring the social ditty a renown it had not known since the unforgettable days of Bruant. Faced with such competition, Corinne could not hope to tread the upward path leading from the small cabarets, through the A.B.C. and the Théâtre de Dix Heures into the Casino de Paris, from there to Monte Carlo and finally to Broadway.

For all that, Corinne had always managed somehow, and had remained independent and free. It was her great pride that she was at liberty to make her own choice of love and adventure whenever they came her way. In her own words: "Je fais l'amour comme je mange." That, of course, was an over-simplification. Her body would never have obeyed unless some part of her mind acquiesced.

In the few weeks she had spent with Velten four years ago, there had initially been no physical contact in their relationship. He had come into a little cabaret late one night to find her reciting the verses of a modern poet who had died in misery. The words in the Parisian argot, much of which was still incomprehensible to him in those days, described the plain, happy love of a worker and his girl. Something in her delivery, her gestures, the whole way in which she interpreted the simple tale, had greatly moved him.

When the cabaret closed, he had suddenly found her standing outside, wearing an ordinary blue coat but no hat, and holding a bunch of red roses presented her by some customer. By degrees they had got into conversation. It appeared that he had attracted her attention as an appreciative listener. Her act was difficult for a foreigner to understand, she thought. M'sieur wasn't French, was he?

57

As they made their way on foot through a nocturnal Paris it had turned out that she loved this walk home. She needed fresh air after the smoke-laden atmosphere of the cabaret: it gradually settled her keyed-up nerves. Very soon the two of them were walking side by side with the feeling that they had for years led a common existence. They came to a halt on the Pont de l'Alma and looked down into the river. A light mist hovered around the Trocadéro. Each found the other was unfashionable enough to be fond of Baudelaire, Rimbaud and Verlaine.

It did not surprise him, when they reached her home, that she should ask him in to continue their discussion. They need not disturb the concierge, she explained, as the door of this house, which was unique by Parisian standards, was open day and night.

Velten shivered as they stood in the hall. "Was that why your forefathers stormed the Bastille and proclaimed the rights of man, so that you could be as happy as children whenever you succeed in escaping from the tyranny of your caretakers?"

Corinne laughed. "I'd have still taken you up even if it meant waking the concierge. I'm as free as the day is long."

They went up to the fifth floor. Corinne opened a door and switched on the light. They were standing in a narrow hall just big enough to hang coats in. Velten helped her out of hers. The summer night was so warm that he himself had neither hat nor coat. She stood there in a simple, gray woolen dress with a pleated skirt and narrow waist. Except for a shining golden brooch on her right breast she wore no jewelry. She had an odd, jumpy manner, as if she were under some strange tension. Noticing his look, she smiled fleetingly.

"Voilà ma carrée," she said, steering him into an almost square room. The furniture was simple. A broad settee along one wall. A round table in the middle. A few chairs. A bookshelf. A few vases with flowers in them. A radio on a stand. The walls were papered in dark blue and hung with pictures of Corinne. Most of them were photographs, but there were also one or two charcoal sketches and quite a large pastel portrait. There was Corinne in evening dress before a performance. Corinne in a bathing suit on the Riviera. Corinne's head in profile and *en face*. Among it all were a few plaster-of-Paris masks, including Sarah Bernhardt's death mask.

She drew back the silver-gray curtains and opened a glass door. It led onto a tiny balcony on which geraniums were blooming in window-boxes.

"I'll make some coffee," she said. She pushed open a door in the background to reveal a minute kitchenette without a window, ventilated only by an air flap.

She soon had the coffee ready and served it with a plateful of cold rabbit and a long loaf of white bread. There was no butter.

"I'm a poor girl," she explained.

They ate at the table, Velten squatting on the settee and Corinne sitting in a blue-covered armchair she had pulled up for herself. They ate the bones with their fingers, gnawing the meat off and drinking the hot coffee in short gulps. Suddenly she laid her hand on his arm and looked him in the face.

"To think that a complete stranger should come here and sit in my apartment and that I should find nothing queer about it and feel it had always been that way! Are you actually Belgian or Dutch? You're certainly one of the two. Shall I guess?"

"Both wrong," Velten told her. "I come from Berlin."

"In that case you're an offshoot from the Napoleonic wars. A lapse on the part of your great-grandmother. That's if you're not a descendant of the Huguenots."

"Good lord, no," he retorted, amused at the thought. "I'm a real Prussian."

"If only my mother knew. She's from Lorraine and talks only of . . . oh, well, you know the flattering expressions they use."

The nationality issue was settled then. It was never mentioned again, and he sensed that she found these things just as unimportant as he. She was Corinne and he was Victor. Each understood the other as a single personality, free of all the dross of origin and alien environment.

As Velten's mind skimmed over the recollection of those first days with Corinne, he found it impossible to imagine that this woman had contracted a bourgeois marriage. What had been strong enough to swing her self-appointed destiny into another channel? Would he ever find out? Corinne had confines inside her beyond which no one would ever be admitted. Even in those early days he had sensed certain ultimate barriers.

Of these there was no sign, however, in the unconstrained atmosphere of their first hours together that night. After their simple meal Corinne had rolled herself up on the settee and Velten had lain on the far side, half facing her and with his back towards the wall. It marked the beginning of a crystal-clear exchange of thought delving into their innermost beings and uniting them till morning came. It had brought them closer together than any physical union could ever have done.

To talk to each other like this, as the lamplight receded before the approaching light of day and the air became bluer and bluer from the smoke of their cigarettes, inspired them with a feeling of sensual intimacy. It was an intellectual foretaste of the fusion to come.

Velten, who despite his appearance and education was still a Teuton possessed of all the obscure impulses of his race and all the unfathomable depths and dangerous fervors of the German soul, was much affected by this first direct experience of the Latin clarity of reasoning and by the healthy Gallic realism apparent in the simple utterances of this woman, who, unspoiled by any of the formal refinements, was cultured in the true sense of the word.

"I don't like to force my style of life on others," said Corinne. "Most of the French, in my opinion, lead bad, stupid lives. They are glued to their possessions. They retain medieval conceptions of the family and the obligations of the woman. But, if that makes them happy, they can go on living like that as far as I'm concerned. If only they leave me to live my little life as I want it. I've no time for reformers. Nor for socialism. I see all the social misery and even get my inspirations from its injustices. But I can't accept the idea of changing everything with doctrines. Probably my attitude is wrong if applied universally. But it's right for me and my life. I simply feel things that way. I earn my bread and the few rags that clothe me, and I've got a longing—an irrepressible desire—to get my big chance in life. I want to rise out of the milling crowd of small people and enjoy all the glitter of fame for just a few years. I want to see big posters of myself on the pillars and long columns about myself in the world press. And then sometimes I'd like someone to keep me company for part of the way. Without passionate outbursts. Without any of the fireworks that go with what people

60

call the great love. Without any tearful goodbyes. J'ai horreur de ça! We're all of us alone right down inside. But it does us good to have someone to smile at when the day's done—someone to share the fireside with and cherish in our hearts. It warms the soul and gives us new courage to roam on alone."

They were to grow to love such conversations later on. Even when they had found each other physically, this mutual unburdening of their feelings and thoughts remained the decisive factor of their relationship. It occasionally happened, for example, that Corinne, lying on her bed by the open window late on a warm summer's night, would respond to Velten's advances with a smile of consent, saying: "You may love me if you wish. But you must not expect everything of me tonight. A soft, warm caress—yes. But nothing more."

Yet Corinne loved the intoxications of the senses, too. Once, when she had been without an engagement for a short while, she and Velten had spent a few days of undisturbed physical pleasure together on the Marne, in the Varenne, a small town where an innkeeper rented little wooden huts built on piles sunk into the shallow river. To get to them one had to row out in a worm-catcn boat smelling of tar, tie up to one of the piles and clamber up a rope ladder to a veranda which ran round the whole structure. It was possible to lie quite naked on the little platform without being seen. One could also hire canoes in which to paddle through the reedy water to little islets bordered with undergrowth and bearing the same absurd kind of names as those in the lakes of the Havel back at home; Island of Love, Swan's Nest and Paradise.

Once they were invited to visit friends in a little château near Chinon. With the sumptuous evening meal they drank a tremendous amount of the powerful red wine of Touraine, which settled the old conflict between Venus and Bacchus. It stimulated the men and made the women more passionate.

"Viens que je te viole," Corinne had whispered, throwing herself upon him. The bed was broad and solidly built. The room was like a vaulted chamber. There were bars over the uncurtained windows in the thick outer walls. Moonlight flooded into the room. Corinne's expression was lost in the black remoteness of the arched roof. Even in the lazy contentment which followed, every look,

61

every gesture and every caress seemed to say: It is I, Corinne, and that is my own pleasure—mine alone.

Velten drained his glass and beckoned to the waiter. As he paid for both of them he sensed a fleeting sign of relief in Corinne's face. The man was already out of earshot. With the frankness to which he had been previously accustomed he asked point blank: "What are you actually living on?"

"Why, I get the normal allowance for soldiers' wives who have no income of their own."

She mentioned a ridiculously small sum.

"And how do you feed yourself?"

"The food situation is still very bad. There's very little bread and no vegetables. If you're lucky you may occasionally get carrots and parsnips. There are no meat, fats or milk."

"I'll get you some food. There's already a market in Versailles. The farmers are bringing quite a lot of stuff in. There are even poultry, butter, meat and eggs. Transportation is probably the only real trouble in Paris."

She smiled gloomily.

"You can't come into my house in that uniform. There's a concierge. And neighbors, too."

"I promise I'll come and see you tomorrow. I'll bring you what you need—and I shan't be in uniform."

Corinne got up.

"Come with me for part of the way. As far as the Porte Maillot. Then I shall go on alone."

They walked through the streets in complete silence, and took leave of each other with a brief handshake.

"Until tomorrow," said Velten.

"Adieu," Corinne replied, with the slight suspicion of a smile.

As it turned out, nothing did come of his projected visit to Corinne the following day. Instead, he was given a whole series of jobs by Mattersen, who in spite of the armistice was still overloaded with work and had not found a single free day to visit Paris. Velten had to go along with two officers as an interpreter, but before he left Mattersen gave him a very special job to do. "Now then," he said in his resolute way, "what are we so near to that damn city of wickedness for? This time you can bring back a few really decent

62

filthy pictures ("really decent" *and* "filthy," Velten noted), you know, some typical Parisian specialities. The old gentlemen here want their fun too."

"Good lord, sir," said Velten in alarm, "are you serious? There's pornography everywhere. I once saw a whole truck load in Berlin that had been confiscated from a dealer. I wouldn't know where to look for such a thing in Paris."

"Nuts," said Mattersen. "Official business. If you can't get any you're useless."

He thrust a few currency bills into Velten's hand. He counted them; there were 1000 francs.

"I've no idea how much the stuff costs."

"We shall know that by this evening, when you've done your errand. 'Morning!" Velten was already dismissed.

Down by the Seine he stopped at one of the bookstands which were already doing business again.

"I'm supposed to get something else for friends with rather peculiar tastes," he told the dealer with some hesitation. "Photographs of a special type, you know."

The man scented business. He naturally hadn't anything like that in stock, he said. First, it wasn't in his line; and secondly, m'sieur must know what a sharp watch police kept. But if Velten would come along that evening he'd certainly have something for him.

In the Samaritaine Velten bought a necktie to match his civilian suit. The two other officers found nothing surprising in this, for they, too, were buying ties and silk scarves. He next went to the hat department to try on a beret. His companions laughed.

"Let's hope you don't make the mistake of sticking that thing on with your uniform!" one of them said.

"Don't worry," he rejoined, "I'm sending it home with the next lot of 'WD property.'"

When they came past the bookstand on the Seine embankment the dealer made a sign to Velten and, with a sideward glance at a nearby policeman on his beat, pushed a fairly large parcel into his hand. It included a very special item, he stated with a wink: La mère et sa fille. Velten gave him Mattersen's thousand francs. The man seemed entirely satisfied: probably he had reckoned with far less and was now making a sizable rake-off.

Velten showed the pictures to his companions. They were unanimous that such things were only possible in France. It was just one more sign how degenerate these people were. High time the country was cleaned up.

"Of course," retorted Velten, "and every Frenchwoman is a whore and every Frenchman a dipsomaniac. . . ."

He was feeling angry.

Just as Velten appeared in the G1(I)'s outer office with his latest acquisition, Colonel Herder, the operations officer, unexpectedly came in about some urgent matter or other.

"What's happened to that stuff of mine!" Velten suddenly asked when he had gone. The photographs had vanished from the desk. The clerks on duty grinned and pointed to a gap between two filing cabinets where, of all people, the lieutenant who was an inspector in the Ministry of Justice in civil life was going through the pictures with a face as red as a beet. Velten took the pictures from him.

"Far too dangerous for our senior judiciary," he said.

He left the material with Mattersen, who displayed every sign of satisfaction. "You see?" he said. "I knew you wouldn't disappoint me."

Velten was mistaken if he thought that was the end of the disagreeable affair as far as he was concerned. When the pictures had gone the rounds of the headquarters, Mattersen suddenly got the idea that Velten paid too much for them. He hadn't in the least intended him to blow the whole sum, he declared, pushing the collection into his hand. Velten could either re-sell the stuff or pay the thousand francs out of his own pocket.

Velten was furious. "Herr Major surely isn't inciting me to commit an offense?"

"Ach, nonsense," said Mattersen. "You misunderstand me. You weren't supposed to spend the whole amount, and I'm only prepared to pay a quarter. Now just start getting the money back in again. We shall see—the stuff'll sell like hot cakes. I'll make sure you get publicity."

As it turned out, Velten got rid of his wares in no time at all. They all approached him one by one, each buying one or more photographs in order to apprise himself of the peculiar habits of the French . . . When Velten still had a considerable stock, an elderly Bavarian colonel who commanded a technical unit attached to the headquarters appeared in his hotel room. He'd been hearing about those filthy pictures, he explained rather uncertainly. "Got a cousin who collects that sort of thing. Perhaps I can do the old guy a good turn. I'd like to see whether the things would be of any use to him."

"May I suggest the Herr Colonel examines the pictures in here at his leisure to ascertain whether they are what his cousin requires? I've work to attend to in the meantime."

The colonel agreed with alacrity and took over the pictures. By the time Velten returned half an hour later he was slightly breathless and had pocketed the entire series. Apparently they were just in his cousin's line. He paid the price Velten asked without a murmur.

When Velten reported to Mattersen it was found that he had made a clear profit. The major took the money, commenting that the staff's expense account was very much in Velten's debt.

"When I put on this uniform," Velten told him, "I never imagined I would be going into the pornography business."

The major growled something about there being "far worse things in the Army," and Velten was dismissed.

He ran to the elevator and went to his room on the fifth floor. If he hurried he could get a ride to Paris with Merrem, who had to collect some equipment there. He packed his Brussels suit, the tie and the beret into a weekend bag. He also put in a bulky parcel containing new potatoes, vegetables and butter from the Versailles market. In addition, Schloyka had supplied him with a slab of steak out of mess rations.

He had timed it nicely. As he came out of the building Merrem's car was still in the drive.

"Brrr," he shuddered, seating himself next to Merrem, "I need a change of air. Drop me anywhere in Paris near a métro station. After that you needn't bother about me. I'll get back somehow." How, he had really no idea. But at that moment it was sheer salvation to get away from the whole set-up. He had a sort of feeling he did not need to return once he had parted from Merrem. He just wanted to get away.

In some way Merrem seemed to understand his mood and did not talk. Velten asked him to stop when they reached the place de l'Étoile.

"I'll be at the Colisée at about five o'clock," Merrem told him. "If you want a ride back, that is." Velten nodded. He couldn't have cared less.

He did not need to pay on the subway, and went through the gate without a ticket. That was a prerogative of the victors. He boarded a train going in the direction of Neuilly. Porte Maillot was the very next stop. He got out and went up the boulevard Gouvion St. Cyr.

On a street corner he found a bistro. With a sigh of relief he discovered that the bar was empty at this early hour. Sitting down at one of the tiny tables he asked the corpulent landlady to bring him *une fine.* As she served him she glanced inquisitively at the suitcase and parcel which he had placed on a chair. They soon fell into a desultory conversation. She called her husband:

"Come and hear how well the gentleman speaks French."

They were typical Parisian publicans, with a frank curiosity for everything foreign. When Velten asked the landlord to have a drink with him, the man accepted gratefully.

Having established friendly relations with the man, Velten took the plunge.

"Listen," he said, "I have a request which may sound a little strange to you. In that bag I've got a civilian suit and I'd like to change into it here. I'm off duty, and one feels freer out of uniform."

The landlord immediately suspected some amorous adventure and stroked his mustache with a knowing smile.

"But of course, m'sieur. I'm human myself. Things would be worse still if we men didn't help one another now and again. I was in the army of occupation in the Rhineland myself."

And with a sly smile he proceeded to tell a rather long-winded story about a fräulein in Wiesbaden whose favor he had enjoyed. His wife had meantime disappeared into the kitchen.

The landlord led him into a back room. Velten changed at lightning speed and stuffed his uniform into the suitcase. Just like a clerk in his Sunday best, he thought, as he saw his reflection in the mirror. The landlord was delighted with his appearance and was glad to look after the suitcase. With a friendly nod Velten took his parcel under his arm and left.

It was a wonderful sensation to be an ordinary man in the street. For the first time in ages he felt he really belonged to the scene around him. In uniform his movements had been ungainly and awkward. Now he enjoyed the pleasure of free, unhindered movement.

He quickly found the street and house where Corinne lived. The front door was latched. He pressed the button, and as the release mechanism buzzed the door opened under the pressure of his hand. The light went on in the wide, gloomy hall, and a haggard old woman stuck her prying gray head through the window of the caretaker's room on the right. Velten mentioned Corinne's name. Third floor, he was told. The elevator was out of order.

He climbed the stairs. The house was deathly still. Most of the apartments were probably empty and their occupants in flight. He rang at the door of the apartment and had to wait for several minutes. She was certainly at home, otherwise the ever-alert concierge would not have let him come up. At length he heard a light step and the door was opened a chink. Two black eyes peeped out. She recognized him immediately. With a cry of surprise she pushed back the safety chain and let him in.

"I wouldn't have thought it possible! Bold as brass aren't you?"

"Come on, Corinne, no flattery," Velten parried. "I feel just like a clerk. But what a sight you are! Did I get you out of bed?"

She was wearing a banana-yellow dressing-gown and black slippers. Her hair was in disorder, and he now noticed that it was damp, too.

"Nothing of the sort—I'd just got out of the bath. A pretty strenuous bath it was, too. We've got warm water today for the first time since the occupation. I made up my mind to really enjoy it."

She noticed his parcel.

"You kept your word then. Victor, you really are an angel. Just put it in the kitchen and sit down while I make myself presentable."

She led him into a big airy room with large windows and a few tasteful items of furniture. Corinne's brightness and simplicity had been at work here to good effect. A few excellent pictures, among them a portrait of Corinne, adorned the walls.

"You seem to have climbed several rungs up the social ladder," said Velten appreciatively, knowing her childlike pride. He let himself sink into a comfortable armchair and reached for a book lying on the table.

"I won't be more than ten minutes," Corinne said and disappeared. She left behind the light aroma of her freshly bathed body, blended with that of the bitter-sweet perfume she loved.

Velten stretched out his legs in their blue ready-made trousers and leaned back in his chair, luxuriously absorbing the atmosphere of culture around him. It was a pleasure that he had long been denied. Sitting there, he could hardly believe he had spent whole months in that gray uniform existing in shabby rooms or impersonal, if luxurious, hotel suites to which his military environment had lent a certain transient quality.

Deliberately he lit a cigar, a genuine Henry Clay. The Germans could buy these inexpensively at an elegant shop opposite the Opéra. Then he picked up the book again. It was *Le Pain des Pauvres*—the first work of Thyde Monniers, the Marseilles author. He turned over the pages, letting the magic of the simple, vivid experiences of young Olivier, the seaman and shepherd's son from the south of France, react upon him. He had the book at home in the German translation and found it fascinating to come across the familiar narrative in its original language.

Corinne soon reappeared, carrying two cups of steaming black coffee and two crisp brown croissants on a tray. Velten inspected her critically. She was in trousers and wearing a Circassian jacket of black quilted silk. With its yellow braid it made her boyish figure even more slender and daintier than usual. The collar fitted so close to her neck that her narrow shoulders looked broader than they really were. She used a dark red lipstick; a lighter shade would not have suited her languid pallor. She smiled in response to his commanding look.

"Satisfied, sir?"

"Captivated, madame," said Velten, kissing her hand. She sat opposite him on a low stool and nibbled at her roll.

"You must look the rest of the house over afterwards. Then we'll go in the kitchen and unpack what you've brought. Will there be enough for a meal for the two of us?"

"More than enough, I should think, if you aren't too hungry."

"Victor, I've really starved these last few weeks."

She said it lightly, yet with the slightest trace of a blush.

"I've gone hungry before," she went on, "in my time as an artiste. But that was a different kind of hunger. It was deliberate and had a definite purpose. I knew all the time there was food to be had if I said the word. I was only going without because I wouldn't make any concessions and wanted to go my own way. But to be hungry for no reason at all, simply because there's nothing to eat—that's hard. At first I still had a little English canned food. Then there was still sugar and a few cans of milk. Then there was not even any bread."

Velten was silent with embarrassment. But the moment was already past. "I'll have to give some of the food to the concierge," she said reflectively. "She's not very well off either, and in any case it'll prevent her from wondering too much about my visitor."

She got up to show him the apartment, after a short tour of which they went into the kitchen. Corinne assured him that the butter and meat were a full month's ration. Taking two knives out of a drawer, she handed him one of them. They sat down together to clean the vegetables and peel potatoes. The cauliflower was to be boiled and then steamed in butter in a closed saucepan, Corinne decided, and the steaks done blood-red, "so that the blood trickles out when they're cut." They would finish off with a cheese she had bought.

As soon as the pots were on the stove, Velten went out to his bistro to get some wine. The landlord produced two bottles of Bordeaux, inferring from the purchase that the adventure he had surmised was taking a favorable course. He treated Velten with amicable secretiveness, like some fellow conspirator.

For the sake of convenience they ate in the kitchen. Corinne ate and drank with concentrated enjoyment. Afterwards they took their coffee in the living room. Corinne was pensive and had very little to say. When the telephone rang she jumped up in nervous haste to answer it, but it was only a wrong number. Velten had the impression she was expecting, and simultaneously living in fear of, a particular call. She said nothing, however, and when they found themselves reveling in recollections of their earlier days together she lost her constraint. In this way the evening passed until the hour of curfew (after which he could not appear on the streets in civilian clothes) was almost upon them. He took a quick leave, promising to come again soon or at least to arrange another visit by telephone.

At the bistro he swiftly changed back into uniform, jokingly parrying the landlord's inquisitive and confidential questions about the outcome of the adventure. After they had drunk a quick *fine* together, Velten left with an assurance that he would return soon, perhaps the very next day, for the same purpose. "Always at your service," the landlord told him, beaming with courtesy as he held the door open.

Velten went by métro to the Porte de St. Cloud. As he could no longer meet Merrem, he was hoping for a ride in some vehicle or other. His luck was good. In the very first car he stopped there was a paymaster who was heading for Versailles and who didn't know the exact location of the unit he had to visit. He was only too happy to learn Velten could put him right, and asked no whys or wherefores.

CHAPTER IX

VELTEN began to lead a thoroughly double life. Thanks to Schwierig's conscientiousness and to the casual approach to duty of everyone else, he was able to visit Paris, bag in hand, at least every other day. As a precaution he had privately advised the understanding Hagestein where he could be found in the event of any unforeseen occurrence. At the bistro where his regular transformation took place he was invariably treated as an old friend.

He and Corinne roamed Paris just as they had done in the old days. He felt absolutely safe in his civilian suit. He had a prearranged plan to meet all possible emergencies. Should he get held up by the French police in the course of one of their raids, he could establish his identity as a German by producing his officer's pay-book and special pass. His motives for being in civilian clothes were, in any case, no concern of the French. And if he were picked up by the Germans he would point out that he belonged to the Intelligence branch of the General Staff and say he had been sent to sound out public opinion. Mattersen was sure to cover up for him if they checked back: first, because it conformed to the spirit of the officer corps to do so; and secondly, the little matter of the pornography would hardly encourage the major to adopt too officious an attitude as far as Velten was concerned.

Life had meanwhile become progressively more normal. The curfew had been extended till ten in the evening. Food supplies were running smoothly again, and almost all the restaurants had re-opened. It was an exception for them to eat at Corinne's flat now that they could again visit the places they had frequented in the days of their earlier relationship. At the old Reine Pédauque in the rue de la Pépinière, that ancient establishment dedicated to the legendary web-footed queen, they ate succulent lobster and drank mellow Corton Charlemagne, the only white Corton in existence. With the meat courses they would sip wonderful red burgundies, a heavy, sweetish Nuits St. Georges or a racy Beaune, on whose labels, in Old Franconian and Gothic lettering, were the words:

> This wine shall be drunk only by our gods,
> our ladies and ourselves.
> By the gods standing, by our ladies sitting,
> and by us on our knees.

On one of these occasions they were sitting in a colorful little restaurant on the boulevard de Rochechouart. Velten loved the place because of the gay mixture of people from all walks of life who gathered at its long tables—eating, drinking, gossiping, laughing and filling the air with a lively hum of unaffected gaiety. A mustached proprietor in a blue apron supervised the bustling waitresses from behind his counter. The girls wore black dresses and red-and-white check aprons of the same material as the wine-stained tablecloths. The walls were decorated with antique china and kettles and cans of yellow brass and red copper.

"Geneviève, another half-bottle," Velten had been about to call

71

to the buxom beetle-browed Corsican girl who was waiting on them—and then the words stuck in his throat. There was actually a man in uniform coming in—into this place where one seldom saw a stranger, let alone a soldier. And that man was none other than good old Hagestein. He was accompanied by an unprepossessing civilian with a black patch over his right eye, and the pair of them were conducting some business or other with the proprietor. Hagestein, vigilant as ever, cast his gaze around the crowded restaurant as he talked and soon spotted Velten and his companion. With a broad grin on his face he bore straight down on their table. Velten had no choice but to effect a muttered introduction.

"Well, well," said Hagestein, "Mr. Velten dressed up as a Frenchman. Since you come to feed your face here as a civilian, I'd better tell you where the dainty morsels they serve you with come from." He proudly informed them that for some time past he had been catering for a number of Parisian *restaurateurs* who needed lobster and various other delicacies in short supply.

He and Velten spoke French out of consideration for Corinne, and the nearby guests were already pricking up their ears. Velten sensed how unpleasant the conversation was for her and strove to end it. Fortunately Hagestein was required that very moment for the negotiations with the proprietor; as soon as he had taken his leave they left quickly.

"I'll never go anywhere with you again where we're likely to run into your brother officers," Corinne told him when they were outside.

"Next time I'll take you to a place where I guarantee you won't meet any," Velten assured her.

On none of their extensive excursions through the city had they ever had such an unexpected encounter as this. They seldom went anywhere near the usual focal points of sight-seeing and pleasure-seeking—the place de l'Opéra, the Champs-Élysées, Montmartre, or Montparnasse. They had been on the Île St. Louis and seen its drowsy, shaded streets of old middle-class houses with broad doorways and silent courtyards. They had enjoyed the unique view of Paris from the famous cemetery of Père Lachaise.

When they visited the cemetery of Montmartre, that idyllic nook in the stony sea of houses under the iron archway where the métro emerges as an overhead railway, they found two graves adorned with fresh flowers. One was the marble slab commemorating Marguerite Gauthier, and the other the somewhat tasteless monument to Heinrich Heine. Velten asked the caretaker who on earth had had the courage to bring flowers for Heine, the forefather of all Jewish émigrés from Prussian Germany. The man scratched himself behind his ear.

"Real live German officers—believe it or not! Quite a few of them come here," he declared, seeing their astonished glances. "They look at the grave, and then some of them come back with flowers. No one'll ever get to the bottom of these Germans."

Corinne, who was in a rather soft-hearted mood that day, was quite moved. "You see," she said, "there's many an opinion you can't kill with political programs. Perhaps the poet's spirit is after all stronger than the will of your Führer."

By the time they left the cemetery it was almost evening. "Today," she told Velten, "I'm going to take you to a place where no German will surprise us. But you must try not to forget you're supposed to be a French civilian."

Something in her tone told him she had at last taken a long-considered decision and that he was destined to experience some revelation or other that evening. They went by subway to Villiers, where they got out. Corinne took him along the rue de Tocqueville into a district of small streets and back lanes.

"Don't get alarmed," she smiled, "but this is un quartier mal famé. In peacetime the police used to keep a sharp lookout around these parts. Gambling and opium dens. Now and again there was a stabbing affair and the next morning there'd be a corpse in the gutter."

They turned off to the right into a narrow street where most of the houses were one-storied. Almost every one of them was a tavern. Rue de la Félicité, Velten read on the plaque.

"Now I'm really beginning to wonder what raptures you're leading me into."

"Whatever happens, you'll get a good meal, and there may even be a stimulating conversation with some people who are worth getting to know."

Flabby women sprawled at the windows of the houses in the

73

warmth of the summer evening, watching the children play in the street. There was a smell of refuse, sewage and cats. They halted before a narrow-fronted two-story house. The ground floor was a tavern and its narrow window was heavily curtained. A sign over the doorway proclaimed the place to be "Chez Tante Amélie." A pale young man with insipid blond hair parted in the middle was leaning against the door-post. He was in shirtsleeves and had his arms folded.

" 'Evening, Corinne," he smiled. He made way for them with a smile and nodded a "Bon soir, m'sieur," to Velten too. There was a peculiar familiarity about both greetings which had none of the professional politeness of a *restaurateur*.

"Bon soir, Gaston," Corinne replied. "Any guests there yet?"

No, Gaston told her, they were the first. But some of the others would certainly be coming. "Some of the others," Velten noted.

Inside was a small room containing five or six tables. A door at the back led to the kitchen. On the left was the bar, the *zinc,* stocked with a battery of bottles. The proprietor's wife behind it was a mulatto with a complexion like café au lait. She had large, soft animal eyes and her small, painted lips were parted. Velten noticed from the greeting they exchanged that she and Corinne were on familiar and friendly terms. Constance smiled at him in the same uninhibited manner as the young man at the entrance. Corinne introduced him simply as "Victor, a friend of mine." There were no questions.

They sat down at a table by the wall opposite the bar. The land-lady brought them the drinks they ordered—a Noilly and cassis for Corinne and a gin and French for Velten. Velten was amazed to find they had real English gin.

"Would you like to eat right away, Corinne, or are you going to wait for the others?" asked Gaston, who had now come inside.

"Let's start," said Corinne, "or else it'll get too late."

Gaston seemed surprised.

"Why, you know you don't have to bother about curfew when you're with us." He darted an appraising look at Velten. There was suddenly a feeling of embarrassment and uncertainty.

"All right, Gaston," said Corinne. "We'll see how the evening turns out." Gaston went into the kitchen.

74

"There's no menu," Corinne told Velten. "We just take pot luck. But Gaston and Constance never disappoint you. Not since supplies got normal again, anyway."

As they were nibbling their crayfish tails and drinking a light dry white wine a new guest appeared and exchanged friendly handshakes with the *patron* and his wife just as Corinne had done. He was a lean little man with a shock of white hair. He must have been somewhere in his middle sixties.

"Now, pull yourself together, my little civilian," Corinne whispered as the newcomer approached their table.

"Aha, Corinne in a tête-à-tête with a strange man. Is that why we've seen so little of you recently?"

"Please sit down, Caporal," said Corinne. There was respect in her voice. "Caporal," Velten reflected. That wasn't his name. What a queer way to address anyone.

He took a closer look at the man, who was regarding him with a smile. It was the face of an intellectual. The mouth was ascetic and surrounded by sharp wrinkles. The deep-seated, clever eyes were mournful, but seemed to hide a certain kindness. There was a high, rugged brow below the white hair. Scepticism and generosity, intelligence and experience intermingled in his vital countenance. But—corporal! It suited the man about as much as it would to call me sergeant, Velten mused.

Corinne did not mention the name of her "corporal." She introduced Velten as "Victor," a friend of many years' standing. The old man sat down opposite them and raised the glass Gaston had brought to his lips slowly.

"You're a foreigner," he told Velten after exchanging a few initial formalities with him in French.

"Yes," Velten lied, "I'm Dutch."

Corinne threw him a look of merriment from the side and nudged his leg with her knee as if to say: "Look out, now you're in for it!" It was no idle warning. The old man, who until that moment had spoken impeccable, extremely cultured French, switched with no apparent effort into equally perfect Dutch.

"Where do you come from then?"

"From Mokum Aleph," Velten returned glibly, "where all the smart boys come from."

75

He would have done better not to use this Jewish slang expression for Amsterdam, with which he had hoped to fake a little local color. For the other immediately began to jabber like a Jewish street trader who had never left the district between Rembrandthuis and Waterlooplein. He had an amazing knowledge of the city and juggled with names like Kattenburgh, Rapenburgh and Uylenburgh and other parts of Amsterdam's Jewish district. Although Velten could acquit himself pretty convincingly in the dialects and slang of Dutch, the old man was very much better at it. After Velten had stumbled once or twice, the old man planted his arms on the table. He paused for an instant, looking from one to the other in amusement.

"Wouldn't it be better if we spoke your mother tongue, verehrter deutscher Freund?"

Velten began to go hot and cold. The Corporal's German was just as perfect as his French and Dutch. Velten preferred not to answer immediately. The old man acknowledged his silent admission with a smile and turned to Corinne.

"I've already realized that you're aware of his real identity," he said in French. "But what's the whole story?"

"There's no cause for suspicion, Caporal," she replied. "I was sure you'd get wise to him."

"The fact that you brought him here is good enough for me," the Corporal told her soothingly. "Apart from that he seems a pleasant enough fellow. Émigré?"

"No," she said, and looked him in the face. "He's a German officer."

The old man whistled softly through his teeth.

"I couldn't hold out any longer," said Corinne. "We're old friends from earlier days. He came across me again quite by chance. I didn't want to hold any secrets back. He must understand me for what I am. I just had to bring him here."

"You know the responsibility's yours and that you must accept the consequences in the event of . . ." He left the rest unsaid.

"If it were possible to deceive oneself to that extent," Corinne retorted, "the other thing couldn't be any worse. What else is left to us but the bond which links ordinary human beings? If we were

76

once to lose that too . . ." She looked fondly at Velten and gave his hand a secret squeeze under the table.

Velten now felt the moment had come for him to abandon the role of silent listener in an argument which was revolving around his own head.

"I feel most honored that you should devote so much attention to me," he said to the old man. "But don't you think you owe me an explanation? After all, I'm in a public place. You have Corinne's word for it that this concealment of my nationality was done in Corinne's interest and not from any evil intent. So what's the point of all this talk about me? What's going on here anyway?"

The old man's reply was carefully phrased: "You won't hear the answer to that from my lips. But if you should find it out for yourself"—"and he'll see soon enough when the boys come," he interpolated to Corinne—"then I don't think Corinne will have any reason to be disappointed in you." And with a look of heartfelt sincerity he held out his hand over the table. Velten took it unhesitatingly.

"And if we are mistaken about you," the old man went on, his eyes once again sceptical, "it still won't matter much. There's nothing but our lives at stake." He said it quite undramatically and turned his attention to his loaded plate.

Though their conversation covered a number of topics they carefully avoided anything explosive. The old man gave a connoisseur's appreciation of the Bordeaux they were drinking; he criticized the style of Paul Valéry; he talked of the charms of the Scottish highlands. He seemed to know most of the world and gave a remarkable demonstration of his unique talent for languages. It was impossible to ascertain his profession or identity. In contrast to the usual frankness with which Frenchmen discuss their own affairs and ask about those of others, personal matters were left out of this conversation.

Velten was so fascinated by this man's unusual personality that he entirely forgot to wonder into what sort of environment he had wandered. The three of them were so immersed in their talk that Velten was hardly aware that three other persons had entered one after the other. They had greeted the Corporal with the same

77

respect and Corinne with the same familiarity. Each had given Velten a friendly nod. Apparently Corinne and the old man made his presence acceptable. There were no introductions. The new-comers were now dining at a table near the kitchen door. One of them was a stocky young man in his late twenties. His appearance and manner betokened a worker. He had a hard face and taciturn manner and was addressed by the others as Jules. The second, a man of about forty with soft features and well-kept hands, was, despite his layman's clothes, obviously a priest. They called him Rix—a cover-name which later proved to be a derivation of Vercin-getorix, the Gallic leader in the liberation struggle against Caesar. The third was a young Jew with a pale face and melancholy eyes. It was not difficult to tell from his pronunciation that he was an émigré from Germany. The others called him Léon. Everyone was on friendly terms. Velten did his best to follow the conversation at the neighboring table, which was not difficult in that uninhibited atmosphere. Constance and Gaston, who had not noticed the clash between the Corporal and Velten, also put in a word now and again. Occasionally some item of information would be relayed to the Corporal from the nearby table, or else one of them would reply to a question from him. There was a great deal of play with cover-names, some of which Velten swiftly comprehended. "Nono," for instance, clearly meant unoccupied France, the *zone non-occupée*.

"Fritz" was, clearly enough, a German soldier. An "orphan" was the term used for a soldier who had either evaded or escaped from captivity and had to be supplied with identification papers. There was also much talk about groups of people in the coastal towns, radio communications and liaison personnel.

Velten leaned over to the Corporal just as he was devoting all his attention on a leg of chicken. "I'm already in the picture," he murmured. "You seem to be doing things in a pretty big way, I must say."

"This chicken really is extraordinarily tender," said the old man with a merry smile in his eyes. "I must urge you to try a leg. Or do you prefer the white meat from the breast?"

Velten looked at Corinne. What could have brought her into this business? She, who had always been so proud of going her own way, belonged to a resistance group which undoubtedly subjected her to cast-iron discipline. Corinne was marching—but for what? For France? For freedom? Ridiculous. Watchwords and slogans had never before made any impression on her. It couldn't be the few weeks of hunger which had changed her so.

Suddenly Velten jumped up in alarm.

"My God," he cried wildly, "the curfew! How are you going to get home, Corinne? I must go and get . . . I mean I must get changed."

Although he had spoken in French the others were struck by something disturbing in his behavior. Though the Corporal and Corinne remained quietly in their seats, the others had got to their feet and come closer to the table. Constance and Gaston also joined them. Velten had failed to notice the latter barring the door and drawing the blinds a good half-hour ago.

"What's biting him?" Jules asked the Corporal. His voice sounded brutal and his face was hard.

"Nothing in particular," the old man answered lightly. "He's a friend of Corinne's she brought along this evening. A German officer, incidentally."

"*What?*" Jules's mouth hung open with amazement. The priest rubbed his hands in embarrassment. The German Jew's eyes had gone dark. His face was as white as chalk. Constance's eyes wandered from one face to another like those of a frightened gazelle.

"He's in with us, you mean?" Jules asked at length, a trace of conciliation in his voice.

"No, not in the least," said Corinne. She got up and stood by Velten. He felt her arm rest lightly on his shoulder. "You should know by now that human feelings come first with me. The rest after."

"The girl is crazy!" Jules shrieked. "D'you know what this means for us—and for him?"

"A little game with death," the Corporal said gently. "Time you got used to that, Jules."

"With death?" asked Jules. He took a deep breath. "Then it's his life he's playing with. Not ours."

He looked round the circle of his companions.

"I think we'd better talk to him out in the back yard. You, Léon, Gaston and me."

He stepped close up to Velten, who could feel Corinne's arm trembling on his shoulder. His hard gaze bored into Velten's eyes. He caught the man's hot, wine-laden breath.

"Hand over your gun!"

"Pas de conneries," said the Corporal, suddenly at Velten's side. "You can see the man means no harm, Jules. I bet he hasn't got so much as a pocket-knife on him."

Velten released himself from Corinne's arm. Without a word he slipped off his jacket and handed it to Jules. He pulled out the lining of his trouser pockets and turned round to show that there was no suspicious bulge in his hip pocket.

With an embarrassed air Jules returned his jacket without feeling it. "But what's the sense of it all? You're endangering our cause and him too."

He shrugged his shoulders as he said it, already somewhat mollified.

"It has a very definite sense, my dear fellow," the Corporal told him. It struck Velten what authority his words had in this circle. "It means we're human first and foremost. All of us, on this and on the other side of the barrier. It means that you'll lose the fight for your motherland if you're a better Frenchman than you are a human being."

"Human!" raved the Jew, who had been staring dumbly at Velten till that moment. "Human, did you say? Tell *them* to be human beings first! They killed my family. They tortured me."

Quivering in every limb, he turned abruptly away and flopped on to a chair. The priest moved over to him and started to comfort him in an undertone.

"Listen, Léon," said the Corporal, "Victor doesn't look as if he'd have murdered your parents. But that's not the question. He's entered our circle, and you'll not persuade me to let anything horrible come of it. I've told you all before; I'll have nothing to do with your principles. I'm not fighting for a program. That policy will hold good here as long as I have any influence over you. What conclusions this German has to draw from his evening with us are something he must sort out for himself. As far as you are concerned I'm making myself responsible for ensuring that he leaves this house tomorrow morning in the same state as he entered it."

80

He turned to Velten.

"You can't go out on the streets now. I won't take the risk of your being picked up in this neighborhood and asked where you've come from. There are several rooms upstairs. We can spend the night there without disturbing each other. You will appreciate that we didn't come here to sleep."

The others raised no objections. By asserting his authority the Corporal seemed to have settled the matter. Velten had not uttered a word. He felt relieved that the old man's directions spared him the necessity of making decisions. Even now he refrained from comment in order not to endanger his position by some inept remark.

Léon got up and walked in silence to the door at the back. The others followed. Without waiting to be told, Velten went along with them. Gaston, being the last to leave, put out the light. They passed through a small kitchen in which there was a lamp burning dimly over the hearth. They went through a door into a dark passage, Jules lighting the way with a flashlight. Some narrow wooden steps led upstairs. One behind the other they climbed the creaking stairway. At the top was a small landing from which there was a view, through a single window-pane blurred with age, of what appeared to be the back yard. Against the wall there was a basin with a tap dripping into it. Opposite was a door, which Jules had already opened. He switched on the light beyond, thereby brightly lighting the staircase. They entered, and Velten found himself in a small room in the right-hand corner of which two sofas stood at right angles against the wall. In front of them was a low table and two armchairs. The windows were hung with thick red plush curtains. A few family photographs adorned the walls. The whole effect was one of mustiness and hidden vice. Perhaps one of Corinne's gambling dens had once been located here. A door on the right evidently led into a further room.

"Come on, men, let's get down to work," said the priest, going over to the door and opening it just enough to slip through and not so wide as to reveal the interior of the other room to prying eyes. No light was put on until Jules, Léon and Gaston had entered in the same manner. Constance, who had been busying herself

81

at a little cupboard, put a bottle of cognac and three glasses on the table.

"You know where there's more in case that isn't enough," she told Corinne, who nodded dumbly. The mulattress cast Velten a trusting look from her velvet eyes. "I'm glad it's turning out so well—for you and us." The last part sounded more like a pleading question, and Velten gave her an affirmative nod. She disappeared into the next room with two bottles under her arm.

"Give me a shout if I'm needed," the Corporal called after her. Then he pulled a heavy plush curtain across the door. Not a sound was to be heard from within.

Corinne had huddled up on one of the sofas and was leaning against the wall with a few cushions in her back. With her arms twined round her drawn-up legs she watched Velten out of half-closed eyes. Her look was full of meaning. They were accomplices now, it seemed to tell him: "This is how I really am and this is how you must take me."

The Corporal had switched on a standard lamp with a yellow silk shade and put out the bright light on the ceiling. He indicated one of the armchairs by the table, and Velten sat down in it. The old man pulled out a packet of Gauloises and offered one to Velten.

"No, thanks," he said. "I haven't acclimatized myself to that extent. I can't take black tobacco."

He drew a package of Players from his pocket. "Booty," he explained, offering one to Corinne.

"We often get them too," said the Corporal, blowing the smoke of his black cigarettes through his nose. "But not as booty."

With meticulous care he uncorked the bottle and poured the amber liquid into the glasses.

"Let us drink, Victor," he said. "Let us drink to life—to the great life which is greater and stronger than all political programs. Let us drink to the freedom which is more powerful and more sorrowful than all hate and suffering. To the freedom to which all of us are born and all of us damned."

They raised their glasses and looked into one another's eyes. Velten felt curiously touched by that strange toast. How did this man and Corinne come to be mixed up with those others in there, he wondered.

The Corporal seemed to have sensed Velten's thoughts. "Those people sitting next door," he said, "have all got something to fight for. Jules believes in his fatherland; Gaston and Constance are Communists. For the Curé it's his faith. Why the Jewish refugee is with us I don't need to explain to you. You've made such a wonderful mess of things that all those who were once at sword's point are now united against you."

Corinne caught Velten's eye. She sensed how that "you" hurt him.

"Well," said the Corporal with his keen perception of others' sensibilities, "you're all one unit as far as the people in there are concerned. One single authority unified under the same terrible will. How else could they fight with the uncompromising harshness that their struggle demands of them?"

He filled the glasses again and took a deep sip.

"And what have they made of this Europe with their ruthless conglomeration of might!"

Velten was grateful to note that the other had changed from the aggressive *you* to an impersonal *they*.

"What did France mean to those of us who thought themselves the spiritual leaders of the nation? Nothing more than a multitude of warming, cheerful firesides. Our vineyards in the glow of eventide. The cathedrals of our cities. And the proud knowledge that in her thousand-year history France had supplied fuel for the torch lighting the dark road of Western humanity."

"Hasn't my nation contributed its own share to that, too?" Velten interjected.

"Certainly, my boy," said the old man. "The best elements in all the peoples of Europe had long outstripped all the laughable self-interest of nationhood. This pathetic old Europe of ours was longing to escape from the disruption and decay of the nineteenth century." He raised a clenched fist in sudden violence. "These countries didn't only succumb to Hitler's aircraft and artillery! How could there be any will to fight for the maintenance of a European order when it already seemed outmoded? Europe simply lay there and waited for a conqueror. Anybody could have taken her—German or Chinese—so long as he overcame her with the might of a new idea. A new spirit—even if it had come by force of arms—

83

would have been met with shouts of joy. Yes, even if it could only have been felt on the points of bayonets or sensed in the fluttering of a new flag planted on the summit of European thought!"

He let his hands sink. With the bitterness of resignation he continued: "No conqueror came. A ravisher came instead. He brought brute force with him. And just as the clock has been put back centuries in Germany, so are the peoples of Europe now putting theirs back. Once again they are going the way of national hatred, destruction and catastrophe."

For Velten there was a tremendous appeal in the man's arguments. This was how he, too, had always felt and reasoned. Once again he found himself wondering how so independent and strong a spirit as this had become embroiled in the underground work of those conspirators next door and, what was more, how he had come to occupy so obviously dominant a position.

"Let us drink," said the Corporal. He re-filled their glasses and held the half-empty bottle critically up to the light.

"One of the wings on which the soul may soar over the abyss," he reflected. "The other"—this with a sidelong smile at Corinne—"has gone lame on me."

"Don't be cynical, Corporal," she said. "You should know that I've only been soaring on one wing myself for a long time now."

At that moment the curtain over the door to the next room jerked to one side. Constance appeared and cocked her head to the Corporal to indicate that he was wanted. He got up and went inside. Constance smilingly examined the cognac bottle and put a fresh one by it. Then with the grace of a wild animal, she glided to Corinne's side and wound an arm round her shoulder.

"How swcct it was of the old man to save your little Prussian for you," she cooed suggestively. A slight frown of annoyance appeared on Corinne's brow.

"Don't act silly, Constance," she said, releasing herself from the woman's embrace. "You know both of us. There's no warmed-up soup being served here."

"Mon petit chou," cried the mulattress, "you know I'd have been the first to wish you every happiness." And, turning to Velten, she babbled: "Ivon, Corinne's husband, is good at other things beside selling cars. He's one of our best men down in the south. She's had him here for exactly two days since the demobilization."

"Get back in there again," said Corinne with an angry push, "and try to keep a check on your tongue for a change." The woman made a playful curtsy in front of Velten and disappeared.

"Victor," Corinne told him, "I'm angry with myself for bringing you here. You shouldn't be bothered with my problems. But you were a fragment of better times gone by—a vestige of my Paradise Lost."

"Warmed-up soup after all then." Velten stretched out a hand to her and smiled. "I've no regrets or reproaches, my dear. Meeting your Corporal alone has made the adventure worth while."

"It came very near to being more than an adventure," said the Corporal, who had inaudibly re-entered the room. "Invasion or no invasion—that's the question now. And Jules proposed that you should be forced to give information."

Velten shrugged his shoulders. "Some hope. Do you think an unimportant body like me knows more than our generals?"

Corinne showed signs of agitation. "You're surely not going to permit anything like that, are you, Corporal?"

"Don't worry, the question was settled almost before it was raised. Incidentally," he added softly to Corinne, "Ivon has left for Lisbon." Velten's start did not escape him.

"Aha, the German intruder is in the picture," he observed. "An old fox like me should know better than that. But that's enough shop for now!"

He reached for the bottle to pour more drinks. "Drink up," he told Velten with a sly smile, "you've every reason to get well primed. Just imagine how it would be if we were to be raided now! I wouldn't give a *sou* more for your head than ours. Do you think anyone would listen to our explanations?" This was precisely what Velten had just been thinking, and he gulped his cognac down quickly. What a damned fix to be in! A juicy catch for the Germans if they were to break in now. With himself as the *pièce de résistance* at the military tribunal which followed!

"Give me another cognac," Velten said, holding out his glass. "You know you've got me where you want me."

85

"But it excites you just the same," the old man grinned as he replenished the other's glass. "Live dangerously! Isn't that your watchword, too, in the new Germany?"

Velten drank in silence. The alcohol was gradually taking effect. Though he was not drunk, he was conscious of a warm glow surging through his body. He was quite indifferent to the outcome of this business. The strange thrill of his situation had him completely in its spell. He hung eagerly on the words of the old man who, with the rhetorical lucidity of one who is slightly drunk, was propounding a strange and bold philosophy. Since hearing the news of her husband Corinne had become very quiet. She sat there with a faraway look in her eyes and did nothing but raise her glass to her lips from time to time or motion to the old man to refill it.

The latter developed his theories with an ease of expression unusual even in a Frenchman. He used French one moment, German the next and English the next, depending on whatever language best suited the context.

"I am the only one of my comrades," he declared, "who is in this game without any preconceived ideas and without being committed to this or that objective doctrine of values. Even our brave Corinne—whose manly spirit comes closest to my own—is propelled more by the powerful motor of her husband, who like Jules gives complete allegiance to his fatherland. Strange that I still enjoy authority over them—or is it because of that? They gave me the name Corporal after the first Napoleon, but left out the 'little.' Is that a sign of insufficient greatness or of less affection?

"You see, when everything comes crashing down, when 'fatherland' becomes an empty phrase, when God is no longer anything but a metaphysical cypher, when humanity's ideals are trampled in the gutter by dirty jackboots, all that is left in this icy solitude is the naked ego—the consciousness of the individual cast out into the cruel freedom of conscience and responsibility towards himself alone. All other bonds go to the devil. Think of the development of modern science. Where chemistry with its many affinities once created more and more new compounds and kept re-integrating the elements of our planet, atomic physics have now brought about a radical dissociation. The life-giving molecules which built up a world of carbonic compounds are disintegrating into the atoms of their elements. And these atoms are reduced to functions so remote from our comprehension that we don't know whether they are matter or energy. Yes, power and matter, those mighty deities of the nineteenth century, have been dethroned to make room for a phenomenon which is either the two in one or else a third which we do not yet know.

"When Copernicus wrested the earth from the focus of human attention in the Middle Ages and cast it into the whirl of the universe like a fleck of dust amid dancing microbes—a ball for the cosmic forces to play with—a similar shock must have convulsed mankind: but Man has found other anchorages since then. Descartes countered despair with his recognition of human existence based on human thought. Newton found gravity to be a regulating force in the apparent chaos of the worlds. Leibnitz devised cosmic harmony as an intrinsic equilibrium of forces. Darwin evolved his doctrine on the development of all organic matter as a reassuring pledge of perpetuity. Spencer extended this for society to the theory of the differentiation and integration of forces. The nineteenth century's optimistic belief in progress was the result. Its heritage is still preserved today by the cadres of the socialist and communist movements. There was radiant promise in our own great Revolution; and the afterglow of the torch it kindled at the threshold of that century has lasted to illuminate the chaos of our own age. Today this light offsets even more sharply the shadows cast by the débris of our hopes."

He had long ago uncorked the second bottle, and now he helped himself and Velten to more brandy. Corinne had slumped to one side in a doze, only starting up now and again when a loud word was spoken.

The Corporal quoted Nietzsche—in German: " 'Wer das verlor, was du verlorst, macht nirgends halt.' Just as we today no longer have any standpoint from which to comprehend cosmic happenings, so have the revolutionization of the masses, the atomization of social and national orders and the collapse of all ethical standards created a chaos in which we grope despairingly for new points of support. In this sense your Hitler is a terrible revolutionary. A social atom-splitter. The tear-the-bandage-from-their-eyes kind of revolutionary. A disillusionist.

87

"What remains? Nothing more than the gray but sublime realization of human freedom. The recognition of human freedom on the basis of human existence. The perception that *I* am, that *I* exist as a character of my own with these or those qualities, that my being, plunged into the uniqueness of my existence, compels me to accept the responsibility of going my own way and condemns me to the freedom of my conscience. Such is the realization which I owe to this era of disintegration.

"Armed with my freedom of conscience and convinced of the essential purpose of my existence, I stand and face the earthly forces of this age. These forces, however, are currently incorporated in the powers which have broken loose over France and Europe—the powers under which Germany is suffering just as much as ourselves. This conviction gives me more courage and confidence to face life and death than my companions can find in the obligations to which they cling.

"Perhaps," the old man added with a smile, "that is why they made me their leader."

Such was the case the old man presented. As a philosophy it was at once infinitely sad and immensely intrepid. Velten realized that it could not make the slightest difference to this independent spirit if Corinne's ill-considered introduction of a stranger were to lead him to the ultimate consequences of his illegal activity. He incorporated that spirit of resistance which had to resist simply because it was a spirit. He had no program to fight for. He fought his own fight. And he would fight against every force which was not of the spirit, regardless of the scheme behind it. Thus did Velten that night come to regret his own weakness and the way he had drifted along in the wake of the power whose certainty of success had so overwhelmed him.

The night had drawn on. Constance appeared with a tray bearing coffee and a simple breakfast. Velten had not noticed her go downstairs some time previously to carry a similar repast into the next room. Having attended to the Corporal, Corinne and himself, she went back in again.

Corinne awakened from her doze, and the three of them sipped the hot coffee. The Corporal, sobering from the effect of all they had to drink and his own flights of eloquence, now spoke of simpler things—the old farmhouse on the Norman coast where he used to spend his summers; the way of life of the peasantry in those parts; and so on.

"I think you can now go out in perfect safety," he told them at last.

He was tired and visibly suppressed a yawn. Velten wanted to settle the bill with Constance, but the old man firmly declined.

"You were our guest last night," he said. "This place isn't really a regular restaurant. Besides, it would be better if you went without saying goodbye to the others."

Having got the key from Gaston, he took them downstairs.

"All clear," he said, opening the door and cautiously surveying the street. He gave Velten a farewell slap on the shoulder. "Au revoir in this life or another."

They stood out in the empty street. The cool morning air made them shiver, but it did them good after the stuffy warmth indoors. As they walked in silence down the street two policemen came round the corner. Corinne immediately clung to Velten's arm and snuggled close up to him. The two *flics* came straight towards them along the narrow pavement and glanced at them sharply as they stepped to one side. Then one of them began to smile and clicked his tongue. The ruse had succeeded. The two men evidently took them for a couple of lovers who had spent a clandestine night together in some local establishment which specialized in that form of hospitality.

Corinne stole a look over her shoulder when they came to the corner. The two policemen had passed Chez Tante Amélie without a sign of interest.

"They're most punctilious about their obligations to the occupying power, our police," she whispered. "You've always got to be on your guard against them."

They walked along the rue Jouffroy and turned off to the left into the boulevard Malesherbes.

"Let's enjoy the early morning and wander round the streets a bit," Corinne suggested. So well did they play their role of two closely intertwined lovers that a group of workmen coming towards them laughed into their weary faces.

"T'as fait la foire chez la fille?" one of them called to Velten.

"Ta gueule!" he retorted, and Corinne stuck her tongue out. The workers roared with mirth.

By the time they entered the dewy park of Monceau the turf and trees were already being warmed by the sun's rays. Girls were exercising their dogs and keepers were busy tidying the paths. No scene could have been more peaceful.

"Well, Victor," said Corinne, "it's goodbye. It was nice to be with you again and experience the echo of a feeling you and I once called love. I was afraid at first you might want to start off again at the place where it ended. But I think I really expected you all along to feel as I did. I'm grateful to you for not disappointing me."

A warm wave of emotion surged up in Velten, for she had for the first time addressed him with the familiar "tu" of earlier days.

"Corinne," he said, gently stroking her arm, "we both sensed that that was all over. I know that you weren't moved any more than I was by the ties each of us has formed since. Even if they hadn't existed we could still never have tried to recreate what had become just a dreary routine. Let us take both memories with us to be cherished in future years: the happy exuberance of the past and today's sad smile."

Corinne stopped and looked him straight in the eyes: "You do know then—this really is goodbye. I am very happy that you know what road I am taking, and I hope for your sake that you will find your own. I'm not ungrateful, Victor. That fragment of life with you was wonderful, then and now.—My dear," she said with a sudden rush of tenderness, and held up her cheek to be kissed. Velten held her for as long as it takes a heart to beat.

Then the book was closed. They left the park. The street was busy now, and as they walked along together they were as cool and composed as two acquaintances who happened to be going in the same direction. The pretense of being in love was no longer necessary.

They got into a subway train at Villers station, feeling thankful to the crowd for making personal conversation impossible. They got out at the Porte de Champerret and hurried to the street where Corinne lived. As they came to it Velten stopped dead in his tracks and pointed to a military vehicle parked a short distance from Corinne's house. It bore the tactical sign of the Army Group. The driver was behind the wheel.

"That must be Hagestein," said Velten. "Something's up."

They found Velten's tavern already open. The landlord was obviously gratified at this unexpected insight into the love affair he believed Velten to be having. All their protests could not deter him from standing a round of drinks, in the course of which Corinne did a perfect act as the soldier's sweetheart. Velten soon had his uniform on.

"It's a good thing for me to see you in that get-up once more," Corinne whispered. "It makes everything much easier."

Beaming with delight, the landlord did his best to appear discreet at the sight of what he imagined to be a fond farewell. He was disappointed when Velten took leave of both of them with a handshake. Obviously he had expected something more.

Velten found Hagestein by the car.

"Thank God you've come!" cried Hagestein. "The devil alone knows where you've been prowling instead of looking after your girl friend. Lucky you'd given me the address. That old hag of a concierge wouldn't talk, though. Made out she didn't know a tenant of that name."

With a tremendous feeling of relief Velten gathered that there was nothing seriously amiss.

"I got caught in some dive last night," he lied. "Just wanted to look in here and pass the time of day."

"Too late for that," was Hagestein's reply. "I came to get you because we're moving today. Schwierig has left already with the main staff. You'll have to work today and leave tonight with the operations staff. We didn't get the order till last night."

"Where are we going?"

"Angers."

"So we *are* going there, then."

They all knew that accommodation had been requisitioned in Angers as a precautionary measure. But there had always been the possibility that they might go nearer the coast.

"That means there's to be no landing in England," Velten said when they had climbed into the car. He lowered his voice in case

91

the driver was listening. He was amused at the thought that the people on the staff had been kept guessing as much as the Corporal and his comrades about whether England was to be invaded or not. Now they knew: the venture was abandoned.

"What are we actually supposed to do in Angers?" he asked.

"Enjoy life—what else?" retorted the incorrigible Hagestein.

As they drove past the bistro, Corinne was standing in the doorway. Unnoticed by the other occupants of the car Velten managed to give her a reassuring wave.

On their arrival at Versailles, Velten got Hagestein to let him out at the prefecture before he drove on to deal with various mysterious matters of his own.

There was considerable confusion in the sub-prefect's office. Most of the military equipment had already been loaded, only a radio having been left behind so that Velten could listen to the day's broadcasts. He stretched himself out in one of the red leather armchairs to catch up on the sleep he had missed last night. He instructed Trooper Rudolf Altenkirch, who was likewise in the rear party, when to wake him.

"The old place takes it out of you, doesn't it?" Altenkirch remarked in his ponderous Brandenburg dialect.

Velten resorted to military authority:

"Don't be impertinent. I was away on duty."

"Jawohl, Herr Sonderführer," Altenkirch assented, standing to attention in a slightly exaggerated fashion and thinking his own thoughts.

CHAPTER X

VELTEN left for Angers late in the evening. It was already dark when he left Versailles. This time he was alone with the driver. Hagestein had not shown up again and Altenkirch had started off earlier with the rest of the equipment.

They made for Chartres, taking the lonely highway which passed through Rambouillet. Now that hostilities were over movement in columns was no longer obligatory. The country seemed peaceful enough in the general exhaustion which had followed the campaign. Had the German command given any thought to the resistance that was already beginning to crystallize in the prostrate people of France?

Velten frankly admitted to himself that his experience in the dingy house in the rue de la Félicité had severely shaken him. There really were people, it seemed, who refused to be daunted by the spectacular successes of a policy of violence. Inevitably this resistance would toughen and expand: popular sympathy was bound to increase the clearer it became that the war was to drag on indefinitely. The abandonment of the invasion made it clear that "lightning war" had found its natural limits on the Atlantic and Channel coasts. But it was not these external circumstances which exposed the limitations of brute force. The decisive factor was that human spirit and human will were steadfastly opposing it in its very hour of triumph.

Velten had the feeling that the last time he had put on his uniform in the back room of the bistro he had somehow failed to resume that spurious military identity with which he had almost willingly allowed himself to become infused in recent months. Never before had uniform and military routine been so far away as they were at this moment. His military role felt like a mask. If he had even taken an oath of loyalty he would now have had to regard it as broken. It was one of the peculiarities of his staff job, however, that neither he nor Schwierig had ever been sworn in. Mattersen, ever the cynical realist, had made it clear that he had no time for this pantomime.

"Deserters get shot anyway, oath or no oath!" was the way he put it, thereby expressing the essence of military coercion in one terse formula.

Velten wouldn't run away. He knew only too well how little he possessed of the stuff that makes heroes and martyrs. But inwardly he had finally deserted the night before when he shamefacedly recognized how long he had ridden on the band-wagon. It did not occur to him to wonder whether this revulsion was due to his appreciation of the portent of spiritual resistance to barbaric brutality, or whether it had come about because the course of the war now gave such sinister corroboration to the Chief-of-Staff's aphorism on the Second Battle of the Marne. The question whether he was a genuine adherent of the spirit of resistance, or merely a little man of the masses dashed to and fro by the tides of fortune and adversity, must therefore remain unanswered.

The cathedral of Chartres, seen in the wan light of an overcast moon, was shrouded in shadow. In that gloom the simplicity of early Gothic was unusually impressive. The whole edifice rose up from the mists of obscurity to the light of true faith.

At Angers they quickly found the Duc d'Angers, the hotel where he was to be quartered. The hour was late and the town seemed dead. The old servant who came shuffling out in his slippers in answer to Velten's ring had obviously been warned by Schwierig of his arrival. He opened the iron-studded door to the courtyard to let the car in and then took Velten to his room. Velten looked round. It was a simple clean hotel room of a marked provincial character. He smiled when he noticed the inevitable bidet in the corner by the washstand. After undressing, Velten sank into the broad double bed and soon passed into a long and dreamless sleep.

It turned out next morning that only a small section of the staff was accommodated at the hotel. Like the interpreters, the others living there were officers who, because their duties were unimportant from a strictly military point of view, had a negligible social status—the chaplains, the paymasters, the mess officer and so on. A back room had been turned into a dining room, and an Alsatian cook prepared them monotonous meals.

The headquarters had split up into a number of small groups, all of whom had apparently adopted Hagestein's campaign slogan about the necessity of enjoying life. Since each of these more or less independent units had settled in one or another of the neighboring châteaux, carrying out the most elementary duties led to a large consumption of petrol which was at variance with the existing shortage.

The camp commandant had chosen the residence of a man in the liqueur business, one of the city's most important industries. Be-

94

fore long the pretty secretary who had been left behind in Düsseldorf put in an appearance. Blüthner, the commanding officer of the defense company, was sent to collect her by car so that "Camp" could cope with his paper work. She went riding with him on horses from the liqueur millionaire's stable.

The general commanding the engineer troops had his own château, as had the artillery commander and the chief of the supporting air formations. On the other hand, Goebel, the judge whom Velten had accompanied to Orléans, had arranged for a private lodging.

The most select section of the headquarters, that headed by the Commander-in-Chief and Chief-of-Staff, resided in the Château Serrant, a vast moated castle built at about the turn of the sixteenth century. This mass of ramparts and ditches lay on the Loire, not far from the road to Nantes. Finding it too expensive to maintain as a private residence, its owner, the Duc de la Trémouille, opened it as a museum and allowed people to visit it for a small fee. For the accommodation of his own family he had built a modern country house in the adjoining park. This was where the chief intelligence officer and his branch were housed. The operations staff was as little troubled by the Duke's economies as by the inconveniences of the ancient pile. The Commander-in-Chief used the Duke's suite and his Chief-of-Staff slept in the Duchess's historic four-poster. When either of them wanted a bath, they had eau-de-Cologne brought by the gallon, for the water which ran in the marble bathtubs came from the lake, and stank.

A big banquet was given at the castle. The Führer had delivered a pompous speech in the Reichstag solemnizing the victory and had announced the promotions of his generals. The Army Group Commander, together with a number of others, had become a field-marshal. He had taken the salute at a parade that same afternoon. The tables were laid in the big ballroom, over by the high French windows which opened on to the terrace. Candles supplied the illumination. The only drink served was champagne. They sat down to dinner in fours at the small tables. The Commander presided at a larger table, surrounded by his closest colleagues. Drinking etiquette was observed with a parade-ground precision which Velten found amusing. A mess waiter appeared at the table at which

Velten and three other officers were seated. Standing stiffly to attention he announced:

"The Commander-in-Chief wishes to drink to Herr Captain!"

The officer thus addressed sprang promptly to his feet, took his glass in his hand and adopted a rigid stance facing the Commander. The glass was raised with a sharp jerk to the prescribed height, its brim opposite a certain tunic button. When the Commander finally deigned to raise his glass and direct a patronizing smile at the officer concerned, the recipient of this distinction duly whisked his own up to his mouth. Then he returned the glass smartly to its initial position and inclined his head in a smart bow. The simultaneous crash of spurs as he brought his heels together was most effective.

"Wonderful!" said Velten. "Just like the theater. I always thought they were exaggerating."

The building where the interpreters worked was in the Street of the Good King René, not far from the gloomy walls of the castle which dates back to the time of the Moors. Not only Hagestein and Velten but even Schwierig were seldom to be found at their office. Duty was taken very lightly, for there was really nothing more to do.

There had been much talk about the victorious powers making good their New Order by some decisive act. But there was no sign whatever of a change of policy. One moment the attitude towards conquered France was hesitant and dilatory; the next it was full of inconsistencies. The German authorities tried their hand at making gestures in little, unimportant things which cost them nothing and were calculated to be good propaganda. For instance, the Führer had directed that the horses of the famous cavalry school of Saumur should be returned to the French in recognition of the heroic resistance put up by the cadets to the invaders. When inquiries were made of the different units regarding various individual horses, Army Group Headquarters submitted a "whereabouts unknown" for the stud mare Fatimah, despite the fact that everyone connected with the Commander knew she was in his stable and being ridden by him every morning.

Velten heard this little anecdote from his Brandenburg companion as they stood at the window of the castle library watching some grooms exercise the horses in the paddock.

"I see," said Velten with a laugh. "While the others are working themselves into a sweat looking for the mare, she gets ridden into one every morning by our Chief!"

"If you weren't such an unsoldierly plebeian," the Count told him, "you'd know that a cavalryman of his class doesn't ride his horse into a sweat!"

Smiling in mock condescension, he went on to declare ironically: "What will become of Germany if you proletarians are the only ones to survive? Are you aware that the German nobility has paid an immense toll of blood in this war? Do you think their sacrifice is unintentional?"

Velten frowned. "I suppose it always was the privilege of nobility to die for their warlords. Look, it's even chiseled up there in stone!"

Velten pointed to the fireplace at the far end of the long vault-like library. Above the huge hearth was a life-size equestrian statue in high relief of a de la Trémouille. Over it stood the words "Le chevalier sans peur et sans reproche." "The knight without fear or fault who gave his life for his king at the battle of Pavia," Velten read to himself.

"François I of the House of Valois," said the Count somewhat piqued, "and Adolf the First of the House of Schicklgruber—that's a fine comparison to make."

"What do you mean?" asked Velten demurely. "The nobility die for both. You said so yourself. And the long-nosed François has shown Adolf with the lovelock where you land your people when you set out to fight for the mastery of Europe—on the edge of the abyss."

The Count became thoughtful. "I can't say I've any urge to challenge you. Are you aware that most unpleasant things lie ahead of us?"

Velten raised his eyebrows expectantly: "What now?"

The Count looked down at his left hand. As always his other one hung motionless at the end of his stiff right arm.

"You know we aren't going to try anything with England. But have you any idea what the next thing is?"

Velten looked him straight in the face, thinking. The Count was very grave. They were both silent for a while.

97

"God," Velten muttered hesitantly, staggered by the enormity of it.

"You mean," he said at length, speaking with deliberate calmness, "he's going to start on Russia?"

The Count nodded. "According to all we hear—yes. To begin with, of course, he'll pretend to negotiate. Russia's imperialist demands will be rejected—and then he'll cross the Njemen. . . ."

"But not like Caesar over the Rubicon," said Velten. He took a deep breath. "Like someone else who crossed the Njemen in summer and came back over the Beresina in winter."

They were silent once more.

"Oh, well," Velten observed with a light wave of the hand, "the nobility will die just as heroically in the snowy wastes of Russia as on the fields of France. Like the old knight there on the battlefield of Pavia."

"God in heaven!" exclaimed the Count in tormented tones. "What could we achieve by ourselves? Every class of society is riddled with the same poison. Even this staff, however reactionary it's made out to be. That fellow"—here he mentioned the name of an officer of middle-class background—"said the other day that if the Führer ordered him to drown himself he'd do it."

"I don't think you've got it quite right," Velten told him. "That man is in his early thirties and already a major on the general staff. He's not driven by conviction. He's out to make a career. He's an efficient officer. Don't you realize that the successes of our country are all due to the co-operation of efficient people who are ready to put their qualifications at its disposal in every sector of the war effort? They don't do it because they believe in the Movement. They co-operate because they smell success. Success for themselves and the whole. That's your celebrated German specialist for you. No other nation has got anything like him. He works away like a beaver in his own special field and doesn't give a damn on whose behalf or to what end. He's unpolitical, and proud of it. Isn't the nobility likewise proud to offer military prowess and a predilection for death on the battlefield?"

Velten did a calculation. It was now almost the end of July. They would hardly march into Russia before winter, particularly if the whole crooked game of diplomatic deceit was to be played beforehand as at the time of Munich. Presumably it would be next spring or summer. That, he felt, would be the beginning of the end. The Russians had a treaty with Germany which they were said to be fulfilling with punctilious care. The German papers said as much. The newsreels told the same story. Wheat and oil rolled into Germany in an apparently unending stream of railway trains. Under what pretexts would the treaty be broken? And what would the consequences be when the end came? For it was palpably clear that the affair would finish badly.

"Can't anyone do anything?" he asked the Count, who was still lost in thought before the fireplace. "Even his own people must see it's madness!"

"Oh, fiddlesticks," the other snapped, his mood suddenly changing. "You won't be able to alter it, Velten, and neither shall I. A handful of men can't make the same stink as a dung-heap. When they were arming against Napoleon in the old days, Goethe told them: "Go on! Rattle your chains! The man's too big for you!" And now *he,* and all that goes with him, are too big for *us.* Do you think it would be possible to revolt now? Not a single man would support us after all those successes. Today no one believes that he'll march on Moscow. And when he does so tomorrow they'll all follow meekly."

He pulled out his case and offered Velten a cigarette. Because the Count could only use one arm, Velten took one for him too, holding it till he had put his case away. Then he gave him a light.

"Well," the grand seigneur went on, "nothing came of that shoot." He was alluding to their recent visit to the Duke's game-keeper. Asked what game there was to be had on the estate, the old man had raised his hands in despair. It seemed that the few deer had been shot by the divisional commander who had been in the area before them. Otherwise there were only one or two rabbits and pheasants.

"But now," said the Count with satisfaction, "we've found a catapult and a few small-caliber rifles for clay-pigeon shooting. And I've got a job for you which should please you. Tomorrow you will drive to Paris to buy small-caliber ammunition and a few thousand clay pigeons."

"Well, I'll be damned," Velten exclaimed, somewhat startled at

99

the turn taken by their discussion of high politics. "Since I succeeded in buying filthy pictures for the staff's edification I ought to manage this job all right. All the same, I don't at the moment know the French for clay pigeon, and, ignoramus that I am, I must confess that until now I didn't know such a thing existed."

The Count laughed. "You see what the State's doing for your education. You'll be getting instructions to pick up Captain Count Galbern at the Hôtel Meurice. He's being transferred to this headquarters. Count Helmsfeld is returning to regimental duty. Galbern is the new Aide-de-Camp. He's already been warned by teletype that you're coming. You'll use the opportunity to collect the hunting ersatz." The Count became official. "You can get your orders as soon as you like. Mattersen's been informed." With marked severity he added: "That's why I sent for you, Velten, understand?"

Victor Velten had not the slightest intention of falling in with the other's official tone.

"Very well then, Herr Graf—Heil Hitler!" he said, raising his right arm ironically. "So we're going to Russia. Anyone who shoots clay pigeons in France will certainly want to have a go at hunting Russian bears or catching sturgeon."

The Count gazed at him in bewilderment. Then he said just one word. It was very unsuitable language for a staff officer and most unaristocratic.

"Precisely what I think, Herr Graf," Velten retorted, and took his leave with a sharp bow.

He was given a staff car and a three-ton truck. He left in the car at six in the morning, instructing the crew of the three-tonner to meet him early in the afternoon at the city commandant's office at the corner of the rue Royale and the place de la Concorde.

In Paris he had just enough time to eat a quick lunch on the boulevard Rochechouart. Although in uniform he went to the same modest restaurant in which Hagestein had found him with Corinne. He took his driver in with him.

Velten had to stop at a number of sports shops before he finally found some clay pigeons in a toyshop near the place Vendôme. The place was called Au Nain Bleu, and the emblem of the blue dwarf over the entrance was the good gnome of the French fairy tale which protects little children against wicked fairies and witches.

He had a few boxes of the pigeons packed up, and sent his driver to the commandant's office to get the truck. Then he asked the assistant for small-caliber ammunition. The man rushed off in alarm to call the manager.

"But m'sieur," this worthy told him reproachfully, pressing his chin against his winged collar, "small-caliber ammunition is subject to confiscation. We've handed all ours in."

"Damn," Velten said. "But look, I *must* have some. Where's the stuff been sent to?"

The manager couldn't tell him. "Soldiers came and took it all away. They took the shot-guns, miniature rifles, air-guns and toy pistols. Everything."

He shrugged his shoulders. When Velten pressed him he finally suggested that the Usines Nationales must stock all types of ammunition. But that was probably all impounded as well. "It makes no difference," Velten said. "I must try them anyway. Where's the office?"

The man gave him an address in the rue La Boétie where he found the factory management on the ground floor of a big business house.

The director listened to Velten's request with a deprecating frown. "My God," he said, "everything's requisitioned. We can't let anything out of the depot."

Velten sat facing him over his desk in a small, dimly lit office. He offered him an English cigarette. "My dear fellow," he said, "do be reasonable. You can see I'm a member of the German forces. You can't do yourself any harm."

A German soldier, the Frenchman argued, could surely get an authority from the commandant's office without any difficulty.

"Has an inventory of your stock been taken?" Velten asked the director. "I'm positive no one knows exactly how much of the stuff you've got lying here."

He explained his dilemma. He simply had to produce this ammunition, otherwise his position on the staff would be untenable.

"After all, you French had soldiers too," he said. "You know how things are in the Army."

The director stroked his smoothly shaven chin, and smiled. Human contact was gradually established. At length it was agreed that

Velten should have a few hundred rounds. The Frenchman categorically refused to accept any payment, pointing out that this might be interpreted as a breach of the confiscation order. Instead he asked Velten for a certificate that he had taken such and such a quantity of ammunition for the requirements of the German Army. Velten thanked him, shook hands, and took his leave.

He cursed himself when he was back in the car. Just one more demonstration of efficiency on his part. And he'd go on being efficient—in spite of Russia and in spite of Corinne and her Corporal. He had an unpleasant feeling in his stomach.

The ammunition was swiftly loaded into the truck out in the factory yard. Velten sent it on ahead and drove to the Hôtel Meurice to pick up the cavalry captain.

They caught up with the truck on the road between Le Mans and La Flèche. It was burned out. The driver was busy transferring his cargo to another truck which he had stopped. The carburetor had caught fire, he reported. He proudly pointed out that he had saved the whole load on his own, in spite of the fierce blaze. His face was blackened with smoke and his uniform singed. You're just as big a fool as I, thought Velten. We've both put on a damned fine show —so that the top brass gets its clay pigeons to shoot at!

When Velten reported back to the Count and started to tell him how difficult the mission had been, the latter cut him short: "Most unsoldierly! You'd have reason enough to talk about your difficulties if you'd come back empty-handed. You've done the job—enough said!"

Not until he reached his hotel room in Angers did Velten realize that it had not occurred to him to ring up Corinne. He was glad. They had parted for good.

Shortly afterwards Velten got the periodic leave—"recreational leave" was the Wehrmacht term—now due him. But when he found himself back in the bosom of his family, tanned like a tourist, he could not help wondering why he was supposed to need recreation. He only wished he could say the campaign had agreed with all other soldiers as well as it had with him. He filled in the time by getting down to work and devoting himself to his practice.

When his four weeks' leave was almost up he received a telephone call from Angers. It was Bellman to tell him not to come back. He could obtain fuller details at the rear headquarters of the Army Group.

He went to the red-brick building in the Kaiserallee. "That's right," the officer on duty told him. "The honeymoon in France is finished. The staff'll be back in Berlin in a day or two. What it's all about, I have no idea."

Velten, remembering the conversation in the library of Serrant, knew the reason. In due course the others arrived. That same headquarters which in France had used incalculable quantities of fuel for the most frivolous purposes now traveled by rail. Petrol had to be conserved. They remained in Berlin for four weeks, awaiting orders.

One day Mattersen sent for Velten. The decision was made. The headquarters was going to Poznan and they'd be needing interpreters with a knowledge of East European languages. Hagestein, meanwhile promoted captain, had been posted to a propaganda company. Mattersen wanted to keep one "western" interpreter and was leaving it to Velten and Schwierig to decide between themselves which of them it should be. He could readily imagine that Velten, a man working on his own account, would have more interest in getting released than civil servant Schwierig, who presumably couldn't care less whether he served the State in civvies or uniform.

Velten was glad to seize the chance offered him. Schwierig was happy enough to stay. In some way he was proud of his uniform. The first time he saw Velten in civilian attire in Berlin he was horrified. How could anyone do such a thing! Whatever would people think in Landsberg-on-Warthe if he, Schwierig, were suddenly to return there in everyday clothes?

When the day of the Headquarter's departure for Poznan arrived and the "eastern" interpreters had still not put in an appearance, Mattersen decided that Velten must come along with them after all. He had to maintain his war establishment.

Thus Velten found himself in Poznan. The quarters were not as good as in France. He was lodged with a German family which had been put into a flat formerly inhabited by Poles. The Poles had probably done the same thing to the Germans in 1918, he told himself.

About this time secret-service agents produced a film which had been stolen from the archives of the Soviet Ministry for War. It had been made during the Russo-Finnish war and covered successive phases of the operations. The events filmed were genuine. It was no propaganda film for the people but instructional material providing object lessons for the specialist.

When they had seen the film through, the gentlemen of the staff were unanimous: So that was the famous Red Army! Laughable! No proper training of armored troops and infantry! No co-ordination of air and ground forces! Error after error in the exploitation of the terrain! No tactical instinct for the weaknesses of the enemy's defenses! How had they come to beat the Finns? Simply by the brute force of numbers!

"One thing's a hundred per cent certain," said Mattersen, putting his opinion in a nutshell: "the Red Army doesn't constitute a serious opponent as far as the Wehrmacht is concerned."

At long last Velten's transfer to the depot came through. He received a movement order and a rail ticket to Berlin, with instructions to report to the Seeckt Barracks at Spandau. There he was given a series of documents to sign, including a declaration that he had not suffered any physical injury and had no claims to make. Then he got his demobilization clothing, fourteen days' pay and subsistence allowance for the same period. Finally he received a gratuity of fifty marks.

His release all but came to naught because no officer could be found to sign his demobilization certificate. They eventually got one from the canteen to sign on behalf of the captain responsible.

At long last Velten saw the barracks gates behind him. He had had the foresight to come in civilian clothes. In one suitcase he carried the clothing so generously bestowed on him. In his record-of-service book they had entered everything he was supposed to have accomplished in this great war.

Part Two

CHAPTER I

THE TROOP TRAIN was a long one. Whenever it stopped at a station the locomotive and the first few cars stood well past the platform, while the end part lost itself in a maze of rails, points and signal lamps. Stops at stations were few. In most cases the long chain of red cattle cars with the one passenger coach in the middle had to do its waiting in the sidings of freight yards to make way for supply and leave trains and the occasional civilian passenger traffic. The train carrying the battalion had already been crawling eastwards for three days and three nights.

There were forty men to a car. Straw for them to lie on had been stacked into each one, leaving only a patch of flooring free in the center, opposite the sliding doors on each side. In that space was a tin plate with a little iron stove standing on it. It was winter, and the stove glowed almost continuously. There was plenty of coal to spare, as it could always be "organized" during the longer stops.

The stove radiated a dry, acrid heat, and the perspiration of forty male bodies made the air thick and heavy. On top of that there was the odor of dubbing and the smell of uniforms long held in store. Forty men lay tightly packed along the walls of the clattering, jarring car. Their packs, haversacks and other equipment hung from the transverse beams under the roof. In the uncertain light of the tallow candles they cast grotesque, flickering shadows on the walls.

Velten tried to roll off his back on to his right side. It was impossible to do so without moving the two neighbors pressing tightly against him. They cursed in their sleep and made room with ponderous reluctance. Their unaccustomed clothing was partly to blame, as everyone wore a second suit over his normal field-gray—

107

the winter camouflage uniform. It consisted of wide, baggy trousers which buckled round the boot at the ankle, and a similar kind of jacket with a full hood and sleeves fitting tightly to the wrist. The suits were weatherproof and waterproof, and padded with cotton wool. They could be worn either way—the white side being intended to match a snow-covered landscape and the brown to camouflage the wearer in normal terrain.

Velten could not restrain a grim smile as he tore open his camouflage jacket to make the oppressive atmosphere a little more bearable. Everyone had sworn that whatever happened they wouldn't go to Russia. Thanks to that capacity for wishful thinking which four years of war had developed so highly and which repeated disappointment had ever failed to dampen, every conceivable rumor about the probable destination of the Zorn Infantry Battalion (Zorn —the German for "wrath"—being the name of its commanding officer) had already gone the rounds. The private soldier contemptuously referred to these rumors as latrinograms, but he loved them dearly and fell for them every time. They brought fresh food to his perpetually fruitless dreams and new rays of hope to his sorely tried faith.

The latrinograms of Infantry Battalion Zorn had it that the battalion was bound for Italy. The Italy of which a piece was still occupied, though the front was gradually being pushed farther and farther north. The truth of the matter was that the front in the south had attracted the German soldier ever since that pious ejaculation was wrung from some private's breast in the heyday of Axis friendship: "Oh to be armed like the Russians, fed like the Americans—and then fight against the Italians!"

Velten had held his peace whenever the others sought to justify this certainty that they were bound for Italy. For he knew that in his file back at Command Headquarters there was a note which said: "Only to be employed in a combat unit in the East." This was the word of authority which guided his destiny. This was the order which had borne him for months on end: from the claws of the Paris Gestapo into the barracks of the Interpreters' Company— from the rue des Saussaies in the center of Paris to a gray street in the East Berlin suburb of Lichtenberg. "Einsatz nur bei der kämpfenden Truppe im Osten"—that curse had accompanied him

108

through the nightly bombings of Berlin's fourth wartime winter, torn him from the relative security of the Interpreters' Company and pitched him into the bug-ridden huts of Hegermühle Camp near Strausberg. It was there that the final order had caught up with him: Off to Wandern to the Zorn Battalion! Such was the designation of this extraordinary rabble commanded by Captain Zorn—in civil life a full-time official of the Party which ranged itself alongside the Wehrmacht as a pillar of State.

"Jesus!" they had said in the Hegermühle orderly room, where in the course of six weeks he had established friendly relations with the clerks and found a certain basis of existence, "you're on draft for the East! Return to be submitted inside twenty-four hours. Now don't give us any trouble—get straight off to Wandern."

The movement order they had given him had been endorsed "Personal documents to follow." Velten knew what this meant. A reliable soldier being posted or drafted was entrusted with his personal papers (Record-of-service book, extract from Part II Orders, training record, medical history sheet and so on) in a sealed envelope; but in the case of a man with a bad record all these items were forwarded through the official channels. The fat company sergeant-major, Parkowski, had shot a keen look at Velten, when the latter, redirected from the battalion orderly room to No. 2 Company, had presented himself with the routine announcement "Private Velten reports himself drafted to the Zorn Battalion."

"Brought no papers along, I see," observed Parkowski, frowning heavily. "All I can say is that they'd better get a move on. We're moving off day after tomorrow."

The words Velten had been about to utter stuck in his throat. He had been on the point of asking for the usual draft leave to which everyone in his position was entitled on the strength of an edict from the Führer. They had been unable to grant it to him in Strausberg because the "order from above" had had to be implemented forthwith.

That was that, then. Goodbye, Gaby-Marie! Goodbye, little Suseli! Goodbye all you old folks living under that patched, blast-torn roof! We're to be spared the tears and melancholy leave-taking!

At all events, Velten, the man drafted to the East, had one advantage over those others: *he* was not to be tormented by doubts

109

as to whether they were going to Italy or not. He knew where he was bound for.

Even when, having been issued with gas masks, battle kit and iron rations, they had mustered out for their winter camouflage clothing, there had been some who thought they were going to Norway. Only now, when Bereza-Kartuska lay far behind them and the train still went on crawling into the wide open spaces of the East, did their destination dawn on even the most stupid of them.

Russia, the Eastern Front. The words weighed like lead on a man's breast. Stalingrad was already a thing of the distant past. Kharkov and Kiev were the names of long-lost withdrawal actions, as were Zaporoshye and Kremenchug. Russia's vastness was no longer as limitless as it once had seemed. The front had drawn appreciably nearer. These forty men had had little enough to say to each other from the start; now they were even more taciturn.

Velten had sat up and was staring absent-mindedly before him in the half-light. Somebody nudged him in the side. His neighbor was also awake. It was Willy Specht, a bricklayer who lived in the Lynarstrasse in Berlin's thickly populated Wedding district.

"Listen," he whispered excitedly into Velten's ear. "I've got it! Now I know why that big ape over there from No. 1 Section is always staring in front of him."

Velten glanced over to the opposite wall. Leaning there, quite motionless, the upper part of his body propped against the woodwork and his legs stretched out before him, was a man of about Velten's age. He had sunken eyes below his bushy brows and a low, greasy forehead. His complexion was sallow and his face puffy. He was gazing into space with unseeing eyes. He looked indescribably evil.

"Well, Willy, what do you think?" asked Velten, who knew very well what interpretation to put on the facial expression and demeanor of their brutish-looking comrade.

"I can tell you that easy," Willy whispered. "We had some like him in Sachsenhausen. They wore the green patch. They were generally in charge of a block and led us a hell of a life. But there were decent ones too. You can bet that one was doing hard labor."

"You can be sure of that," Velten smiled. "Whenever he comes

110

to a door he stands and waits for someone to unlock it for him. He hasn't been used to open doors for years."

The state of being "unworthy" for military service, once accepted as a natural consequence of the degradation of penal servitude, had been abolished. To serve with weapon in hand had once ranked as an honorable duty to the German people: now it was indispensable to Germany's salvation from mortal peril. As a result, all those whose attitude and offense did not seem to threaten the State—primarily common delinquents—were being released from the jails and penal camps, and the habitual criminals and lesser political offenders from the concentration camps. Willy Specht was one of the latter category, having spent three years in Sachsenhausen on the suspicion of collecting for the *Rote Hilfe,* the Communist welfare fund.

Naturally this motley collection also included a number of respectable, law-abiding artisans who until recently had gone about jobs of national importance back at home. Then it had suddenly emerged that they could no longer be reserved. On re-examination they had been upgraded from g.v.H. (*garnisonverwendungsfähig Heimat*—fit for service in a home unit) to k.v. (*kriegsverwendungsfähig*—fit for active service). Despite their manifold incapacities, their ruptures, flat feet, false teeth and thick spectacles, the machinery of the Director of Medical Services had turned them out as Fit for Duty at the Front.

Like a ship tossed about by fate on an unfriendly sea, the red cars and their human freight swayed through the night. The occupants were all strangers to one another—such strangers that each man regarded his neighbor with suspicion. Those longest with the battalion had been together for at the most three weeks. The rest, including Velten, had joined only a few days previously. It was this that created the furtive wariness which told Willy Specht that the man opposite him was an ex-convict. It was this that led to the brutal inconsiderateness with which the toughs in No. 1 Section of the first platoon—the section to which that brooding giant belonged—had monopolized most of the room in the freight car. For them it was a matter of complete indifference that the others had had to cram together in the narrowest of spaces. A corporal's appeal for a more comradely attitude had evoked nothing but dumb opposition. The strong men lay there like logs of wood, stirring only to eat and drink or to perform the opposite function whenever they were in a station.

Velten, who had not landed among this motley crowd by accident, had already provided himself with a hard outer shell of insensitivity. Here, too, he was aided by the same innate capacity for adapting himself to circumstances which had helped him to find his way about in the strange environment of a military staff. It was hard to say which he found more difficult and more alien—the rarefied atmosphere surrounding the highest managers of the war, or the proletarian climate of the death factory. In view of what lay between, he found no difficulty in settling down in his new situation. He did not fail to realize that here, too, he had cover and protection from the powers that had pursued him. As a member of No. 2 Company of the Zorn Battalion en route for the Eastern Front, he was a cipher, a speck of dust moving along in, and propelled by, the great cloud. What wonderful immunity there was in uniformity, in being a particle among other particles!

Velten had joined No. 2 Section of the first platoon. The main thing was to belong somewhere. Chance had smiled on him here. When they had marched in front of the gas chamber on Wandern to test their respirators, a hand had tugged at the tail of his blouse. He had wheeled around. The short, stooping man behind him, with the gray hair on his temples sticking out untidily from under his cap, and those blue, rather watery eyes staring good-humoredly up at him, had been, of all people, Martin Scholtz!

"Martin Scholtz—spelled T-Z!" Velten had cried. The man was an old school chum. Mentally the least well-equipped member of the class, he had with great difficulty been carried along by the others to his matriculation. He was the boy they had all helped because of his thorough, if slightly doltish, integrity—and probably, also, because he just happened to be one of them anyhow. He had an impediment in his speech which made all his sibilants thick and indistinct. Whenever they had to state their names during their early years at school or on the arrival of a new master, the assiduous Martin always proclaimed himself to be "Scholtz—shpelt T-

112

shed." Thanks to the mischievous humor of his classmates the designation had come to stick.

Now Martin Scholtz's eyes shone with pathetic pleasure. Velten, too, was happy to have encountered this living reminder of a past life in an environment devoid of human relationships.

Martin tried to explain to Velten how he came to be there. As ever, he found difficulty in expressing his thoughts lucidly. Velten deduced from his somewhat confused account of things that he had been a *sonderführer* in Stalino with some economic or administrative function. As long as he had been there he appeared to have had a comfortable enough existence. Then the great retreat had come. Stalino had been evacuated after being completely demolished, and Martin had ultimately been conscripted into the Zorn Battalion.

At this moment Martin Scholtz, grimy and unshaven and always slightly dirtier than anyone else, was asleep on his back, openmouthed and snoring.

Meanwhile Velten talked in a whisper with Willy Specht, who was also in their section. Willy was a wide-awake character, resourceful and full of practical ideas. After they had finished their minute ration of sausage and fats, he had been the first to think of toasting the dry rounds of army bread on the stove. The husky, dampish rye bread thereby acquired a fresh, appetizing taste which made it easier to do without margarine.

Velten offered his open water-bottle to Willy, who took a long drink from it.

"That schnapps is all right," he remarked contentedly, passing the bottle back. Velten smiled to himself. It was genuine Scotch whiskey—his one remaining bottle—which he had brought with him from home and secretly decanted into his water-bottle in the latrine in Wandern.

It was a sheer delight to let the aroma of the spirits slowly mingle in one's mouth with the sharp flavor of toasted rye. He had not washed for three days and three nights now, and even before that the problem of ablution had been solved more "by numbers" than individual requirements. Though Willy Specht was at least as dirty as Velten, he accepted the flask from his hand, wiped its mouth

113

lightly with his palm and tilted it up to drink. With the same equanimity he took the bread from Velten's dirty hands, broke it between his own grimy fingers and stuck it in his mouth piece by piece, chewing it with epicurean relish.

Such was life, thought Velten: community of nation, community of bread, community of schnapps and community of dirt.

CHAPTER II

THERE WAS one passenger coach in the long, lumbering train. In one of its two second-class compartments the man who had bestowed his name on the whole set-up sat with a number of his officers: Captain Zorn. Zorn was just over fifty, thick-set without giving any impression of stoutness. His gray-blond hair was cropped short, but on the front of his skull he wore it in a little tuft which, when heavily greased, allowed a short, neat parting to be made. It was the extraordinary hair style affected by reservist officers and former members of students' corps. To keep it company Zorn sported the famous toothbrush mustache.

In his tunic buttonhole Zorn wore the black-and-white ribbon of the Iron Cross Second Class which he had won in the First World War. Otherwise he had no stars or decorations. After returning home as a second lieutenant in 1918 he had long shared the fate of the Great War generation—an existence without present or future. That was why for him, too, the year 1933 had marked a happy turn to better living conditions. In due course he had taken over a full-time job in the Party which he had originally served in an honorary capacity in the hope of winning this very reward. When Germany regained her military sovereignty he had gone on all the army maneuvers, for the Party attached great importance to the men in its ranks assuming leading positions in the new Wehrmacht. At the outbreak of war, of course, it had been necessary to use these reliables in posts at home, where political conviction and its propagation were more important than at the front. There the soldier obeyed automatically, particularly when on the advance.

However, the position now was that even these loyalists were needed in the field, either because the gaps out in front had become too big or because the new units created from the amorphous mass of the manpower reserves required strict political leadership. At all events it was hardly fortuitous that Captain Zorn, who was on probation for promotion to major, had been given command of this ill-assorted bunch with its many doubtful elements. He himself, for that matter, was inclined to ascribe his assignment to the intrigues of a personal enemy in the Party organization. He was convinced that his exertions on the Home Front had been of far greater value to the war effort than the military role in which he now found himself. At the same time he felt it was probably a good thing to take an active part in the war, as this could be of great importance "later on." The main thing was to look out for the first opportunity to get back home again, pending which he would simply have to make the best of the society of his subordinate officers.

The officers had one advantage over the enlisted men. While the rank and file were entirely oblivious of where they were being sent, these gentlemen were well aware that this dreary collection, about whose deficiencies as fighting men they harbored no illusions, was not destined to be thrown into the front line. On the contrary, the initial plan was to commit the battalion in the partisan-riddled areas where the lines of communication, those life-lines of supply, were constantly exposed to the annihilating attacks of an unknown adversary.

Meanwhile, Zorn felt the time had come for him to tell his officers the details of the situation and the commitments they were to take over. Putting down his cigar, he reached for the map-case which 2nd-Lieut. Schwinger, his tall blond adjutant, was holding out to him.

"At approximately 0800 hours," he announced in a voice which hundreds of Party harangues had turned chronically hoarse, "provided we don't get stuck in some other filthy dump, we shall arrive in Iwacewicze."

With Schwinger holding up its top edge, Zorn spread the map out on his knees and indicated a reference. "This blasted hole, where there are probably more lice than thieves, is where Battalion Head-quarters is to be. No. 3 Company will provide a scout platoon, which will be commanded by 2nd-Lieut. Brandstätter."

He glanced over to a tanned young officer who wore both Iron Crosses of the Second World War and the crimson ribbon of the first winter campaign in Russia. Brandstätter made a slight bow. His face remained expressionless. He had realized from the outset that among all these older men he was bound to get the dangerous jobs.

"The scout platoon," Zorn continued, "will be quartered in the same place as Battalion—that is, in this lousy nest Iwacewicze. I personally shall decide its employment in the light of the orders I receive. With naive pride he added: "We are an independent bat-talion directly under the command of *Korück*.

"You will select the most useful non-coms and men from No. 3 Company," Zorn told Brandstätter. "Weapons will be issued from the armory. The rest of the Company will remain at my disposal to provide guards for my headquarters. You will now understand, gen-tlemen, why No. 3 Company, of which 2nd-Lieut. Brandstätter has so far acted as commanding officer, is not to get a commander." He was addressing the three officers sitting opposite him—Capt. Zweig, the colorless commander of No. 1 Company who looked more like a civil servant than an army officer; Lieut. Mortensohn, commander of No. 2; and finally No. 4's well-fed, jovial skipper, Capt. Quandt.

Zorn felt unsure of himself vis-à-vis Quandt. A lawyer by voca-tion, he was a *Landrat* in civil life—the administrative head of a Mecklenburg rural district. Apart from sensing the superiority of the man who had attained maturity in a civilian sphere of existence, Zorn was unable to decide to what "philosophical" category Quandt belonged. During the hasty assembly of the battalion he had picked up no information to go on, and so far he had received no reply to the inquiry he had lodged with the Party organization in the place where Quandt was quartered.

Lieut. Mortensohn of No. 2 Company, on the other hand, was a man more after his own heart. Admittedly he wasn't exactly weighed down with military distinctions, but the crimson ribbon of

116

the "Frozen Meat" medal, his sole decoration, did mean that he had military experience in the East. Mortensohn was in his late thirties. He was slim and wiry—almost emaciated. Above the protruding cheekbones of his ravaged face he had dark eyes of indefinite color in which at times a strange light burned. Mortensohn was an abnormal character. His unusual manner served to conceal a gaping intellectual and spiritual void. His whole personality was merely a mask calculated to impress those around him, and his artificial smartness arose from an inward uncertainty. Furthermore, he was a dipsomaniac, and when intoxicated was subject to dangerous choleric frenzies in which he reeled close to insanity. Of all this, however, there was as yet no sign. Mortensohn wore his accustomed mask to perfection.

Zorn handed his adjutant a cognac bottle to pour out a round of drinks.

"To good comradeship!"

The officers each made the short, sharp bow demanded by military etiquette and tipped the contents of their glasses down their throats. Zorn went on with his briefing.

"Even though our task may seem purely defensive to begin with," said Zorn, "we obviously can't confine ourselves to mere guard duties to keep the line and road clear for traffic. On the contrary, once our men have done the necessary training, we shall increasingly tend to go over to the offensive, so that we can hunt the bandits out of their hide-outs and put a stop to their activity once and for all."

Having delivered this little speech, Zorn drew a deep breath and glanced around the circle of his officers. Lieut. Mortensohn gave a sharp bow of acknowledgment and snapped out a stereotyped "Jawohl, Herr Hauptmann," though he had hardly been listening. Capt. Quandt stared dreamily out of the window at the telegraph poles, now looking like wooden spoons in a milk soup in the first light of day.

Second Lieut. Brandstätter had started violently at the revelation of his commanding officer's military intentions. This was just about what he had been expecting. He cleared his throat and, in response to Zorn's questioning look, risked voicing an objection. "Excuse me, sir," he began with emphatic politeness, "but I think we can consider ourselves fortunate if these three companies succeed—

117

under the continuous strain of their patrol duties—in protecting the rail installations against large-scale attacks. About the best we could expect would be to keep up a more or less steady flow of traffic. As for sending our inexperienced men into the forest, we shall have to confine that kind of operation to the scout platoon. Even then I would suggest that Herr Captain start off with small-scale reconnaissance patrols. I think I know this territory. It's always had a bad reputation for widespread and systematic partisan activity."

At this point Zorn broke in with an impatient gesture: "Whatever you do, my dear Brandstätter, do get out of the habit of talking about partisans. That may have been fashionable before the full menace of those criminals was recognized. There's an Army Council Instruction prohibiting all reference to the scum as partisans. We're dealing exclusively with *bandits*. I attach great importance to our only using the term *bandit*—particularly in the presence of the men. That will create a sense of moral superiority from the outset."

"Let's hope the partisans—bandits, I mean—are convinced of their moral *inferiority*," Capt. Quandt interjected. Zorn's furious glance told him he had blundered; he bit his lip and relapsed into silence.

"Whatever the bandits think about it," said Zorn, raising his voice, "doesn't matter a damn to us. We, at all events, have the advantage of disciplined troops and"—he hesitated very slightly—"experienced leadership. Finally, I really do feel we are better armed."

Brandstätter, at Zorn's last words, raised his head. The battalion had set out without any weapons. Only some twenty ancient carbines and five rounds of ammunition per head had been issued to the few men detailed as train guards.

"Has Herr Captain any idea how the battalion is to be armed?" he asked.

"I only know that we are to take over the arms of the battalion we are relieving," was Zorn's uncertain answer. But he caught himself and once again assumed the leader's role which he enjoyed so much: "I'm taking for granted that in accordance with the overall equipment of our Army we shall receive sufficient automatic weapons, as well as heavy infantry weapons such as mortars."

118

Mortars, thought Brandstätter, oh you poor fool! Aloud he said: "Excuse me, sir, but I think I've got some idea of what things are like. To my mind we shall get only enough machine-pistols to arm the outpost commanders. And as for machine-guns, there'll be at most one LMG 34 to each outpost."

At this point the head of No. 1 Company, the bespectacled secondary school teacher Zweig, meekly announced: "Not one of my people is trained on the machine-pistol, and according to the records only fifteen on the light machine-gun. I had the sergeant-major inquire how many can actually handle an LMG, and there aren't more than eight."

At this point Mortensohn sounded off. "May I say something?" he snapped with a half-turn towards Zorn. When the latter threw him an encouraging look, he let go: "Typical of this bunch—comes close to sabotage! I wouldn't even bother to ask the fellows what they've learned. It's quite natural that they'll evade the issue. The first time they smell powder when they've got a plaything like that in their hands, sheer panic will tell them how to handle it."

"I quite agree," Zorn interpolated. "That brings me to another most important point. As a general rule our men will be operating at night. I believe I'm right in saying that the bandits only carry out their cowardly attacks under the cover of darkness." He directed an ironic look of inquiry at Brandstätter, who this time concurred.

"In other words," Zorn continued, "the troops will be free all day long. We're now at the beginning of February. The days are getting increasingly longer. Obviously we shall use the daytime for completing and supplementing the men's training. That, by the way," he added as an afterthought, "is of great importance for another reason. You will be aware, gentlemen, that only a very small number of our soldiers can be regarded as completely blameless in the political and moral sense. Even some of the non-coms have questionable pasts. For reason of discipline alone, therefore, the men must be kept continuously occupied. I would particularly impress on you the need to exercise strict discipline among our troops, and—if need be—to proceed with the greatest severity."

The officers nodded their agreement. Only 2nd-Lieut. Brandstätter privately wondered how many times the battalion would have to be shot up at night before its chief lost his taste for sen-

119

tentious maxims. Lieut. Mortensohn, on the other hand, felt deeply stirred.

"Herr Captain can depend on us," he barked. "With material like this we shall never manage unless we apply the strictest measures." Whereupon he rapped his gleaming boot with the riding-crop he constantly carried around with him.

Zorn's adjutant had stuffed the map back into its case. Now that the conference seemed to be over, Mortensohn felt it incumbent on him to enlighten his commanding officer on one or two further details.

"Yes," he reflected, "it's astonishing what queer customers we've got in this outfit." Poking his head round the corner, he called into the next compartment where the battalion medical officer, the paymaster and the orderly room sergeant were sitting:

"Hans, what was that fellow I've made my clerk before the war?"

"Consistorial counselor!" the medic bawled back, scanning each syllable with the tip of his tongue.

"That's right," laughed Mortensohn, "I can never remember that beautiful title." He slapped his thigh. "He's not a parson, though, he's a lawyer. They badly need his sort in the church administration. He belongs to the Congressional Church—or what's its name?" he yelled into the next compartment.

"Confessional Church!" the doctor roared back at him.

"All right, Confessional Church. Anyway, the guy was in a concentration camp, and now he's been released as "reformed." No, no, don't you worry, sir," he added with a reassuring wave of the hand as he saw Zorn's eyebrows go up. "He can't do any damage. In the company office he's under surveillance: I'll soon sort his ideas out. Besides, my sergeant, Parkowski, is a very reliable man. He'll keep an eye on him."

He paused for a moment, but the faces of the other officers told him that he had not yet made the desired impression. So, clearing his throat slightly, he went on: "Yes, so much for our holy Confessor. To offset him I've got a man—well, it certainly shook me when Parkowski showed me his papers. Four convictions for pimping! They stuck him in the concentration camp last time, just like the holy one."

Mortensohn laughed noisily and again flicked at his riding-boot.

120

"Just imagine, sir, what'd happen if he took up his trade again out here. He's quite capable of catching a few partisan wenches and putting them out on the beat."

"You mean *bandit* wenches, of course, Herr Mortensohn," Brandstätter corrected him ironically.

"Couldn't care less which it is," Mortensohn grinned. "The main thing is he'll liven the place up a bit."

At this stage the conversation promised to become quite stimulating. But Mortensohn still did not achieve his object, for after a long-drawn-out screeching of brakes the train came to a stop. Outside it was already quite light. A sign told them that they were in Iwacewicze.

Shortly afterwards Regimental Quartermaster-Sergeant Hornemann, who had been acting as train commander, came along at the double. Catching sight of his commanding officer at a window, looking the worse for a sleepless night, he stopped, came to attention and reported that the train had reached its destination.

Zorn thanked him with a gesture of the hand, put his cap and belt on, and, accompanied by Schwinger, climbed down from the coach.

"No maids of honor to welcome us," he growled. "They don't seem to have expected us yet. I'll find out myself at the town mayor's office where the hand-over's to take place."

CHAPTER III

THE TRAIN backed out of the station and, after a great deal of shunting, came to a stop down a siding. They heard the engine being uncoupled and go puffing off. Before long it was being noised around the cattle trucks that the journey was over. A few men jumped down through the sliding doors on to the track. More and more followed.

"God, where in hell have they dumped us?" they asked each other in amazement as they inspected their immediate surroundings. "I-va-ts-e-vi-chi," one or two men spelled out with difficulty from the signboard outside the station building.

"Just you wait till you get farther out in the country," warned the few who already knew Russia and the Eastern Front. "That'll make you think. This place is still quite civilized. It's even got streets and walls to the houses. Almost a city."

The main thing at this stage was that they were able to find a hydrant. It was a delightful sensation to strip to the waist and let the thick, ice-cold stream of water play all over one's head and the upper part of one's body. Martin Scholtz, who attached less importance to washing than to the possibility of taking a little sustenance, came running up in great excitement. He was still several yards away when he called out to Velten that he had found something.

"Just by the station," he stammered moistly, "right next to it, in the *Soldatenheim,* you can get a very good breakfast with coffee—and no coupons!"

Velten hastily completed his toilet, and they set off together for the enlisted men's recreation center, the *Soldatenheim.*

Like the other buildings in the vicinity, it resembled a block-house. Inside everything was spick and span, and on the walls, just as in all other recreation centers, hung pictures of the Führer, Goering and the popular Field-Marshal Rommel, as well as the familiar poster showing a black human shadow whispering "Sh!" as a warning against dangerous talk.

In the middle of the room there was an enormous stove which gave out a pleasant warmth. Trim, friendly lay-sisters brought them malt coffee and three slices of bread each, spread with artificial honey or jam.

As it turned out, they were to spend most of the day in the center, as the battalion was kept waiting until evening. The men had their own theories as to the reason. Some suggested that the hand-over was to take place under cover of darkness to escape the notice of enemy spies.

Finally a corporal appeared. "Come on, let's go," he shouted. "Get your kits! Fall in in ten minutes!"

They poured outside. Already the gray twilight was fading into night. The few lights on the station blinked mournfully through the mist. Soon the battalion had formed up in three ranks on the platform and along the rails, and the various companies began moving off by platoons. By the time No. 2's turn came it was pitch dark. Silently and in broken step they marched through the night, guarded in front and on the flanks by the few men who were armed. With the village behind them they covered several miles of country road. In the village they had sunk ankle-deep in mud: now they stumbled over pot-holes and obstacles. At last they came to a few miserable huts.

Just as Velten felt they must be through the place, they were ordered to halt. Gradually they picked out the contours of a strange-looking fortification consisting of a high wall of tree trunks, furnished with loopholes and a watch-tower at each corner. In the middle there was a wooden gate with spikes along the top. After one or two shouts from Parkowski at the head of the column, the gate was opened a fraction and a soldier appeared. Pushing the barbed-wire barrier to one side he swung the gate wide open. They stumbled through.

Inside was a fairly spacious courtyard lit by torches. Mortensohn was standing in the center. His figure stood out lean and lank in the flickering light. The inevitable riding-crop whipped against the leg of his boot as his piercing, impassive eyes appraised the new arrivals. Then, as if bored at the sight, he strolled towards the back of the courtyard in the direction of what appeared to be a fair-sized building. In front of it towered the wooden superstructure of a well. Parkowski had hastened on a few paces ahead and as they heard him bawl the word of command "Companeeeee . . ." from the middle of the yard, they pulled themselves together and marked time on the stamped-down clay.

"Halt!"

"Damn fool!" murmured Willy Specht, who had been marching next to Velten. Parkowski had naturally given the command on the wrong foot, with the result that, instead of the usual even jerk, an undulating movement ran through the ranks. However, they came to a halt somehow. Parkowski was then able to give the next word of command: "About—face!"

At this juncture Mortensohn sauntered out of the background. Then his penetrating voice sawed through the night air:

"You lazy dogs—I'll teach you to move a bit faster! You've taken half the night to crawl those few miles. You're in for it from now on! I'll have you out marching till the pants fall off your arses!"

He took a deep breath preparatory to further invective, and then relapsed into silence just as unexpectedly as he had begun.

"Dismiss," he told Parkowski in exasperation, and turned away without returning the salute.

"To your quarters—fall out!" the sergeant commanded. The men made an about-face and remained standing stupidly where they were. "What does the twirp think he's doing?" said Willy. "No one here knows a thing about any quarters."

The non-coms had gone to speak to the sergeant-major. After a short consultation they came back. It was only too clear that no one had thought of detailing an advance party to prepare accommodation, despite the fact that the troops being relieved would obviously continue to occupy the available quarters until they left.

They stood around in the dark courtyard for a good half-hour. Most of the men took their packs off and sat down on them. A steady drizzle started. Of the sergeant-major there was no sign. At last a sergeant appeared and led them into a stable-like building to the right of the big blockhouse. They sank into the straw dead tired.

They were not awakened too early next morning, and found that the old unit had mustered out beforehand. When they mustered out themselves, they were merely warned not to wander away from the outpost. Otherwise no one paid any attention to them. They learned from the "old" unit that they were on a fortified manorial farm. The place was called Mysonowicze—an appropriate name to German ears, to which it sounded rather like Gloomstead.

In the course of the day, incredibly enough, they received their weapons. Velten managed to appropriate a brand new carbine, with its barrel and breech parts still freshly burnished from the factory. Many of the men got the clumsy long infantry rifle or the old-fashioned carbine.

In due course they were called to fall in again. Mortensohn appeared—in one of his best moods. Briefly he informed them that they were to be divided up into small teams of two non-coms and twenty-two men, each commanded by a sergeant and occupying its own outpost.

The detailing of these sub-units did not take long. The non-coms were in a hurry, since they were supposed to be in their outposts by sunset. One by one the parties marched away. Velten's own reached its destination, Outpost No. 603, just as night was falling, after a march of about three miles.

CHAPTER IV

VELTEN was quite surprised to find that a soldier's existence was not without its pleasant sides. The most pleasant of all was that in this new remoteness one never saw an officer. There was no longer anyone to bawl him out. There was no drill, no saluting, nor any of the trifling annoyances of army life. Things one had previously cursed and done only under duress without realizing their necessity—weapon-cleaning, for example—were now carried out quite voluntarily. It was no longer a question of complying with an order but of keeping one's arms in a fit state for self-protection.

The little body of men was completely self-dependent. The youngsters they had relieved had left them two light machine-guns, one of which was positioned on the firing-step at the southeast corner of the wall to fire out over the railway line, the other pointing in the opposite direction towards the highway. In addition there was a mortar. Guido Reichert, a technician from Schwäbisch-Hall, had persuaded the previous occupants to give him some instruction on it and was now the only man at the outpost capable of handling the thing. He had already fired a few trial shells: the splintered trunk of a birch at the edge of the wood testified to the accuracy of his aim.

The outpost, a wooden structure with a tapering roof, lay between the railway line and the road. Just as at company headquarters at Mysonowicze, the living quarters and adjacent well were surrounded by a wall. The latrines had been dug outside this to avoid pollution of the water supply. The ground had been systematically stripped of trees and undergrowth. This gave the outpost a free field of fire on the western boundary of its sector, part of which was mined. There were two miles of track to be guarded—one in each direction. At the eastern end of the sector two freight cars lay on their sides by the track—mementoes of a raid by partisans. Not far from the outpost a side-road branched off to the nearest village, cutting over the railway track and through the forest. A wooden turnpike protected the crossing, with a sentry box nearby.

Every seven minutes a freight train roared past to the front; and others returned from the east with equal frequency. The locomotives all pushed a truck full of sand before them to deaden the effect of mines on the track.

Though there were no signs of mines or partisans in the first few days, a great deal of futile shooting was caused merely by the crackling of branches, the squeals of wild animals and the rustling of the wind.

The man who carried off the first prize in this connection was Corporal Sternkopf, an elderly, sickly, prematurely aged fellow who suffered from insomnia and chronic headaches. One night when Velten and Krawczyk, a groom in civil life, were out on No. 1 patrol, they ran into Sternkopf doing one of his periodic checks. He reared up before them with such suddenness that they started back in alarm. As usual, he had been keeping timidly under cover and had come creeping up the ditch alongside the railway embankment. Krawczyk, as the senior in rank, made his report with exaggerated correctness.

"Number One picket carrying out assigned task with two men. Password "Rheingau." No unusual occurrences." He grinned as he said it.

"All right," Sternkopf whispered. He was holding his machine-gun at the ready, the butt pressed fiercely against his chest. It was the only one the outpost possessed.

126

"A terribly dark night," moaned Sternkopf. "Wish to God the moon'd rise a bit quicker. All right, do your job properly." With that he hastily disappeared into the gloom of the ditch.

"Damn fool," Krawczyk swore after him. "As soon as they get those cucumber skins"—he alluded here to the silver braid round the collar of a corporal's tunic—"they think they're something better than us."

He stopped speaking and nudged Velten. The latter, too, had heard suppressed shouts. Sternkopf was apparently issuing instructions to the neighboring picket. The crackle of rifle fire followed. Krawczyk and Velten jumped into the ditch and hastened along to No. 2 picket's stretch of railway track, since the patrols had orders to go straight to each other's assistance in case of trouble. Before long they came upon Sternkopf and the other picket. The two men due to relieve No. 1 were also there. All five were lying on the embankment blazing away wildly at the forest. The bark of Sternkopf's machine-gun was audible amidst the whine of rifle bullets.

"D'you see the light?" Sternkopf shouted.

There was indeed a mysterious, reddish-yellow glow in the undergrowth. It was strictly forbidden to show any lights at night. Were the bandits flashing secret signals to each other? Were they asleep round a camp fire? Velten and Krawczyk took aim and let off a rain of bullets. The light seemed quite unaffected by this fusillade. It even became brighter and, slowly losing its reddish tinge, began to take shape.

Krawczyk was the first on his feet.

"Stupid bastard!" he shouted, throwing his rifle over his shoulder and stalking off towards the outpost.

Much abashed, the others had also got up. Velten ran after Krawczyk, shaking helplessly with laughter. Before No. 2 picket's relief could put in an appearance Sternkopf had caught up with them.

"For Christ's sake keep quiet about this!" he panted. "We'll say we got shot at."

"Do you think we want to make a laughing-stock of ourselves in front of the others too?" Krawczyk fumed. "It's bad enough when a damn old fool like you has us shooting at the moon!"

127

Soon after that, No. 2 Company had its first fatal casualty. It happened during a weapon-cleaning session in Mysonowicze. Parkowski came on the scene and took charge of a machine-gun.

"This," he announced, swiveling the barrel towards the window, "is the way to hold it—the nose always pointing away from the squad. Now here is the cocking handle. We'll just pull it back. . . ."

Wham! There was a report, and a shot shattered the window pane. Parkowski turned as white as a sheet but quickly collected himself.

"Thank God for that—you see, I *told* you to always hold the nose away from your mates!"

Outside there was a sudden uproar, and men could be heard running around. Private Tomaszeck, a Viennese lad, had been on sentry duty in front of the living quarters: now he had Parkowski's shot in his belly. He writhed in agony till evening; and then he was white and still.

". . . My sad duty," Mortensohn wrote to the father in Vienna, "to inform you that your son Leopold has fallen on the field of honor. He died for Germany. Heil Hitler!" For the time being they kept Tomaszeck on the ration strength.

"It'll sort itself out somehow," Mortensohn told Parkowski, as the latter stood looking at him like a whipped cur. Whatever they may have done to achieve this, no one ever subsequently noticed that Tomaszeck was no longer among those present.

Apart from the fusillade at the moon, nothing exciting happened out at Outpost 603. The weather had suddenly turned icy cold, making the ground hard and the air dry and clear. The little band went on with its patrols, wrapped in the camouflage suits which relieved its members of the need to wear equipment. They wedged the ammunition belts for the LMG into their trouser-pockets and went out with the handles of grenades protruding from the low-slung side-pockets of their canvas jackets.

Before going on patrol they were in the habit of sitting for a while in the main chamber of the blockhouse which served them as a guardroom. In its center stood an enormous stove which gave out a terrific heat. Velten had already protested against excessive heating, but without success. For these men, in whose homes want had been an everpresent guest, the surplus of fuel was an encouragement to have it too hot.

Velten was lying on the straw in his underwear. Schrader, the non-com in charge of the outpost, was sitting with the two corporals in the other, smaller room reserved for them. The armory lay in between, and on the right of the entrance, connecting with the main room by a narrow corridor, was the cookhouse. Fritz Rötert, the cook at Outpost 603, lived there. His function consisted solely in warming up the hot meal which Company Headquarters sent over every day at noon by horse and cart and in ladling it into their mess tins. His only other job was to distribute knapsack rations.

It was this food which filled the men with the most bitter resentment. What they received from Company did not suffice to satisfy even the first pangs of hunger. There was watery soup with badly shelled buck-wheat groats—known to the Russians as *kasha* and to the men as spit-soup because they had to keep spitting out the woody chaff. To spread on the army bread they were given ridiculously small quantities of margarine, artificial honey and jam, and occasionally some dry tinned fish. They were well aware that they were not receiving their fair share and had not the least doubt that people at headquarters were stealing their rations.

"I've often been out of work," said Tülle, a professional musician from Berlin-Spandau, "but we never got as far as eating dry bread. Dry bread—I've never sunk so low before! Took the army to do that for me!"

Their hunger really hurt. It tore into their entrails in the cold of the re-awakened winter. The only ones who still managed were old hands like Fritz Rötert, who wore the crimson ribbon of the "Frozen Meat" medal. Before leaving the depot back in Germany these wise ones had prudently stocked themselves up with commodities which at the time seemed quite extraordinary—darning needles, black and white thread, saccharine, salt, brightly colored kerchiefs and woolen comforts. Thus armed, they now sallied forth in their off-duty hours—and made for the big village across the fields. In due course they would come back carrying little bags containing up to as many as thirty eggs: *yaitsa* in the vernacular.

129

Or they would have *maslo*—unsalted butter of a greasy, watery quality which always tasted slightly sour. They used also to get *salo* —pieces of unsmoked but strongly salted bacon. In addition there was often *myaso,* or pickled meat. The crowning achievement would be a bottle or two of *samagonka*—a home-distilled schnapps which stank dreadfully and which the peasants prepared by some unfathomable process from a mush of unripe corn.

Those with nothing to trade had a thin time of it. Worst of all, no mail whatever reached them in the first few weeks. It made no difference how often they wrote home, no answer came. At length, they discovered that Battalion had forgotten to report the field post number to the postal unit responsible. Only when this had been rectified did they get letters and parcels.

CHAPTER V

IT WAS the last week of February. Despite the cold there was already the faintest hint of spring in the air. Velten, who was doing the first tour of duty on the machine-gun platform, stood gazing out over the highway. It was past sunset. Suddenly the crunch of footsteps broke in on his thoughts. Through the evening mist he discerned a figure approaching the outpost from the roadway. He released the safety catch of his carbine. The shape drew nearer. It was a soldier, laden down with all the accouterment that goes to make up field service marching order.

"Halt! Who goes there?" called Velten, more for form's sake than from any feeling of anxiety. "Password?"

The other stopped short for a moment, and then started to shout back his reply:

"Corporal Eichberg. . . ."

"All right—you're recognized!" Velten called, jumping down from his platform to open the main gate and push aside the barbed-wire entanglement. He stretched out both hands to the newcomer, full of pleasurable anticipation. "What a treat to see you! What are you doing here?"

The other came in and wrung Velten's hand. He was a short, dark-haired man with twinkling black eyes and lively features. Bernd Eichberg and Velten had met on the latter's last day in the Wandern camp. They had dropped into conversation, and from those few words a mutual trust had been born. The pleasure they felt at the unexpected reunion was genuine and reciprocal.

"How nice that you should be the first person I find here!" said Eichberg. "They've sent me to relieve Sternkopf. He's been moving heaven and earth to get away. I'm coming to you from No. 4 Company."

"Not a bad swap—you in exchange for Sternkopf," Velten smiled.

Eichberg asked what the outpost commander was like.

"He's all right," Velten told him. "So far he hasn't given us a single hour's training or instruction, although headquarters keeps putting it on the training program."

"Well, do a good job," said Eichberg. "We'll have a talk to-morrow."

All at once Velten felt happy. The arrival of this man with whom he felt a common bond suddenly altered the whole aspect of things. His optimistic mood continued until his relief arrived. It was Krawczyk, the perpetual grumbler.

"Sternkopf's being shifted," Velten told him in an undertone as he got down from the platform. "We're getting a chap I know from Wandern. *He* certainly won't have us shooting at the moon."

Krawczyk remained as cynical and sulky as ever.

"Already seen him. Just like the rest of them. Don't you go getting any ideas about him."

On the morrow Velten was on one of the daytime pickets. This time he was accompanied by Eichberg, who had not yet taken over and wanted to familiarize himself with the local landmarks.

Velten showed him the few objects of interest: the overturned freight cars at the eastern extremity which afforded good cover to a cunning enemy; the mine-field at the western end.

"And what got you out here?" Eichberg asked him.

"My call-up order," was Velten's cautious reply.

"Oh nuts!" Eichberg laughed. "None of Zorn's boys are here for normal reasons. You must have blotted your copybook somehow."

"What about yourself?" Velten asked, still on his guard.

"That's simple enough," Eichberg replied with equanimity. "If you like, I'll talk about myself first—though I'm sure your case is more interesting."

They sat down in the doorway of a derailed car.

"My past is soon accounted for," Eichberg began. "I was an elementary-school teacher, a Catholic—very much so—and a district councilor for the Centre Party. The Nazis sacked me in 1933. I was politically unreliable. After that I was a sub-editor on a Catholic periodical. When they banned that I became an insurance agent. And when the fun started, they called me up. I've got as far as corporal, but only in units of the type and quality of Zorn's outfit. Well," and he looked encouragingly at Velten, "I suppose it'll have been just about the same with you."

Velten put his chin in his hands.

"It's a pretty long story," he reflected. "But by the time we've been to 602's sector and back I should be just about through."

It was a wonder to Velten himself sometimes how he had landed here. Out in the middle of this wilderness it was hard to credit the existence of that other, vital world he had only quite recently left. Eichberg listened attentively as he told of his early war experiences on the Western Front.

"Yes," said Velten, "and then one day I was home again. Life was almost normal. When this delightful war of ours still kept on I had to look around for a reserved occupation. That wasn't difficult. There were plenty of clients doing work of national importance, and giving them legal advice was considered equally vital. I was able to get by for quite a time that way. Thousands of others are doing the very same thing in factories, Party jobs and Government offices."

"How d'you mean, am I against soldiering on conscientious grounds?" he demanded as Eichberg demurred at this. "Of course I'm against it, but to be quite frank I don't see the necessity of advancing every kind of noble, humanitarian and ethical reason to justify it. I kept out to the very last moment because of a purely

132

egoistic urge for self-preservation. And I guess that goes for most of the people who've managed to keep out of the business up till now."

Noticing Eichberg's look of pained surprise, Velten added soothingly: "I know you feel differently about it. But according to my own way of thinking it's quite sufficient to regard the war in its entirety as madness. If six drunks decide to jump over a cliff, that doesn't mean the seventh sober man who happens to be with them needs to produce philosophical reasons for not diving over too."

"You've landed in the pit all the same," Eichberg pointed out with a flash of his perfect white teeth.

"Well," Velten began, "this is how it came about."

As he talked, he found himself living through the whole sequence of events all over again.

CHAPTER VI

IT HAD BEGUN one afternoon at his office. The cases with which he had to deal reflected the conditions prevailing in the fourth year of war. There was a man accused of absenteeism. Next came a weeping, middle-aged Jewess. Her Aryan husband had perished in an air raid the year before, and her teen-age daughter, having erased the capital "J" on her mother's ration card, was now in custody on a charge of falsifying a document. Then there came a tearful matron who was suing for divorce because her husband . . . and so on. Into the midst of all this had burst a tall, blond young man with prominent features and deep-set blue eyes beneath bushy brows.

"Secret State Police," he casually announced, drawing a metal badge from his pocket and holding it out for Velten's inspection. The latter leaned forward and studied the object with care, instinctively sensing the need to play for time. He automatically

133

noted the national emblem, a formalized eagle and swastika, embossed in the middle. Around the edge ran the words Geheimes Staatspolizeiamt.

"Won't you sit down?" said Velten with a wave to the chair opposite. What could the trouble be? His last defense before the Special Court? Had he gone a bit too far that time?

The man sitting opposite regarded him in silence. Velten strained every nerve not to betray his anxiety by asking impatient questions. At length his visitor spoke. Taking out a pencil and notebook he asked for Velten's particulars. When he inquired about national service, Velten felt in his pocket for the Wehrpass which contained all his military documentation. The young man inspected the "certificate of indispensability," the so-called *UK-Stellungbescheinigung,* and thumbed through the pages recording Velten's earlier service. From time to time he made a note. At last, thanking Velten politely, he returned the pass. That would be all, he intimated, rising to his feet and bowing. He held out his hand and allowed Velten to accompany him to the door, thanking him again. Then, with a Heil Hitler, he was gone.

There followed a period of agonizing conjecture in which the entire family participated. The visit obviously had something to do with Velten's reserved occupation, they insisted. Probably his certificate was going to be withdrawn. Would he be called up as an interpreter again, or did that no longer arise now that the Gestapo was dealing with him?

Ten days passed before the next move. On the eleventh day, through normal postal channels, a summons arrived requiring him, "in connection with an investigation," to report a day or so later to Room 370 at Gestapo headquarters in the Prinz-Albrecht-Strasse.

On the appointed day he walked into the gray building which he knew from many a fruitless attempt to intercede on behalf of an arrested client. The man on duty at the reception desk threw a glance at the summons, lifted the telephone received and dialed a number. He was evidently told to send Velten up at once. Beckoning to an SS man who had been lounging sleepily in the background, he handed him the summons and curtly motioned to him to lead the way.

Velten followed his uniformed escort up a few flights of stairs inside the spacious building. The man gave him no time to gather the name and function of the official outside whose door they stopped. Quickly opening it, he crashed his heels together, shot out his right arm, and gave the individual behind the desk Velten's summons.

"Wait outside," was the succinct reply. With a further noisy salute the guide disappeared. The door closed behind him.

Velten took stock of the man behind the desk—the gray civilian suit, SS badge in the button-hole, bald head, fat red hands. A detective-sergeant of the old school, he decided, later embodied in the SS. He was sorting through the bundle of papers he held in his hand. Then came the usual throat-clearing which throughout the world signals the beginning of an official interview.

"Your name is Victor Velten?" the official began with studied off-handedness. He proceeded to read out Velten's personal data, which the latter acknowledged now and again with a murmured affirmative. There was a short pause. Finally the interrogator threw the papers on the desk, leaned back in his chair and looked at Velten for the first time. An unpleasant face, thought Velten. Then it came out crisp and clear from under the gray toothbrush mustache: "You are required for interrogation by an office outside the Reich. You leave tomorrow. Until then you can stay right here." Then it hit him: God in Heaven, he was being put under arrest!

"How am I to understand that, Herr . . ." He waited for a name, but none came. "What is this supposed to mean? What is there against me? If some authority wishes to question me, I must ask for a summons. Naturally I shall comply. On what legal basis am I to be held here?"

"I have orders to take you into custody for your personal protection and to prevent any attempt at collusion. You will start on the journey tomorrow as a free person, but accompanied by a police officer . . . in civilian clothes." He added the last bit after a short pause.

"I protest. I shall put in a complaint."

"Do so, if you wish," said the official, carefully arranging the papers on his desk. "You can obtain writing materials at the reception desk. Anything else?"

Velten realized the futility of further resistance. "Can I telephone

135

to my wife?" he asked. "Can I have a change of linen and toilet articles sent to me here?"

The official indicated the telephone. "Press the red button and dial when you hear the burring tone. Linen and soap can be handed in this afternoon at the main entrance between four and five. Shaving things are not allowed."

Gaby-Marie answered the telephone, almost before the first ring had sounded.

"I've got to go away," Velten told her. "No, no, it's nothing bad —some witness or other has got to be questioned—obviously a misunderstanding. It'll straighten itself out."

How silly, he thought. How often the two of them had talked about those senseless messages which were frequently the last an arrested man's relatives ever heard of him! Nevertheless, she quickly pulled herself together and promised to deliver the things he wanted. Would she be able to see him?

Velten asked the official. "Out of the question," he snapped. Velten bade her a brief farewell over the telephone. "I'll be back soon."

"Yes, dear."

The wire clicked. She had hung up. In the meantime the official in the gray suit had called in the SS man and given him his instructions. Opening the door and throwing Velten a beckoning look, the fellow sourly led the way downstairs. So they were bound, Velten thought, for those celebrated cellars which he knew only from occasional accounts given him by clients. There was no daylight in the subterranean corridors, which were brightly illuminated by many powerful lamps. They stopped at a gray-painted iron barrier extending across the passageway. The guard sitting at a table behind it opened up. Velten stepped through, while his escort gave the guard some papers and exchanged a few words with him. Then the gate closed as the escort hastened away.

Afterwards Velten lay on the plank bed in his one-man cell. The furnishing, atmosphere and smell were familiar to him from his professional visits to the remand prison. From now on he was filled with a curious peace and resignation. He had the feeling of having become a different person from the moment when they relieved him of his valuables, petty cash, wallet and identity papers,

136

keys and pocket knife. Soon he fell into a deep, untroubled sleep.

The next morning he was taken into an office. A uniformed official treated him with brisk dispatch, though not without courtesy. A young man in civilian clothes was standing nearby. He wore a gray raincoat and held his hat in his hand. At his feet were a small dark suitcase and a yellow portmanteau which Velten, with a pleasant surge of surprise, recognized as his own property. The man behind the desk informed him that he would be leaving today with this gentleman, whom he indicated with a nod of the head. The escort had all the travel documents with him.

Velten was handed his bag, and his personal belongings were restored to him. He was required to count his money, and did so with care before giving a receipt. Thereupon he was free to leave the large, sinister building with his chaperon.

As Velten stepped out in the street to breathe in the fresh air in deep gulps, his companion formally introduced himself as Schmidt, a detective-constable. "Herr Doktor," he said, beaming at Velten with all the cheerfulness in the world, "Herr Doktor, do you know where we're bound for? Paris. Just imagine—my first duty trip to Paris!"

Paris. The word hit Velten like a bolt. So that was it. Like lightning the certainty flashed into his mind that Corinne and the Corporal came into it somewhere. But how? There couldn't be all that much evidence against him, otherwise they would have been treating him very differently.

"We're taking the ordinary train to Paris. You're no prisoner, of course, Herr Doktor. We'll act just like two friends traveling together. I'll give you your papers and the ticket afterwards. Admittedly that's against my orders, but I see that I can trust you, Herr Doktor."

"What station do we leave from?" Velten asked abruptly. Apparently it was to be the neighboring Potsdamer Bahnhof. They were already walking towards it. As they still had three-quarters of an hour before their train left, Velten persuaded the friendly Herr Schmidt to visit the refreshment room with him. Over a glass of wartime beer Schmidt handed him an entry permit for the territory under the jurisdiction of the Military Commander of France, together with a transit visa for the zone of Belgium and Northern

137

France, and an army movement order. So great was his confidence in Velten that he let him go to the telephone unescorted.

Velten actually managed to arrange for Gaby-Marie to turn up on the platform before the train left. With her usual thoughtfulness she brought some sandwiches—enough for Velten and Herr Schmidt —and a flask of cognac.

They said a brief and, to all outward appearances, very matter-of-fact goodbye. Gaby bravely choked back her tears. Herr Schmidt repeatedly assured her that it must all be a mistake. Gnädige Frau would soon have Herr Doktor home again.

"Let's hope to God you're right, Herr Schmidt," said Velten when Gaby's slim figure had disappeared from their sight. He sighed deeply and sat down on the wooden bench of the third-class Wehrmacht compartment.

Herr Schmidt chatted away quite affably. He looked forward to Paris with unrestrained enthusiasm. Though he was only supposed to hand Velten over and then take the next train back, he felt sure he could spend at least one night in the city. He had heard fabulous tales from comrades of his. Now he had his first opportunity to savor it all in person.

Velten felt somewhat uneasy at the prospect of Herr Schmidt's coming home without him, and said so.

"Come, come," said Herr Schmidt merrily, "either there really are grounds for suspicion against you—in which case our good old Kaltenbrunner will issue a warrant for your arrest or at least have you taken into protective custody. That being so, you'll stay in Paris, of course! Or else—and both you and I are quite convinced of this—the suspicions are unfounded. Well, all you'll have to do then is to make your own way home as a free man." He took a generous bite at one of Gaby's ham rolls, and winked at Velten.

After one or two long pulls at the cognac flask Herr Schmidt gradually began to open up and actually went so far as to comment adversely on his own organization.

"Even in the SS," he said, "many things could be different. The idea itself is all right"—*what* idea exactly, Velten wondered—"but in practice it often looks pretty unpleasant. Why must everything be done by force? They'd achieve a lot more by good will."

138

Having consented to another cognac, he turned to his experiences as a recruit in the SS depot.

"I was trained in Buchenwald. The SS barracks are next to the concentration camp, you know. The training was good—no senseless Prussian drill. We were good comrades together. But the prisoners were only next door. It gave me the creeps, I can tell you. Many of the others felt the same. But we had other types among us. Whenever we came back from a route march and found the prisoners working by the roadside in their torn overalls, there were always a few fellows who would jump out of the ranks and go for the poor devils with their fists. And that was tolerated."

He looked out of the window. They had the compartment to themselves. For the rest of the night they did their best to sleep. Early next morning they were in Paris.

Velten gathered from a paper Herr Schmidt showed him that they were to proceed to the building of the former French Ministry of the Interior in the rue des Saussaies. They went to the nearest subway station, and as Herr Schmidt was getting their tickets it suddenly struck Velten that he had no French money on him. For some reason or other the two of them had been missed by the currency people at the frontier. This meant that Velten had illegally brought his German cash into the country. For the time being he preferred not to mention the matter to Herr Schmidt, whose time was in any case fully occupied with gathering impressions. The métro struck him particularly by the evident size of its network. On the other hand he thought the Berlin underground "much more clean and modern." The few female passengers drew his special attention. Naturally these factory workers, cleaning women and newspaper vendors hardly corresponded to his conception of Parisian femininity. Velten held out better hopes for later in the day.

"As soon as you've handed me over," he assured him mournfully, "your colleagues will show you round properly."

"Ach, Herr Doktor," protested Herr Schmidt, "I would much rather make an expedition with you."

This, Velten reflected, was just about the last straw. Aloud he said:

"Your people have been here long enough. They are sure to know their way around better than I."

139

In the rue des Saussaies they quickly found the big, box-like building they were seeking. It was an office building with a series of inner courtyards. After a few inquiries Schmidt found he had to hand Velten over to a branch of the Security Service, the SD, in the second of these. A slim SS man with carefully parted hair received them. His manner was correct to the point of courteousness. He was prepared for their arrival. There had been a telephone message from Berlin.

"I'm sorry to say you won't find it very comfortable here," he told Velten. "I fear we shall have to accommodate you in a cell. I'm sure your interrogation will clarify everything."

"I protest against this treatment," Velten declared. "I've committed no crime. No one in authority has placed any restriction on my liberty."

"That," the man with the carefully parted hair informed him in polite but firm tones, "is not my business. You will be given an opportunity to convey your complaint to the appropriate quarter."

Then Velten had to hand in his valuables and wallet. The SS man whistled through his teeth.

"How do you come to be carrying German currency notes around with you?"

"Carrying around with me be damned!" shouted Velten. "I don't know myself why the stuff's still on me. Your people in Berlin put me on the train just as I was and with all my money in my wallet."

Fortunately the good Schmidt assured his colleague that they really had not been checked for currency at the frontier and that the Berlin office had obviously overlooked the matter in Velten's case. He himself produced a certificate authorizing him to bring a sum in French francs into the country. The SS man shrugged his shoulders, put Velten's money and the rest of his possessions into a big yellow envelope and announced that the matter must be decided at a higher level.

"Whatever happens, I shall demand my money back," said Velten, "either in marks or francs."

The other made no reply. Herr Schmidt was in a hurry to leave. He got the man to make him out a pass and disappeared with a friendly "Heil Hitler!" for the SS man and a brief nod for Velten. Then another man came to take him to the cellars.

"One might call a cellar the substructure of the New European Order," Velten remarked. His mood was already one of complete indifference. They could treat him as brutally as they liked. To his astonishment the man grinned.

For three days Velten sat in his cell. Nobody came near him, except to bring his meals three times a day. On the fourth day he was taken out. "For interrogation," he was told. His breath came jerkily as he climbed the stairs behind the SS man. It really was a damnable situation to be in. What did they know and what didn't they know?

He was led into a small office. A desk and a few chairs made up the furniture. The man behind the desk, whom Velten's guard addressed as Hauptsturmführer, the SS rank equivalent to captain, had a smooth, intelligent face, carefully brushed hair and well-kept hands. His chin was vigorous without being brutal. His manner was austere and ostentatiously self-assured.

Near the desk a secretary sat behind her typewriter at a small table. She wore a shiny, black overall which revealed the firm contours of her breasts. Her hair was dyed chestnut and carefully waved. Velten glanced at her hands as she fitted a few sheets of paper into her machine. Her nails were colored crimson. It was a measure of how far Paris had contaminated the Germans in only a few years of occupation. The woman's mouth was painted a rather too dark and voluptuous red. Her cheeks were powdered, her eyebrows carefully plucked and elegantly penciled. She glanced at Velten with momentary interest and then haughtily turned her head away. The SS officer motioned to the wooden chair in front of his desk. Velten sat down. The guard had left the room.

It began with the familiar gambit of question and answer about personal particulars. The luscious creature in the sleek black overall showed not the slightest interest as she tapped it all out on her machine, rhythmically jogging one crossed leg in its sheer silk stocking and high-heeled shoe.

"How long have you known Mme. . . . ?" the SS officer suddenly demanded in a louder tone, mentioning Corinne's surname.

141

So that was it! Just what Velten had long feared. He was immediately ready with his well-rehearsed reply, giving no hint of his inner agitation as he uttered it:

"I know no person of that name."

"*So?* You mean you have never been to the Carrefour de l'Alma to a studio apartment on the top floor?"

"I may have been to a studio on a top floor at some time or other," said Velten, forcing a smile, "but you can't expect me to remember all my Paris adventures, let alone the exact addresses."

"When were you last in . . . ?" The man mentioned Corinne's last address in the Quartier Péreire.

"I'm sorry," said Velten with a shrug. "The street is completely unknown to me."

Then there followed a string of charges about people Velten was supposed to have met in the studio in question. This time he was able to make his denials with an easy mind, for his ignorance of the persons mentioned—some of them by cover-names—was perfectly genuine. There was nothing definite known against him, he kept telling himself to keep his nerves steady.

"During your tour of duty in Versailles you went out in Paris in civilian clothes," was his interrogator's next charge.

"Yes," Velten admitted, "for official reasons and with the approval of my superior officer." He gave Mattersen's name and appointment. *He* wouldn't leave him in the lurch.

"I should tell you, by the way," said the Hauptsturmführer softly, leaning forward to look straight into Velten's eyes, "that your denials are quite futile. You're only getting deeper in the mire. Your girl friend admitted everything long ago."

Velten remained outwardly unmoved, holding the other's gaze as his brain worked frantically. Had she really given him away? Like hell she had—it was one of the oldest tricks in the world!

Without a tremor in his voice he said: "In that case I request to meet the accuser."

The answer came out like a lash:

"By all means!"

The man pressed a button. An orderly appeared.

"Bring in the woman from Fresnes!"

142

So they already had her out there. Mechanically Velten watched the typist, who was looking intently towards the doorway.

Corinne came in, silent as a shadow. She was far thinner than she had ever been before. Her face was a waxen yellow, and there were dark rings beneath her eyes. Her hair was lank and unkempt. She was not in prison uniform but wore a dark gray suit which was wrinkled and threadbare, and under the jacket a black cardigan. At a sign from the SS officer she sat down on the chair next to Velten's. Not a glance reached him or the others from those shadowed eyes. She laid her fragile, slender hands in her lap and stared blankly in front of her. Velten felt as though his heart had stopped beating.

"Send in the interpreter," the Hauptsturmführer called through the open door. A man wearing the uniform of a private in the SS entered noisily. In one hand he carried a dictionary. His face was flushed with zeal.

The interpreter sat down at a small table in the background and looked expectantly at the SS officer.

The latter gave an order:

"Sit facing one another!"

"Asseyez-vous vis-à-vis l'un de l'autre," came the translation in an accent which made Velten's hair stand on end. Without a word Corinne turned on her chair, so that Velten could now look her full in the face. The gaze from her deep-set eyes was fixed and expressionless. She stared straight through him as if he were thin air. Only then did it dawn on him that she had given nothing away.

"What about presenting this lady with the allegations against me, Herr Hauptsturmführer?"

"Hold your tongue till you're told to speak!" thundered the voice behind the desk.

"You know this man?" The question was addressed to Corinne.

"Vous connaissez cet homme?" asked the interpreter, leaning forward intently as if to tear the secret from her pallid lips. Corinne made no answer. Still without stirring, she continued to stare at Velten.

"Answer the question!" the SS officer ordered. His tone was sharp and menacing.

143

"Répondez quand on vous demande," said the red-haired young man. Still she did not reply.

"You know we have ways to make you talk," the SS officer threatened.

The threat lost much of its weight through the halting translation which followed:

"Savez-vous que nous avons les moyens de vous faire parler?"

No answer.

"Stand up!"

"Levez-vous!" Now the interpreter was bellowing as well.

Corinne rose to her feet.

"You too!" the Hauptsturmführer screamed at Velten.

"Vous aussi!" echoed the red-haired zealot, no longer able to distinguish between what he should translate and what he should not.

The synthetic red-head behind the typewriter smiled cynically and examined her finger-tips.

"Stand facing the wall," ordered the Hauptsturmführer.

Corinne obeyed, and Velten made to follow suit.

"No, not you," came a command from the desk. "Come over here. Right up to the desk."

Suddenly there was a riding-crop lying there. The SS officer got up and let it whistle through the air once or twice. "You had an affair with him. Yes or no?"

"Vous étiez sa maîtresse—oui ou non?" repeated the budding pedagogue.

Velten could not resist the flush which suffused his cheeks. By trying to fight it down he only made it worse. Corinne remained mute. The riding-crop whistled through the air.

"Well, mein Püppchen?" the interrogator demanded.

"Alors, ma poupée!" came the voice from the corner. Damn fool thought Velten. Ma poupée!

"Very well, my pretty one," said the officer, "we'll see how your boy friend talks when we use rather more rigorous methods!"

Velten never heard the interpreter's translation. He just had time to see the big-breasted secretary stiffen and catch her breath—and then a wave of cold rage surged through him.

"Don't you dare touch me!" he raved. "You're investigating

144

things I am supposed to have done as a member of the Wehrmacht. I dispute your authority to do so. If there's any investigating to be done, that's a job for a court-martial. A Wehrmacht tribunal—not the SS! Don't think you can hide me here indefinitely. I've got friends who'll ask questions!"

He planted himself firmly on the chair, determined not to obey any more of the SS officer's instructions. The man bit his lip.

"You can leave it to me to decide whose province the case falls in. Apart from that, you know perfectly well as a lawyer that no member of the SS would dream of using force in an interrogation. The whole thing was naturally just a threat to make this creature talk."

Fancy telling that to him of all people, thought Velten. As if he knew nothing of their methods! In any case, the threat alone was a punishable offense. Nevertheless, he preferred to hold his peace now that his adversary had admitted his defeat. At the same time he grasped Corinne's tactics. Obviously she had preserved this silence from the very beginning. What courage! What power of endurance!

"Sit down," Corinne was told.

In response to the "Asseyez-vous" of the interpreter she came slowly back to her chair and sank down apathetically, as if her mind were elsewhere. For a while the room was still.

Suddenly the SS officer bent his whole body over the desk and grinned lasciviously into Corinne's face.

"Dis donc, la môme," he said, "il t'la mise?"

"Sage doch . . ." Utterly confused by his chief's abrupt switch into French, the red-haired fellow had begun translating back into his pedantic German. The SS officer told him to shut up.

Corinne still said nothing. Not a muscle of her face betrayed any reaction to the obscenity. The lady at the typewriter stared pointedly out of the window. Clearly she understood the officer's French. Velten tensed himself. His head was now cold and clear.

"Herr Hauptsturmführer," he said steadily, eyeing the man opposite, "I take off my hat to your command of French. Admittedly it smells slightly of the brothel. Nevertheless, it's grammatically impeccable. But do you really think you'll scare this lady out of her silence by talking that sort of filth?—Je suis sûr," he added,

145

feeling that he simply must make himself intelligible to Corinne, "que madame n'a même pas compris le sens de votre phrase."

"I am sure that the lady did not in the least understand what you said," the interpreter translated mechanically, looking wide-eyed at his master.

Before the Hauptsturmführer could utter another word, something unexpected happened. Corinne suddenly crumpled into a heap on her chair. Her face went a shade paler than before. Beads of sweat appeared on her brow. She drew in her breath through chattering teeth and said with a shiver:

"J'ai froid."

"She's cold," said the interpreter, jumping up and rushing out of the room.

The poignancy of it almost finished Velten. Those two words—the first he had heard from her lips for two whole years! He had to hold himself almost violently in check to refrain from dashing to her side and taking her in his arms. He felt the hard eyes of the SS officer boring into him, and clenched his teeth. No one spoke a word. Corinne was trembling in every limb. It came home to Velten with terrible clarity how much she was suffering. The Hauptsturmführer's gaze did not waver. A cruel smile played around the painted lips of the typist as she savored the situation.

Then the interpreter came back. He was carrying a blanket—an ordinary army blanket. Clumsily, but with extraordinary tenderness, he draped it over Corinne's narrow shoulders. As he did so he gave the Hauptsturmführer a defiant stare. The latter still said nothing. Corinne drew the blanket tightly around her.

"Take her away," said the SS officer.

The interpreter told Corinne to get up and quietly followed her out.

The SS officer preserved a businesslike equanimity. "Send in the Duval woman," he called.

An elderly, simply dressed woman appeared. It soon emerged that she was the concierge of the building where Corinne had her apartment. Velten had felt sure he knew her face. The interrogation was short and factual. Clearly the woman had talked at some time or other. But now, confronted by Velten, she declared that she had never seen this gentleman. However much the officer upbraided her, she stuck to her story, contending that the other man had been shorter and thinner and had had a different accent. Velten was made to talk French to her. She thought Velten's French had more of a Russian intonation. The other had talked French like an Englishman. This was palpable nonsense, for when asked whether she understood Russian or English she had to admit she knew neither. She insisted, nevertheless, that she had never seen Velten. Finally she was told she could go.

"I have no intention of going into a lot of detailed explanations," said the Hauptsturmführer when he was alone with Velten, having dismissed the secretary, too. "Whatever happens, you can expect us to return to the matter at a later date. You've merely won the first round."

"And *I* reserve the right to an explanation," said Velten, merely for the sake of something to say.

The SS officer made no reply. He filled out a form and handed it to the orderly who entered in response to his ring.

"You can go," he told Velten. "This man will take you to the office which will deal with all the details of your return journey."

Velten took his leave with a curt bow, but received no acknowledgment. They gave him his belongings and made him sign a certificate that everything had been returned in good order. His German currency was paid out to him in francs, together with an authorization to have the money in his possession. He also received his travel documents, including a military rail warrant back to Berlin.

Eichberg broke into the narrative at this point. What a burden it must be to Velten, he reflected, to know that the woman who by her unflinching silence had saved him his liberty and possibly his life had gone back into the shadows—the shadows, most probably, of death.

"Did you ever hear anything from her later on?" Eichberg asked.

"No," said Velten.

"Do you mean you've never tried to find out anything about the fate of this woman?" Eichberg asked when they had passed on.

Velten fiddled with the screw cap of a hand-grenade he had absentmindedly pulled from the pocket of his camouflage jacket.

147

"It must oppress you, I mean," Eichberg's warm voice insisted. "You don't live exactly luxuriously, but you do live, after all—*and* you enjoy a certain form of freedom. But this woman . . ."

"So I'm to tell you how I got here," Velten interrupted. "How I landed in this certain form of freedom, as you call it."

Since Eichberg raised no objection, Velten went on with his story as they continued their patrol.

When after his release, Velten had found himself standing out in the Paris street with his little suitcase, a sudden idea had struck him. It was early September, and the air tingled like silver beneath the soft blue skies of that city whose atmosphere can transform a man's blood and spirits so strangely. This air does not intoxicate like the deep blue southern sky of Capri, like the sea around the islands of Greece, like the thaw-wind of the alpine valleys. Neither does it corrupt like the fatal sweetness of Venice, the cloying richness of Sorrento, or the abandoned glow of Naples. It makes the spirit soar and the blood sing. The air, the aura of Paris, have a quality which may be expressed in one single, untranslatable word —*grisant*.

Velten sensed how *grisant* was this September noonday—as *grisant* as the plunging neckline of a woman who, with the first foolish indiscretions of youth behind her, is ready to throw open her heart and bosom to the great new adventure. To him it was as *grisant* as the flashing knife in the hand of the swain from Belleville who lies in wait at the street corner near the bistro for the man rivaling him for the favors of the dark-haired Marguerite. Or as *grisant* as the inflammatory tract of a revolutionary pored over by students at an embankment bookstall as the setting sun turns the Gothic buttresses of Notre Dame blood-red.

Quickly he made up his mind. *They* and their ticket to Berlin could go to the devil. Velten went into the next bistro. He ordered a beer and poured the cool liquid down his parched throat. After that he went to the telephone and dialed a number in Passy, on the Trocadéro exchange. It was a pre-war number which he had often called and carefully stored away in his memory. It was still right, apparently, for a domestic servant answered and informed him that neither m'sieur nor madame was at home.

148

"Madame," Velten noted in some surprise. He had only known Gérard as a bachelor.

Only after Velten had sworn that he was an old friend of m'sieur did the girl divulge his office number. When he finally got through to Gérard, a whoop of delight came over the wire. Having ascertained his whereabouts, the gay Parisian told him to stay put. A car would be collecting him in fifteen minutes. They could hear all about each other later.

Velten was astounded. He had pictured Gérard in captivity or at least reduced circumstances. But marriage, a housemaid, an office and a car—that all looked very different.

The car appeared. Though not a de luxe model, it was nevertheless a respectable, dark-blue Renault. The chauffeur wore a discreet gray livery and politely took his cap off as he opened the door for Velten. Then, with Parisian adroitness, he sped through the maze of traffic to draw up in front of a house of quiet distinction in one of the side streets around the Étoile.

Gérard came rushing down the stairs almost before Velten had got into the hall.

"Victor, vieille branche, what on earth brings you here?"

Gérard Comte de Champtocé-St. Georges was a great towering man over a head taller than Velten, who was himself not short. They were both about the same age. They had much in common as regards character and background but, unlike the passive Velten, the Count was a blunt man of action. With an arm round Velten's shoulders he guided him upstairs.

"I was afraid you might still be stuck in a prison camp," said Velten when the first excitement of welcome had died down.

"No fear," laughed Gérard. "I never went into captivity at all. I was a subaltern in the tanks and my brigade was demobbed in unoccupied territory. After that I made my way up here."

They entered a roomy office after passing through a small anteroom occupied by a smart-looking secretary.

"Me voilà dans les affaires," said the Count. "As you see, business suits me very well."

Not liking to ask after the nature of his friend's business, Velten inquired instead how long he had been married. Aware of his former reputation for being *très* coureur, Gérard smiled. He was

149

already married for the second time, he said, and had a son six months old. "And what about you?" he went on. "You don't exactly look as if you'd come to Paris on a secret mission for your Führer."

"I'll say I haven't," said Velten, once again remembering his plight. "I've come straight from the rue des Saussaies."

"Merde alors! From the boys in black? Have they engaged you?"

"Damn fool—I was in the *cachot*."

Gérard pursed his lips. When he had heard Velten's story he thought for a moment.

"We must consult Georges," he said at length. "He can help you. He's got the right contacts." He asked his secretary to get him a number.

"Georges," he bawled into the mouthpiece, "are you free for lunch? I've got someone here from east of the Rhine. You're needed. He's in a jam. Mais oui, dans la purée. A good friend of mine. Don't be stupid, Georges. You can pass up the casse-croûte in that ridiculous Kasino or whatever you call the place. You're lunching with us in the rue Jean Mermoz. You know, where that little brunette serves who's always got bruises on her arms. We'll be there in a quarter of an hour. A toute à l'heure."

Gérard slammed the receiver back into its cradle. "Come on, old boy, let's get moving. You can leave that baise-en-ville of a portmanteau here."

He clapped his hands: "Germaine!"

"Ring up that old rogue in the rue Jean Mermoz," he said when the secretary appeared, "and tell him to reserve a table for three. A quiet table in the back room where three men can have a serious talk undisturbed."

With that he steered Velten down the stairs, still gossiping away in his own high-spirited fashion.

In the rue Jean Mermoz, a side street off the Champs-Élysées, they entered a small restaurant not far from the Rond Point. From the outside it looked like a shop, and inside there was a bar as in any bistro. But the few tables covered with white cloths and the well-fed men and elegant women who sat around them showed the place was no ordinary tavern.

The proprietor greeted Gérard with the respectful familiarity reserved for favorite habitués. Velten got a polite bow. The man led

150

the way into a second room where a table had been kept for them in the background. There were no other guests in there. As they sat over their *apéritif* a slim man of indefinite age walked in. The cropped hair on his temples was iron-gray, yet there was no hint of a wrinkle in the clean-cut face with its steady gray eyes. His clothes were well cut.

"Georg von Cismar," he said with a trace of a smile as Gérard, after greeting him boisterously, launched into a lengthy introduction. There was something congenial about his brief handshake. Though his French was grammatically faultless, his accent identified him as a Balt. At a sign from Gérard the proprietor appeared at their table with the waitress. She was a pretty brunette and actually did have a few blue and brown bruises on her arms.

"On m'a pincée—somebody pinched me," she informed them naively in response to Velten's inquiring look. Everyone laughed. Then began the solemn business of arranging the meal, a ritual at which Gérard displayed his old mastery. Velten could hardly believe it. Though it was known in the Reich that unrationed meals were obtainable in the occupied territories in spite of the official restrictions, the food now offered to him was sumptuous even by the most generous peacetime standards. They were served a fastidiously planned, five-course luncheon, together with excellent wines. In accordance with custom they talked little, and only of unimportant things.

"This unhappy fellow generally lunches at his office," said Gérard with a smiling nod at Cismar. "They've got a pig-trough there they call a Kasino—the name normal people give to a gaming house. A very Germanic set-up. There they guzzle sauerkraut and swill it down with Pinard. The same sour red wine which made us mutiny whenever we got it with our army rations."

"Oh, it's not as bad as all that," said Cismar. "But whenever there's a crowd of us together, tradition has to be maintained. Just imagine," he said, turning to Velten, "they call me an epicure—and mean it as a reproach, not a compliment."

"Extraordinary folk, these nomads from east of the Rhine," said Gérard. "Is it true, Victor, that you live in tents and make cheese from mare's milk?"

"Of course!" Velten retorted. "And when we come back from

151

our bison hunts we bathe our feet in the blood of three slaughtered Gauls."

"No, not blood," Cismar protested. "Let us not speak of rope in the house of the hanged."

The waitress had brought their coffee, and with it an aromatic Armagnac which shone as gold-brown as her eyes.

"The Germans smell more of sweat than blood," said Gérard jocosely. "God, how they work! Whatever they turn their hands to they pursue with methodical efficiency and fanatical thoroughness —war just as much as trade."

"We must keep off the subject of trade today," said Cismar, "otherwise we'll find ourselves talking shop. That would shock our guest from the Reich even more than it would bore him."

Then he inquired after the nature of the trouble at which Gérard had hinted on the telephone. He listened to Velten's story in silence.

"It's pretty clear what will happen—or already has happened— to that particular resistance group," he said. "Anyway, it's only one of many and certainly not one of the main ones. If it were, we should have heard of it from time to time. You yourself are obviously just as much under suspicion as ever you were. Well, there's only one thing to do—look for protection and go under cover. Where are you guaranteed the surest cover these days? Only in the Wehrmacht. That means you must join up. Himmler's boys can't get you then. We'll have your reservation rescinded and get you called up. Since you were employed as an interpreter once before, you'll be put in your regional interpreter company. There's most likely a note to that effect in your file. In any case, they're no longer letting interpreters loose on Wehrmacht as disguised civilians as they did in 'thirty-nine and 'forty. They drill them as soldiers in interpreter companies first."

Cismar noted down Velten's particulars.

"You can be a recruit by October 1st," he told him cheerfully. "Do you want to stay in Paris till then and enjoy your freedom?"

No, Velten did not. He was keen to return home. Besides, he pointed out, one couldn't hang around on the loose in occupied territory.

"That," Cismar laughed, "would be my worry. People are all busy scratching each other's backs in this part of the world. There'd be no great difficulty about fixing you up with the necessary papers."

But Velten still wanted to get back to Berlin, particularly as his family did not know what had become of him. Gérard suggested spending just one night on the town together. Velten could leave the next day. To this he finally agreed, after Cismar had promised to ring up Gaby on a military line and inform her of her husband's release.

Velten was appalled when he saw the bill Gérard had to pay. "That's almost the monthly salary of a minor official!" he gasped.

"You're in the land of the black market, my friend," said the Count, pushing the entire change, including several fair-sized notes, back to the waitress. "We aren't mean here. We earn money and spend it. Live and let live, you know. Après nous le déluge."

CHAPTER VII

BACK HOME again, Velten enjoyed a few more days as a civilian. Soon he received notification that he was no longer reserved, and shortly after that came the much longed-for assignment to No. 2 Interpreter Company, III Military Region. He had to present himself at the unit's location in Berlin-Lichtenberg at 8 a.m. on October 1st, 1943.

The building had originally been built as an elementary school. In the company office a friendly young corporal dealt with all the formalities involved in the enlistment of a new recruit. When he got up to walk over to a filing cabinet Velten noticed that he dragged one foot. Velten was later to discover that the whole permanent cadre of non-coms in the company were young soldiers whose wounds rendered them unfit for further active service.

Velten was duly put on the ration list and issued with underclothes, socks, laced boots, ankle puttees and a shabby much-patched uniform. At the armory they gave him a rifle, belt,

153

bandoleer, bayonet and scabbard. Then he went up to Room 22 on the second floor, where the recruits were housed, and began to put on the new things. While still engaged on this task the sound of male singing reached his ears, gradually drawing nearer. He opened one of the three big windows and looked out on to a spacious playground forming a gap in the house-fronts. On the other side of the street was another school building in which the military district headquarters was accommodated. The clock in the little wooden belfry showed half past eleven. Then they came marching in through the open gates—a column of men in gray with rifles slung and gas masks worn over their overcoats. They made a complete circuit of the yard, roaring a marching song.

"Aufhören!" a hoarse voice bawled. The singing broke off abruptly. Not till then did Velten become aware of an undersized officer standing in the middle of the playground. In response to his shrill, barked orders the party came to a halt, noisily ordered arms and fell out, jamming the narrow back entrance to the school building. Soon Velten heard them clumping up the stairs. The barrack-room door burst open and in streamed his new comrades.

One of them came straight up to him. The two chevrons on his upper arm identified him as a full lance-corporal. Somewhat pompously he held out his hand.

"My name," he announced, "is Lance-Corporal Winter, and I am the barrack-room senior." He squeezed Velten's hand in a manly grip and directed a searching look into his eyes. "I am therefore your superior and shall endeavor to make a good soldier of you. What is your name?"

"Velten."

"*Private* Velten is the way we say it here," this new superior reminded him with unctuous friendliness. "And that rifle belongs in the rifle rack, where you must put on a label stating your name and rank. Your rifle is your bride from now on."

Dear God, stand by me! Velten groaned to himself. He looked round for the others. But they had all hurried out again without a word, mess tins in hand.

"Off we go to get our food, then," said the barrack-room senior. "And so that you learn right away: here's my mess tin to bring

154

my dinner in." He looked at Velten expectantly. The latter made no move.

"When you're a regular soldier you'll know that the answer to that is: "Jawohl, dinner for Lance-Corporal Winter!" Understand?"

"I suppose I can get mine at the same time?" asked Velten, grabbing his own mess tin and making for the door.

By the time they were all back in the barrack-room and seated at the long table, cautiously spooning their piping hot vegetable soup, Velten was gradually getting to know the others.

"Don't take Winter as seriously as he takes himself," said a man of ample girth sitting opposite, who wore the 1914-18 service ribbon. There was a comforting tranquility about his portly figure and broad expanse of face. He had an enormous bald pate, and the tufts of silvery-white hair on both sides of his head contrasted bizarrely with his carefully trimmed, jet-black mustache. He was Dr. Hans Streif, the secretary of some industrial association, and was known in Room 22 as the Silver Stripe because of his silver hair and cheerful disposition.

"You see," the Silver Stripe told Velten in his deep, pleasant voice, with that slightly singsong intonation which betrays a Saxon long resident in Berlin, "we interpreters are a foreign body in the army of our beloved Führer. An undisciplined pack of intellectuals, as our company commander puts it. The good Captain Hacketanz has the irksome task of making soldiers of us. . . ."

"And what do the Chinese say?" interrupted a man who had been listening attentively from the other end of the table, a lean fellow with a pale, scholarly face and dark eyes which radiated kindness and intelligence from behind glinting spectacles. " 'You don't turn good iron into nails!' "

"Nor good men into soldiers," added the Silver Stripe. "That's the whole trouble."

"Our Franz Wennemahr there," he explained to Velten, "is a missionary from China. They've enrolled him as a Chinese interpreter because no one can tell where the frontiers of the Greater German Reich will end."

He looked round the table. "There you have Otto Heldt," he continued, pointing out a slender man of youthful appearance who

155

blushed to the roots of the dark hair over his fine brow. The Silver Stripe chattered on unperturbed as he spooned up his soup. "Otto joined us yesterday, so he's just as new to it as you are. Used to practice in Paris as a German lawyer. Sorbonne degree."

The man in question shot the speaker a pleading look, whereupon he turned his attention to another.

"There you have Paul Bindewaldt. He knows South America from the Gulf of Mexico to Cape Horn and speaks all the Ibero-American languages and their dialects. Roamed the countries for years earning his living as an export agent and doing philological research for the love of it. When you see his Spanish wife in the peculiar tap-room where we're allowed to have visitors on certain evenings of the week, you'll realize you've lived in vain."

They all laughed. Paul Bindewaldt, a slim, smooth-featured, sinewy man in his late thirties, made an ironic bow in the Silver Stripe's direction. The latter went on with his introduction: "There, sitting next to the missionary, you have our *enfant terrible,* Alloys Remmele, born in the Saarland but a truck driver in Paris for the last twenty years. The French *he* talks would make the average French secondary-school teacher blush with shame."

"Tais ta gueule, vieux con, fous-moie la paix et bouffe ta casse-croûte," came a growl from the bottom of the table in the genuine accents of the Paris suburbs. It was uttered by a tough-looking character with a large red face and thick auburn hair. In due course Velten was to learn that there was nothing in the man's vocabulary or pronunciation to distinguish him from a Paris laborer. Despite this he could neither read nor write a word of French. The letters which regularly arrived from his French wife and girl friend in Paris had to be read out to him. He dictated his replies in his remarkable but quite genuine Parisian argot, and then faithfully copied them out in his own handwriting.

"As you see," said the Silver Stripe, "it would be hard to make nails from iron of this quality. It's the same throughout the company. For all that, Hacketanz is resolved to make serviceable nails of us. He's the very man for the job, too. Did twelve years in the ranks of the old Prussian Army, after which they made him an inspector of municipal graveyards. Not having missed any army refresher courses in the meantime, he's managed to rise to captain.

156

And to make sure we become really good nails he puts nail-makers of Winter's type in charge of us. *That* bird picked up his bit of Portuguese on construction jobs abroad for Siemens—*and* as a staunch member of the Party's overseas organization."

The Silver Stripe imparted this last item of information in English, having first made sure that Velten would understand him.

"Our Mr. Winter," he continued in German, "endeavors in his own fashion to lighten our task of becoming soldiers. Hacketanz takes strict care to see that we respect our barrack-room senior. In his eyes we are only recruits, even if some of us like myself did have the pleasure of taking part in the Great War."

By now they had all finished their soup. They trooped out to a wash-room at the far end of the corridor where the mess tins were rinsed out. Then they all lay down on their beds for a brief spell. Winter had allocated Velten a bunk over that of the Parisian Saarlander Remmele. Just as he was beginning to assimilate the wealth of new impressions and one or two of the others had started snoring, there was a piercing whistle out in the corridor and a shout of "Get dressed to fall in!" They lurched to their feet, cursing and groaning.

Before long came the order to get outside, whereupon they poured down the stairs together with the occupants of all the other barrack-rooms. Out in the playground the company of 150 to 200 men was forming up in three ranks under the direction of Sergeant Sauerbier. A corporal placed Velten over on the left with the rest of the recruits. There were three platoons. The third comprised the beginners, who were employed on military duties only. If they completed the four weeks' initial training satisfactorily, they were moved up to the second platoon. There they did half military and half "language" duty—the latter consisting of reading, conversation and so forth in the various sections into which they were divided. The first platoon was made up of men who had passed their interpreter examinations at Command Headquarters and were waiting for assignments to field units. All three platoons came together for fieldcraft exercises and rifle practice.

Initially Velten, like the other recruits, had the most elementary things to learn. When a grown man is dragged out of a bourgeois existence and stuck in the gray mass of uniformity, the first task

157

is to rid him of any spirit of independence or individuality. The simplest way of achieving this is to knock his spirit out of him altogether. The process starts by imbuing him with a sense of his own inferiority. He is made to realize that everything he has been doing until now was wrong. He learns to stand properly, for instance. Then he learns to walk. Then comes saluting—*das Erweisen der Ehrenbezeigung,* as the handbook calls it. This is particularly important.

Their drill was quite a mild business. All the instructors were younger than their recruits and, having mostly been wounded on the Eastern Front, only too glad to stay at home. Apart from that they were without exception impressed by their recruits' social background and high degree of education. Consequently a pleasant relationship far removed from the traditional picture of the Prussian barrack-square developed between the permanent cadre and the trainees. Another factor was the speed with which training had to be carried out.

By way of contrast, the officers—Captain Hacketanz and the officer in charge of military training, 2nd-Lieut. Humpp—were far from pleasant. Captain Stubenrauch, who ran the language classes, was simply a secondary-school teacher in uniform. Hacketanz was typical of the old Prussian school; and Humpp, down-graded because of heart-trouble, complemented him with the brutality of the "new" type of reservist officer. Humpp, who had taught at a vocational school in civil life and was only half educated, worked off his sense of inferiority on the "pack of intellectuals" by chasing them round the drill square and having them out on bayonet practice for half an hour or more at a stretch in steel helmets and gas masks. Then, still in the same get-up, he would make them march woodenly round and round in a circle singing some merry tune or other, until he had reduced them to a state of complete exhaustion. Whenever they had to march back to barracks from a training ground he never failed to chase them two or three times round a certain block of houses. Rumor had it that his mistress lived there and that this was his way of impressing her.

158

CHAPTER VIII

ONE DAY a new recruit appeared—Georg von Cismar. He did not give any explanation for his presence, but lightly hinted that the time had come for him to take refuge in the protective custody of uniform.

"I must say you rather gave me the impression you belonged to the commissioned caste," Velten told him in astonishment.

Cismar's only response was a shrug of the shoulders. He brought a new spirit into Room 22. Hitherto they had tended to see their own lives and current history in the light of the Silver Stripe's good-humored, if mocking, strictures. Now the dispassionate Balt, with his razor-edged intellect, plunged their discussions in the corrosive acid of his cynical pessimism.

"I have a purgative effect on your spiritual bowels," he would say, alluding to the unappetizing analogy coined by Germany's club-footed propaganda boss in an editorial describing invective as evacuation of the soul.

Clearly Cismar had had a checkered war career. In the course of it, however, he had gathered experience which had never come the way of the majority of his room-mates. Whenever he started a discussion after lights-out, in the meal line-up or during a short pause between formations, they always spoke French. This was Cismar's own innovation to safeguard them against the barrack-room senior, who could scarcely object to soldiers who were being trained as interpreters keeping their foreign languages up to scratch. There was always tremendous suspense whenever some chance remark prompted Cismar to open up, in his own sarcastic fashion, about his own war experiences.

One day Remmele happened to be reminiscing nostalgically in his best Parisian argot. "Christ," he declared, "what a pile I made through the occupation! I used to take stuff by the truck-load to Clignancourt where the SS had that big dump. Those boys were all right, too. Do you know, there were actually a few there who went into "combine" with me."

"What sort of a "combine" was that SS captain, Fahrenbusch, running?" inquired Cismar with a discreet smile.

Remmele darted him a crafty look.

"Tiens, you know him too? Not that *he* knew what was going on, though. I'll tell you the whole story—you can keep your mouths shut. It was like this. I'd drive up with my load right on to the weighing-machine to get my gross weight, sling off the load and weigh again empty, then take the whole issue on board again and drive out the back way. Then I'd come round through the front and go through the whole thing once more. I'd do it three or four times over—it brought in a nice rake-off for yours truly, even if I did have to shell out to four of those boys in black. Had a brand-new outfit tailored for my little piece at a swank place at the Cours de la Reine. *And* I sent the old woman and the kids to Arcachon for four weeks."

Cismar laughed: "If only Ciborius had known about that—or even the Yellow Dwarf!"

This shook Remmele. "Holy Jesus!" he said, his blue eyes opening wide. "Do you know who the Yellow Dwarf is? And Ciborius? Would you happen to know who 'Monsieur Catastrophe' is, too?"

Cismar was still smiling. "You can put your mind at rest," he told Remmele. "An aircraft with Ciborius in it went into a nose-dive over Italy last October. He was going there to introduce the same *Schwamast* system as you profited from in Paris. But Almighty God had different ideas and summoned Ciborius to his fathers instead. And now they're winding up the whole *Schwamast* affair because they've found some fly in the ointment. So you don't need to worry. Today you'd no longer find any opportunities for working your own little swindles in the framework of the Big Racket."

Naturally everybody wanted to know what was behind all this. "Very simple," said Cismar. "Humanity has long emerged from the barbaric stage in which differences of opinion were fought out with chunks of rock or oaken clubs. There's a great deal more to warfare nowadays. That's why they invented economic warfare—

160

the fight for the raw materials and the exploitation of an occupied country's industrial potential. Old Genghis Khan really put the problem in perspective when he asked: 'What is the warrior's greatest happiness?' and gave his answer: 'To gloat over the tears of a beaten enemy, to drive away his cattle and to press his women and daughters into one's arms.' Nowadays, I admit, it's generally agreed to be bad taste to take pleasure in the misfortunes of a beaten adversary—at least, one no longer publicizes one's satisfaction. The rest of the old moral code of war, though, is still very much in force: Thou *shalt* covet thy neighbor's ox, and his ass, and his maid, and all that is his. Where the womenfolk are concerned, one tends no longer to follow this precept in terms of brute force, as the hordes of Mongolian horsemen did. One applies such devices as better food, glittering jewelry and softer beds. As for removing the ass and ox and all the other things this ancient concept implies today, it's not always possible to do so by straightforward robbery or theft.

"That was where Ciborius came in with a really brilliant notion. Just as the process of civilization had prompted mankind to replace the cruder form of appropriation of other people's property by the more amicable method of fraud—thereby affording the victimized party the comforting illusion of having been fully compensated for whatever he had been induced to part with—let us now, Ciborius argued, substitute trade and commerce for confiscation. The human instinct to do another man down in the course of commercial exchange has undergone an astonishing revival despite—or perhaps because of—the rationing with which we've blessed the Europe we liberated. The result is the black market. Since we couldn't suppress it, said Ciborius, we should use it for our own ends. Ciborius was the very man for such a job as this. He combined a warrior's hardness with a merchant's cunning. He incorporated the ideal type of soldier of the second millennium. In the Great War he had been a member of that fighter squadron whose sacred memory has since been taken over by the National Trust. When Germany collapsed after the famous stab-in-the-back, there was nothing left to him but to devote his dual virtues as a soldier and businessman to a calling that is more lucrative than first-hand participation in the mass murder of war: he became an international arms dealer. The bloody

161

International of armaments, brought him the ideal of a lifetime. He equipped the armies of that general in the west of the continent whose rise was to mark a further prelude to the Second World War. Ciborius delivered his arms, and they duly triumphed at Irún, San Sebastián and Madrid. When he presented his bill, his clients stared at him in innocent surprise. They thought all that was supposed to have been fraternal aid—mutual support for the same noble aim. Surely not a business deal to be paid for in cash? Ciborius went home with his pockets empty. Pending the final settlement. This, however, was indefinitely postponed by the outbreak of the Second World War.

"The Führer's most faithful paladin, familiarly known as the Fat Boy, accordingly decided that Ciborius must be compensated, particularly as the war had deprived him of most of his markets. He gave him the sole right to introduce and operate the *Schwamast* system which was Ciborius's own brain child. *Schwamast* was short for *Schwarzmarktstellen,* the official centers in Holland, Belgium, France and the Balkans which under Ciborius's direction skimmed the cream off the black markets in the interests of the Third Reich's war effort. Only in Russia was the Genghis Khan system retained in its original form. A stream of agents poured into the occupied territories, the then unoccupied zone of France and the neutral countries. They were controlled by the purchasing organizations, one of which was that SS depot in Clignancourt whose easy-going methods our Remmele's mistress has to thank for her fine clothes.

"A much bigger and better center was the OO—the Organization Oskar. It was run by an experienced intelligence man who before the war had removed the plans of the Belgian frontier fortifications from the Ministry of War in Brussels. He called himself Oskar: no one knew his real name. He had an office in Passy, in a palace which had belonged to the Bonaparte family. The place was a regular rabbit-warren with God knows how many secret exits. Agents and purveyors used to turn up there openly and in disguise, in broad daylight and under the cover of night. Behind its doors freight papers found new owners and millions exchanged hands. Out in St. Ouen-le-Docks, in the north of Paris, the OO had a well-equipped, up-to-date depot.

"The OO dealt in every known commodity. From the factories

162

of St. Étienne in unoccupied France came the spiral drills used for boring holes in sheets of armor-plating. You could find specimens of them in many a dancer's make-up box, as the best deals of this type were and still are clinched in the cabarets and night clubs of Paris. Ask Private Velten. He must be blind if he didn't spot that only recently. Whole flocks of sheep were driven over the Pyrenees in the mists of nighttime. Wolfram came from Portugal for hardening iron into steel. At the same time, of course, anything else was brought up which made life comfortable and pleasant. The Fat Boy himself got a special train full of *pâté de foie gras,* sardines in oil, champagne and other restoratives.

"Over all this rapacity, gluttony and genuine want of raw materials presided Ciborius's *Schwamasts.* These blessed institutions were intended to endow the whole murky swarm of racketeers, whores and adventurers with a semblance of legality. 'Chaste ears must never hear what the chaste heart holdeth dear!' Ciborius had the diabolically ingenious idea of camouflaging his own black-market activities—which were, after all, officially punishable—by incorporating them into the organization combating the black market! They actually did combat it from time to time—whenever they happened to drop a purveyor who had become too presumptuous or an agent who had fallen into disfavor—and hand the offenders over to the courts. In the main, though, they regulated the activities of the recognized purchasing organizations on the black market with the discretion and vigilance of a procuress. They passed on the requirements of agencies back in the Reich, they checked the quality of wares offered them, and they endeavored to achieve some degree of co-ordination between the conditions of purchase and sale.

"To run the Paris *Schwamast* Ciborius had found a man ideally suited to fulfill the tasks of this sanctimonious organization—that same Yellow Dwarf to whom Remmele has already referred. But what Driver Remmele doesn't know is that the Yellow Dwarf and Monsieur Catastrophe are one and the same person. The man had a name which was quite unpronounceable for Frenchmen, so those in his immediate entourage—the chauffeurs, principally—were prompted by a vague sense of the man's malignancy to dub him 'Monsieur Catastrophe.' He owed this nickname to his outward

163

appearance as well as his activity. He's a tiny fellow with spidery little arms and legs. Buried between his shoulders he has a goblin's head with big protruding ears and a fleshless nose. Apart from that, the weird little devil seems to exude a sort of all-pervading and quite offensive yellowness. His hair is a flaxen yellow; the skin of his face is a grayish yellow. When he opens his wide mouth with its thin bloodless lips he shows little square, waxen-yellow teeth. The eyelashes round his inflamed lids are white, just like the brows over his watery eyes."

"I've got to hand it to you," Velten interposed. "What a wonderful description! You seem to have quite a soft spot for that bird."

"And how!" Cismar retorted. "I've a debt to settle with him one of these days."

He grinned and went on. "The Yellow Dwarf was the ideal man for *Schwamast*. He was a sanctimonious humbug. Every modern State is prepared to murder, rob and cheat. But only the State of our beloved Führer would go so far as to have its dirty work supervised by an expert who can make you and everyone else believe not only that all this sort of thing is fully justified but that it's actually prompted by the highest of motives! And the Yellow Dwarf really was a master at his job."

"There's one thing I don't understand," the Silver Stripe interrupted. "Where in fact did the money come from for such extensive black-market operations?"

"A fair question," said Cismar. "Plenty of people before you have racked their brains over that one. Naturally a way was found. As far as Holland was concerned, there was no difficulty anyway, as the guilder is tied to the mark and not really a foreign currency any more. You can print as much of the stuff as you like. As for francs, the French paid all we needed in the form of occupation costs. For a time all of these occupation costs were being pumped back into the country via the black market. The only difference was that the money decent citizens had paid in taxes out of their own wages now found its way back into the pockets of racketeers. But the really genuine foreign currencies—those with an international status like the Portuguese escudo, the Swiss franc and the Swedish crown—had to be acquired through other channels."

164

Before Cismar could make any further revelations, Corporal Winter called for silence.

A few days later, Silver Stripe reopened the discussion.

"You still owe us an explanation, Cismar. The other day you hinted you knew exactly how foreign funds are acquired for armaments—"

"I never *hint!* I know something," Cismar interrupted somewhat brusquely. "I talk only of things I know from personal experience. I've told you that Cain is at work everywhere. He's as ubiquitous as God and the Devil. I met him once, in a place where I'd never have expected to find him. He casts his shadow right into neutral countries. In May last year I was in Portugal. . . ."

"Well, well," said the Silver Stripe. "Not a bad trip to make in the spring. And you actually came back!"

"It was the worst mistake I ever made in my life!"

Cismar's thoughts were obviously far away. "I'd give a lot to know what impulse prodded me into flying back into the 'Fortress of Europe.' I wouldn't be sitting here in this outfit if I hadn't!"

"Come on, then," cried the Silver Stripe, "let's hear all about foreign currency. You can hardly have been to Portugal without any."

"I'll say so," Cismar smiled. "That was the very reason I went, as a matter of fact."

Then he began his story. As he told it, his hard Baltic accent became a shade softer. "Ach, Kinder," he said. "I spent Whitsuntide of 1942 in Estoril. An enchanting coastal resort close to Lisbon. Ex-kings and beggars stroll there under the same palm trees. And everybody's equally content. Or so it seems, at any rate. 'Tene paciencia' is what you tell a beggar if you can't or won't give him anything. 'Have patience.' And the beggar thanks you quite amicably for your words of consolation.

"This blessed land not only lies on the sunny side of Europe. It lies on the sunny side of the war, too. A large part of the economic power extorted from the people of the continent by their masters flows into the hands of the friendly Portuguese. For here you have a rarity like wolfram—a raw material indispensable to arms production. And though a British corvette is perpetually lying off the

165

entrance to Lisbon harbor, inside the three-mile limit and recognizable with the naked eye, even this breach of international law—only one of many, incidentally—can't prevent the coveted ore from being delivered to the Axis powers through Spain, which winks an eye at such things. Our good friends the Portuguese are in no way inhibited by their 700-year-old alliance with the Mistress of the Seas—always provided that the purchaser pays well and in decent money. Besides, they profit by the mere fact of their neutrality, thanks to which their capital has become the espionage center of all the belligerent powers. Espionage brings money into the country. Particularly if you consider that the activity of most so-called spies consists solely in spending money. Perhaps three per cent of all spying is genuine espionage. The rest is nothing more than mutual surveillance and bureaucratic bullshit. Why should the modern State act any differently in war from peace time, when the mere fact of a man's birth or death, or the removal of his appendix, sets a score of officials in sluggish motion and provides them with a not entirely adequate livelihood? The Anglo-Saxons talk of 'paper war' just as we do of 'Papierkrieg.' It's to the conduct of paper war that the intelligence activities of the belligerent powers in Lisbon are largely devoted. They're all installed as accredited members of their diplomatic missions and operate as so-called attachés. Everyone knows exactly what his opposite number is there for, of course, as well as who the genuine members of the mission are and who are merely attached for intelligence duties. If the Germans seek an *agrément* for one more attaché, the other side immediately puts in for one too. Otherwise, one side doesn't do the other any harm. One can always give tit for tat, but that would be unpleasant and disturb the peaceful routine.

"Once I was sitting in the garden of a white villa, eating hard-baked, golden-red fishes. I had been served with a dry, thirst-quenching white wine to go with them. My host was lounging slightly paunchily in a comfortable deck-chair. At his feet squatted his amanuensis of long thigh and thrusting bosom, gazing out with wide blue eyes at the unending fleece-tipped waves of the great Atlantic . . . 'Donnerwetter,' gasped my host—his name was Müller but he called himself Schulze: they were very smart with cover-names—'just take a look at that!' He was holding out a copy of Army Council Instructions.

"He had been thumbing through various official papers to show me that the southern sweetness of the country couldn't weaken his sense of duty. But what had upset him? He was pointing to a directive issued by the High Command in the East which debarred troops, in view of the 'demoralizing effect' involved, from witnessing executions of Jews. My good friend was horrified. 'My God,' he said, 'what are they doing with the Jews? How do they come to be killing them—and in masses, too?' I had the impression that for the first time in his life he had really come face to face with the consequences of our Weltanschauung. 'Come, come my dear Schulze-Müller,' I said, 'how can the shooting of a few thousand Jews at which soldiers are not allowed to be present disturb you here in your picturesque cliff-top garden on the dream-coast of Estoril? Do you not night after night fight for the same aims at the side of your blonde Amazon? I feel your ideology is at fault.'

" 'Ach, what's ideology got to do with it?' sighed Schulze-Müller. 'We hauled a Jew out of Dachau—fellow by the name of Dagobert Salomon. He's down in our records as Danny Salmon. He's emigrated to the USA in the normal manner as a Portuguese—with false papers. He's got a small short-wave transmitter on which he sends us messages every Wednesday from 23.40 to 00.15 hours. With the best will in the world. Good old Salomon! We know exactly what President Roosevelt eats for breakfast and how his digestion's working. It'd be quite possible to treat the Jews differently without harming our Weltanschauung!' "

"Now let's have a rest from your anecdotes and finally hear something about Cain and the foreign currency!" cried Velten, voicing the general feeling.

"Yes," said Cismar, propping his head in his hands and gazing into the distance. "Yes, I actually met Cain there, besides feeling his shadow over the white villa on the hillside. His greedy talons were close beside me, ready to reach out and claw his victim's throat.

"There was a ship lying in the harbor. The flag on her stern was a yellow cross on a blue field. The same emblem was painted on her

167

gray hull and visible from afar. She was a Swede—the *Drottning-holm*. She had brought German and Italian diplomats back from America and now she was to take the American staffs from Italy and Germany back home. As a result Lisbon was teeming with foreigners of all the belligerent nations.

"I don't know how it happened. One day I found myself strolling through the municipal gardens in the center of Estoril at the side of an American woman. She belonged to the repatriates who were waiting for the *Drottningholm* to sail. Somehow or other I had made her acquaintance. I had passed myself off as a Frenchman. She spoke impeccable French. When I finally told her I was German, it turned out that she spoke German equally well. She was no longer young. But her physical freshness, her straightforward good-fellowship for all her feminine readiness to entice, gave her a vivid charm all of her own. The fact that we were citizens of enemy nations did not perturb us; and the certainty—in view of the peculiar local conditions—that we'd create a sensation only gave our association an added zest. We swam together at inaccessible spots on the shore; we hired a car and drove by night along the coastal road to the fishing village of Cascães. Here a writhing, floundering catch, phosphorescent in the moonlight, was landed and put out for sale on the open market. After a great deal of haggling we acquired a fish, and a bare-footed youngster took it to the guest-house for us. Then we sat under the projecting roof and watched the pot-bellied landlord in his soiled apron gutting and scaling our supple prize. As we waited we nibbled brown olives and drank white port. When our paunchy host brought us our fish swimming in a garlic sauce, we ordered the local white wine. Finally we consumed enormous hunks of strong-smelling goat's cheese and the porous white bread of the countryside. Everything here was simple and still and breathed contentment. A peaceful moon smiled down on it all.

"We spoke of everything but the war. Frances enjoyed the hour even more than I. She had lived long in Europe, and in taking leave of this continent she was bidding farewell to a way of life. After her divorce in America she had lived as a free woman in three different countries. She was one of those untypical Americans who come back here like Columbuses in reverse to rediscover the Old World.

She adored this Europe with the tender, slightly hectic love of the proselyte. 'Now I must go back,' she said bitterly, 'to all those dreadful women—and the worst of them all is my own mother!' And before she went she was for the last time imbibing the fragrance and the soul of Europe. . . .

"A little later we lay naked on the sands. The moonbeams traced green tones through her uncoiled black hair, in the dark shadows of her lap, and from her breasts to her armpits as she pillowed her head in her hands. . . ."

After a brief pause Cismar went on in a different tone: "This little romance lasted longer than we expected. The *Drottningholm*'s sailing date was put off time and again. A few days became a week. I soon found the reason. Among the repatriates awaiting embarkation, I was told, was someone in whom the Germans were particularly interested because he was a 'courier.' He had got as far as this as a result of some oversight on our part. Now instructions had come through that he must not be allowed to leave Europe alive. The problem was how to eliminate him. In answer to my astonished inquiry I was casually informed that he would simply be decoyed into the Marinha, the desolate, unmapped swamp which extended into the hinterland behind the coast. Once out there, he could be quickly throttled or killed by a bullet in the neck. No one would ever find the body. There was always the alternative of arranging for a fast-working poison to be dropped into the victim's morning coffee.

" 'And how does one get the *Drottningholm*'s departure postponed?' I asked.

" 'Very simple: we say our U-boats haven't been warned.'

"The result was that Frances and I continued to meet frequently. Quite naturally our relationship hadn't escaped the notice of the gentlemen of the intelligence organization. They had even made capital out of it by their own lights. On one occasion I had unsuspectingly reported that Frances really had nothing to do with the diplomats being repatriated by Sweden as the protecting power. According to her, she had only escaped internment through being on good terms with someone in the State Department. My friends of the organization had taken smirking note of this. It was a point worth knowing, they told me. It could always be used against the

169

Americans if they objected to the Germans playing a similar trick. After that I naturally kept a check on my tongue.

"One day the *Drottningholm* suddenly sailed. The whole party of Americans left with her, including Frances. When I asked Herr Schulze what had happened about the courier, he told me he'd received fresh instructions. The original information had been incorrect. The person in question hadn't been so important after all, so the liquidation order—I quote his exact words—had been rescinded. Then I asked who the death candidate had actually been. 'Why,' Herr Schulze responded with a smile, 'your very attractive girl friend, of course. That was why your flirtation suited us so admirably.' I felt ready to vomit. I'd been the murderers' cat's paw. Even in those brief moments of happiness we had spent together, Murder had been creeping round us—and I had been its tool.

"By now my own mission was completed. I left Portugal by the next plane from Cintra airfield."

"And what were you actually up to while you were there?" Velten asked.

"Yes, what about the currency business?" the Silver Stripe demanded.

"Oh, yes," said Cismar absent-mindedly. "Where we get our foreign exchange from, you mean? By the sale abroad of things with an international value: 'degenerate art' in the form of paintings and sculpture; jewelry and precious metals taken from the occupied territories and Jews who've emigrated or been deported East. That brings in all the escudos, Swiss francs and Swedish crowns we need so badly. There's a special department under the Four-Year Plan for transactions of this nature. This time I'd been sent off on quite a new stunt. Some resourceful character had had the idea of benefiting the war effort by a smuggling trick often tried by émigrés. Since stamps rank as international tender, many an émigré who had to leave his valuables behind has brought out a large slice of his fortune in the heel of a boot. So off I went to Portugal with a stamp collection. They were a dead loss. I couldn't get rid of them. In that part of the world people know of better means of capital investment than scraps of fancy-colored paper. No one needs to smuggle valuables out of the country for the simple reason that no one wants to leave it. Apart from that there are no currency restrictions. Thus

170

our Four-Year Plan still has to go on dealing in diamonds, pearls and knocked-out gold teeth to raise its funds for purchases abroad."

Cismar was to have little further opportunity to regale Captain Hacketanz's recruits with his reminiscences. A few days after his narrative about Portugal he was summoned to the company office in the middle of dinner. When he returned a few minutes later he was accompanied by two military policemen wearing pistol-holsters. He quickly packed up his belongings and left without a word of farewell, stalking out with his head high and a scornful twist to his lips. From that day on an uneasy atmosphere prevailed in Room 22, and the Portuguese-speaking Winter was treated with extreme caution.

For Velten the days that followed were difficult for other reasons. After an adequate spell of weapon-training he had, like most of the others, been moved up to the second platoon; and from now on, thanks to those of his comrades who instructed on the language courses and had permanent access to the company office, he came into possession of many scraps of information about the internal working of the unit. In this way he did not take long to discover that his own position was in danger. It seemed that General von Unruh, the man vested by the Führer with plenary powers to comb out home units and dispatch anyone he chose to the front, was breathing down his neck. Unruh's department, Velten learned, had called for his immediate drafting to a combat formation on the Eastern Front. The Interpreter Company and Command Headquarters, on the other hand, contended that Private Velten's command of Dutch, a language for which interpreters were in particularly short supply, made him indispensable.

Such was the state of the paper war being fought over his body by the von Unruh Manpower Commission and the Reserve Army when Velten was granted an unexpected respite. The Allies now began to bomb Berlin in earnest. Admittedly there had been raids of steadily increasing violence in the years before this; but now, in the last week of November 1943, the enemy air forces were concentrating their attacks on the Reich capital. Night after night the sirens howled as the spectral fingers of the searchlights, mute harbingers of the impending holocaust, groped their way across the sky. The bark of the anti-aircraft guns, more and more of which

171

were being drawn away for anti-tank defense in Russia, sounded pathetically weak as the hum of enemy machines grew louder. Then the flares of the pathfinders glowed like fairy lights over the defenseless city. A hail of blockbusters, land mines and incendiaries poured down over factories and railway yards, workers' tenements and middle-class houses. A burning, choking, mangling, mechanical death hurtled earthwards to envelop man and beast, soldiers and simple townsfolk, supporters of the regime and its bitterest opponents, male and female, old people and unborn infants. The most oppressive thing of all was the stillness after the Terror had passed: that short space before the all-clear when fires blazed unchecked and the slain sprawled nakedly in the streets. One almost heard a moan of agony rise from the mutilation of the night.

Velten, transformed on such occasions into a wild-eyed creature with trembling nostrils and straining ears, had opportunity enough to register such impressions as these. Evening after evening the Company was detailed for watcher duty. Leave was canceled and all troops were confined to barracks. They fire-watched on the various floors of the main building, on the drill-ground and over in Command Headquarters. Those not detailed for duty, as soon as the sirens went, piled into the pitiful dug-outs which had been constructed in the yard.

CHAPTER IX

ONE EVENING a number of men in the company, Velten among them, were told to stay behind after formation. 2nd-Lieut. Humpp gathered them around him.

"Men," said Humpp in his hoarse voice, "Operation Ikarus has come into effect. You are now members of a catastrophe force. A ring of military command posts, the Ringkommandanturen, has been set up around Berlin. In case of catastrophe their job is to

172

hold up the civil population fleeing from the city and provide for its immediate needs. Each command post is allotted interpreters who must detain prisoners-of-war and foreign workers attempting to escape in the general panic and segregate them until further orders."

The interpreters were given armbands to indicate what language they spoke and told to stand by with full equipment. After the customary period of military delay they were collected by a truck already carrying several eastern-language speakers from the 1st Interpreter Company in Spandau-Pichelswerder. When the vehicle had passed through a number of villages well beyond the metropolitan boundary, Velten and Werle, a man speaking English and Italian, and three others with a command of Russian, Polish and Serbo-Croat were dropped off in Alt-Landsberg, a country town east of Berlin. They found themselves in front of a rustic beer-garden. Several other trucks had drawn up there, and a group of soldiers were busy unloading army bread. In an alley enormous carcasses of beef, sides of bacon and sausages were hanging. Cheese and tubs of butter were stacked everywhere.

Velten spent two weeks of complete idleness in Alt-Landsberg. The population of the German capital displayed the same incredible self-control as the inhabitants of all other German cities in those years of horror. Not even the smallest group of refugees appeared; and neither—this was perhaps the most remarkable feature of all—did a single runaway prisoner or foreign worker show up. Far from giving a thought to escape, plunder or deeds of violence, the latter helped to combat the common danger, and many of them gave their own lives in the process.

Velten exploited this spell of inactivity by making certain inquiries in the orderly room of the Alt-Landsberg Ringkommandantur. The clerk he found on duty was a well-nourished lance-corporal, and to this worthy he confided his qualms regarding General von Unruh. Corporal Weber, who on his own statement had managed to hold out in home garrisons ever since 1939, was fully acquainted with all the regulations likely to arise in Velten's case.

"My dear man," he said patronizingly, "what is there to get excited about? Before they can get you to a field force battalion in the East they must transfer you to the appropriate drafting unit.

173

As soon as they look like sending you off, just you consult me, and I'll provide you with the necessary introduction to the company. But don't forget your old pal Paul Weber!"

When it was realized in Berlin that there was to be no panic, the interpreters were sent back. The morning after his return Velten was summoned to the company office. The sergeant-major was waiting for him in the long, narrow room, feet planted well apart.

"Looks as if you've got good friends up above," he remarked nastily. "Direct order from General von Unruh: You're posted to your unit forthwith—the 3rd Landesschützen Battalion in Strausberg-Hegermühle. Pack up your stuff and get off to Strausberg as fast as you can!"

But Velten was not in all that hurry. Having collected his papers and packed, he first made a trip to Alt-Landsberg. There he handed over a bottle of schnapps to a beaming Weber, who wrote him a letter to Corporal Hahn of No. 2 Company, 3rd Landesschützen, asking him to take the bearer under his wing. He, Weber, could report favorably on Velten. All further details by word of mouth. Placing the letter in an envelope, Weber carefully licked and sealed it.

"Just you take that to Strausberg-Hegermühle," he said, "and ask for Corporal Jack Hahn at No. 2 Company. Give him the letter and everything'll be in the bag. But bear in mind that Jack Hahn's always hungry and thirsty and very fond of his smokes."

Velten took the train to Strausberg with mixed feelings. Outside the station there he caught a tram out to Hegermühle. He soon reached the camp lying in a clearing in the woods. He asked the sentry where he could find Corporal Hahn, and learned that the company was celebrating Christmas. It was December 17th. The party was being held in the camp movie, and Velten managed to get admitted to the ante-room. There he asked a private just coming out if he would call Corporal Hahn. After a short delay the door to the main room opened, and over the threshold stepped a stooping figure with corporal's epaulettes.

Jack Hahn's outward appearance alone sufficed to mark him down as a home-front warrior who could never be usefully employed in any theater of the Second World War. He was an emaciated fellow, with an enormous Roman nose in the middle of his

174

haggard face. One stained, jagged tooth protruded from his upper jaw and bored into the lip below. Wisps of scrubby gray hair stuck out around his temples. Though as thin as a rake, however, Jack Hahn was possessed of a gargantuan appetite. Every single clerk in his department had something or other to do with foodstuffs in civil life. He had a dairyman, a fishmonger, a grocer, a mill-owner, a leading member of a farmers' association, and so on and so forth.

Having perched himself on the edge of a table, Jack Hahn read the note from Weber. Velten pushed over two packets of cigarettes. Hahn stuck them in his pocket without even looking up.

"Very nice of you, I'm sure," he commented unctuously. "Though you don't really *have* to, of course.

"Right, son," he continued, having digested the letter's contents —Velten found this first "son" from the lips of a superior extremely reassuring—"I'll bear you in mind. We'll fix you up with a soft little job in the company to start off. All you've got to do is to make sure no one spots you. When some soft job turns up, I can put your name down right away. But if someone's after you up above—well, even Jack Hahn can't help you then."

Velten hastened to assure him that he quite realized that.

"But," Jack Hahn went on, "no one's goin' to worry about a poor lousy private like you. They'll leave you in peace, and you'll be well looked after with us. The main thing is to get you into my outfit, so just you take a bus ride as far as the Klosterstrasse, and tell them in the orderly room you're posted to No. 2 Company. Say Jack Hahn knows all about it."

No sooner said than done. Velten was put into No. 2 Holding Company and initially found himself in one of the camp's long wooden huts. Those who passed through No. 2 Holding Company comprised fresh draftee groups, front-line soldiers who had been wounded and patched together again, old shirkers, and men who, having for years ranked as unfit because of some genuine physical defect, were now suddenly adjudged suitable for active service.

The huts teemed with bugs. The moment the lights were extinguished legions of these loathsome vermin descended on the occupants, leaving behind itching, running rashes. Fortunately for Velten, he spent only a few days living under these conditions: he was moved into the company office. His task was to help the leave clerk

175

issue the special Christmas leave passes. This particular clerk was an actor, and the company commander, Captain von Blauert, had obviously been struck by his cheerful disposition and talent for entertainment.

Velten spent five whole days writing out passes under the direction of his theatrical colleague, who lightened the proceedings by cutting grimaces and maintaining a flow of partly recondite and partly bawdy quotations. Naturally Velten did not forget to issue himself a pass. On the advice of the furlough expert he did not give Berlin as his place of residence but Bernburg-Anhalt, where relations of his lived, the distance entitling him to two extra days for travel, making a total of nine days' Christmas leave.

Once again Velten savored the pleasure of being a human among other humans. He was hardly inside the porch of his home before he had pulled off his tunic and slung it down the cellar steps. His boots went thumping down after it.

On reporting back to his unit he was transferred to the receiving department. A third man was required there owing to the tremendous influx of troops lately up-graded for active service. The department was presided over by Lance Corporal Edwin Kroschel and Leading/Able Seaman Anton Mühlenseifen. The former had secured his niche there through being the brother of a famous racing cyclist who counted their sergeant-major among his fans. Young Mühlenseifen had got stuck in the job after being wounded on a mine-sweeper. The three of them lived and worked in the room that served them as an office. Along the walls stood their beds, with mattresses, pillows and blankets.

The three of them were kept frantically busy. Every soldier posted to the company from another unit or coming there straight from civil life had to be processed by them. On one occasion it was Velten's pleasure to be present when a small party of his former comrades from the Interpreter Company arrived. They clustered anxiously together like a herd of scabby sheep. To Velten there was something pathetic about the deferential attitude of the simple soldiers who passed through his own humble hands. Even the interpreters now being returned to regimental duty because of unsuitability or a falling demand for their services brightened up at the

176

sight of him. Timidly they inquired whether Velten could help them.

"Any of you fellows drive?" he asked expansively. It appeared that several of them held driving licenses. Velten actually succeeded after conferring with Jack Hahn, in getting them transferred to the motor transport holding battalion in Rathenow. They gazed at him in grateful awe, as if he were some superior being.

Early one morning Jack Hahn came round to the department. "Trouble," he announced. "Brigade's just rung up from Fürstenwalde to ask if there's a Private Velten in the Company. Yes, I said, we've got him in our office and we were just goin' to send him on draft leave. Do you know what they said? Leave canceled, they said. He's to remain here till further orders!"

Kroschel and Mühlenseifen did their best to console Velten. They could send him off to the front, submit the necessary return to this effect—and then quietly post him back again. "Mind you," Mühlenseifen added thoughtfully, "if you get wounded in the meantime, that'll put the kibosh on it."

The day passed wearily. The following noon Jack Hahn showed up again.

"There's an order from Brigade that authority to draft Private Velten has been withdrawn from the Company," he announced indignantly. "What a lousy suspicious way to treat me! The draftin' order's to come from Command."

Velten looked at him hopefully.

"Tell you what I'll do," said Jack Hahn. "I'll write 'No action to be taken without informing Command' on your card. With that against your name you can sit here in Strausberg and wait for Final Victory to roll along. As for seeing as no one at Command drafts you—you'll have to fix that up yourself."

Velten endeavored to "fix it up." All he succeeded in doing, however, was to discover that his personal file at Command Headquarters contained a strict order from General von Unruh: "Only to be employed in combat unit in the East. To be complied with by 30.1.44."

A few days later Capt. von Blauert sent for Velten. "Don't stand around like that—sit down," he told him when Velten stepped in and froze to attention in front of his desk. "It's quite clear that some dirty trick or other's being played at your expense. What I have to do is to ask you if you consider your training to be of a sufficiently high standard for service against partisans in the East."

Holy Jesus, thought Velten. Partisans. This was it in earnest. After a moment's deliberation he looked the captain straight in the face. A pair of benevolent brown eyes met his own.

"Now try to get this straight," said von Blauert. "I've instructions from Brigade to find out whether you are adequately trained to fight partisans. According to your papers you're trained as an infantryman, but I'm leaving it to you to say whether you consider you're fit for drafting. If you tell me you still feel unsure of yourself I'll report accordingly and you'll be sent to the training battalion at Fürstenwalde. By doing that you'll gain further time—and that means a lot these days."

Velten thought rapidly. They had driven him thus far and didn't mean to leave him in peace here, either. They had got on to his track and would find him everywhere he went. It wasn't that he was a coward. He was damned if he was. It simply made him nearly spew to think of being drilled again. No, he wouldn't let them humiliate him to that extent. The will behind this manhunt was stronger than he. He wasn't going to make himself look despicable now.

Very quietly, he gave his answer. "I thank Herr Captain for being so helpful. I consider myself fully trained. I know the .98 carbine, the .34 machine-gun and the .09 pistol, and I can throw grenades. Apart from that I couldn't care less."

He sprang to his feet. "I beg Herr Captain's pardon."

Von Blauert waved the apology aside. "That's all right. I'll report that you think you're up to scratch."

In eleven days the orders came through: "Confirmation of Pvt. Velten's transfer to Zorn Inf. Bn. to be submitted within 24 hours."

"Do us one favor," said Jack Hahn, so impressed by the gravity of the hour that for the first time he spoke decent German instead of his native *Berlinerisch*. "Scram off to Wandern as fast as you can. Don't go taking a powder, whatever you do—they're bound to catch up with you."

Velten received a smart, brand new uniform and an issue of soft, warm underwear. In place of his "fore-and-aft" forage cap they gave him one of the peaked type with ear-muffs buttoning up at the

178

sides. In addition, he was given a knapsack, a steel helmet and a gas mask. Last of all he was handed an enormous bundle of newspapers: this last item was based on an order directing that every soldier proceeding to the Eastern Front be supplied with enough newspapers to pad his uniform and protect himself from the Russian winter.

And so Velten came to join the battalion commanded by Capt. Zorn.

CHAPTER X

NATURALLY Velten had not been able to tell Bernd Eichberg all this in the course of one patrol. It had taken several days to relate the full story of his career. Eichberg was a silent listener, but his warm-hearted interest evidenced the lively sympathy he felt. To Velten this was a precious consolation in the gray solitude of his present lot.

In the meantime their day-to-day existence was swiftly taking on a different complexion. One night those members of the outpost due to go on patrol were sitting in the flickering candlelight of the blockhouse. Every man had received an issue of rum—a quarter-liter mug full. Animated by the unaccustomed spirit, and accompanied by the quavering tones of Tülle's mouth-organ, they were singing an artless, clumsily composed song taught them by Rötert, the cook, and a few others. They sang of the alien, hostile land whose flabby, indolent womenfolk lie around in the heat of the summer chewing sunflower seeds and spitting out the husks on the ground before them, while their grimy children play in the dust of the roads. The long-drawn-out, melancholy rhythm lent a mournful background to their own dismal existence.

As they took up the last refrain, it was an abstracted Velten who sat with chin in hand. In that moment he was so acutely conscious

179

of the homesickness felt by tens of thousands of his fellows, all driven into an unknown wilderness by the order of one man who thought he was Germany's destiny, that tears of anguish and compassion came into his eyes.

Then the door was kicked open. Everyone swung round. Stodolka burst in, reluctantly followed by Albert Schnupphase. The two of them had been out patrolling together. With a sudden movement Stodolka reached for his cap and threw it on the table. Then, with his little black eyes flashing beneath their thick brows, he dug his hand in the pocket of his camouflage jacket, pulled out something and threw that on the table, too. At this point, attracted by the noise, Sergeant Schrader came in. The object which Stodolka had thrown down was a foreign-looking head-gear: a round cap of short, frizzly fur with a red velvet top criss-crossed with gold braid.

"I was patrolling with that half-wit there," Stodolka began, with a nod towards Schnupphase, "when all of a sudden I saw a whole line of dark shadows dart over the railway, crossing from the road towards the wood. Just as I was trying to creep nearer, this damn fool Schnupphase yells 'Who goes there?' and in his panic starts loosing off into the air. They jumped like rabbits and were off into the darkness in a second. This here is the only proof I wasn't dreaming."

Schrader took charge of the evidence. Then he rounded on Stodolka, demanding what he meant by returning before his time was up. Hothead that he was, Stodolka had apparently had no other thought but to pass on his news as rapidly as possible. By this time the relief—Velten and Martin Scholtz—was due anyway. Velten, who had not the slightest desire to come up against any partisans, found the prospect a little gruesome, particularly as his companion seemed even less fitted for such an encounter than he. It was thus with some hesitation that the two of them set off into the driving snow. Nothing happened, however.

After that the situation changed rapidly. The next evening the outpost was fired on for the first time. The shots came from rifles at the forest edge, their flashes being clearly visible. Schrader gave permission to return the fire and they let off a few rifle shots and one or two bursts from the machine-gun. Guido Reichert fired his mortar twice. Then there was silence.

180

Two days later, while Eichberg was giving instruction on the machine-gun in the main building, a freight train drew up outside with a scream of brakes. A minute or two later the sentry from the main gate brought in the engineer, bleeding profusely from a wound in the neck. Schrader questioned him as Rötert applied a first-aid dressing. The shot seemed to have been fired at the level crossing—in other words from the same patch of forest as the volley two days before.

"Let's comb the wood," Eichberg suggested.

"Right!" Schrader called. "Ten volunteers to go with Corporal Eichberg!"

To his own surprise Velten jumped to his feet, buckled on his belt and seized his rifle. Stodolka and Reichert naturally stepped forward, as did Knaus and his fellow Swabian, Vogler. Even Willy Specht and Alfons Schindler did not hang back. As the party came past the level crossing they hurriedly asked Martin Scholtz, who was on sentry-duty there, whether he could give them any idea of the probable position of the sniper. It turned out that poor old Martin had entirely missed the incident. Not even when the train stopped had it occurred to him that there might be something amiss.

They moved through the wood in extended order, rifles ready. They found nothing. As they wheeled left to approach the eastern fringe, they spotted a figure lying under the trees. Cautiously working their way nearer, they saw that it was a dead man. He was on his back, staring wide-eyed into the sky: a powerfully built specimen about thirty years of age. Everything about him was clean and tidy and in striking contrast to the raggedness of the local population.

Willy Specht searched the corpse with expert speed. He had been shot through the left breast, and one foot was smashed, apparently by mortar splinters. All the pockets were empty. There was no trace of identity documents or money—not even the tiniest scrap of paper. Obviously his comrades had seen to that.

There had been a two-day lull after that. Then things really started. They were fired at night after night. Whenever the shots came whistling out of some black recess of the forest, the patrols simply dived into the ditch and fired blindly in the direction of the muzzle flashes. Every time one of these skirmishes occurred, a mine exploded under the next train. Then the alarms and excursions began. The train guard would leap down and start shooting all over again. Next, since this was an important stretch of line, a breakdown train would arrive at short notice to clear up the mess. Once the damage was repaired the seven-minute traffic would be resumed.

As a result of all this, more rigorous instructions were issued. Officers began to carry out snap checks on the pickets and the sections of railway for which they were responsible. Mortensohn was given the assistance of a second-lieutenant who cursed and swore as he stumped up and down the company's sector with five enlisted men. It took him a whole night to do the double journey. From now on pickets were no longer relieved at fixed times. None of these innovations made any difference, however. The racket went on night after night just the same. Once Outpost 603 set up a record by having three stretches of track blown up between sunset and sunrise. No casualties in dead or wounded were suffered.

Higher up people started to get alarmed, and a general came down to inspect them. Naturally his trip was announced days in advance, and equally naturally he did not come at night when things were humming. The usually easy-going Schrader enforced strict measures for keeping the premises clean. Stodolka was given the important task of keeping a look-out for their visitor and letting the outpost know when his arrival was imminent. The neighboring outpost was to telephone through a preliminary warning.

"Now!" cried Schrader at a quarter to eleven. "He's just leaving 602!" Then they heard Stodolka's whistle, and a few seconds later the trolley bearing their general whined straight past. Outpost 603 had been passed by.

The general was said to have expressed profound displeasure with the results of his visit. To judge by his comments, one might almost have thought the Zorn mob alone were to blame for the delay in attaining final victory. They were to be replaced as soon as possible.

After a week or two the relief arrived: Hungarian troops in khaki uniforms. They brought their gear on farm-carts which they sent away again after unloading. An enormous copper kettle and

182

pots and pans of every shape and size figured prominently among their belongings. All their cooking was done at the outpost, and Rötert soon found himself crowded out of the cookhouse.

The Germans had to stay a few days longer to give their allies time to settle in. During this period the Hungarians slept on the floor wrapped in their overcoats and blankets. Not one of them spoke German.

One night—the two nationalities were sharing duties on a fifty-fifty basis for the duration of the hand-over—Velten went out on patrol with a mustached Hungarian. Though his comrade-in-arms was obviously keen to be communicative, their respective vocabularies did not extend to even the bare minimum necessary for conversation. Naturally the Magyar's chief standby was the word *Scheisse*—with which the German soldier could convey a whole range of emotions—and of this he made exhaustive use. With the help of a few other scraps of German and many gestures he explained that he had already been in the army for seven years. A movement of the hand across the throat served to indicate what he thought of this station in life. Velten subsequently gathered that he had soldiered in two armies—first the Rumanian, then the Hungarian, and then the Rumanian again. His opinion of both was identical—*Scheisse!*

In this dejected frame of mind he trotted alongside Velten. At the far end of the stretch of track they had to patrol he suddenly ran off to the left of the embankment and, before Velten could warn him, was in the middle of the minefield. "Mina mina!" Velten yelled. His companion, however, had already let down his khaki trousers.

At that moment they came under fire from the edge of the forest. As Velten took cover on the far side of the embankment, the Hungarian plainsman came bounding over towards him, one hand holding up his trousers and the other grasping his rifle. Conscientiously Velten took aim at the spot where he had seen a muzzle-flash and fired across the rails, ducking under cover after every round. Hearing someone call softly to him, he glanced over to his right. The veteran of seven years' military service was lying unconcernedly behind the embankment, tapping his forehead and pointing to himself as if to say: "You're crazy. Do it my way!" Velten saw that he

183

was holding his rifle like a howitzer and, from this position of perfect safety, firing one shot after another into the air. The fool was right, Velten decided. Why the hell should he risk his skin? At last a Hungarian picket, drawn by the sound of firing, came crawling over from the neighboring sector and, having briefly conferred with Velten's prudent friend, set up a machine-gun. After a few bursts from this, the invisible sniper in the forest left them alone.

On the day of the final hand-over the Germans marched in to their company headquarters at Mysonowicze, whence, following a day and two nights of futile inactivity, they finally went on to Iwacewicze to entrain. Then they waited around in the siding for a further day and a night. At long last they steamed off at a snail's pace on a journey broken by innumerable long stops. They traveled through day and night, losing all sense of time. Having finally detrained somewhere or other in pitch darkness, they stumbled off, listless and sluggish with fatigue, on what seemed an endless route march. They came to a village—but marched straight through. Not until the next village did the order to halt finally come. They saw now that only their own company, No. 2, was still present. They were standing in a spacious courtyard weakly lit by a few storm lanterns and apparently part of a large estate. Part of the company, including the office staff, were directed into the main building; the rest were sent out into the village to fend for themselves.

Next morning Velten awoke with a splitting headache. They had been told to muster out in the yard at eight o'clock, but as there had been no reveille he got there too late. Velten's tardiness was very much to his disadvantage, as the sergeant-major had already nominated the complements of the various outposts and Velten, together with a number of other latecomers, found himself allotted to Sgt. Seidenspinner, a man entirely unknown to him till that moment, long, lean and bony. When Seidenspinner had gathered his little flock of sixteen men around him, Velten found that, in addition to Reichert, Stodolka, Knaus, Vogler and himself, there were also Tülle, Senkpfiehl and Schnupphase from the old outpost.

There were also eight new men who kept to themselves.

Seidenspinner appointed them to their various duties in a voice which was querulous and overbearing. When he called for those who were trained on the machine-gun, a fourth man stepped forward in addition to Stodolka, Velten and Guido Reichert—Herbert Berger. Herbert was an indescribably silly fellow. He was restless and jumpy, afraid of superiors and partisans alike, and quite insufferable on account of his unending chatter. "The answer to a soldier's prayer," Stodolka groaned.

As it turned out, this assessment was entirely incorrect. In moments of danger the fidgety, floundering Berger was a man transformed. Cool as a cucumber, he would drop behind his LMG and take aim as calmly as if he were at the butts, quite unmoved by the enemy's fire.

"And now," said Seidenspinner doubtfully, taking stock of his force, "who's going to be cook?"

They studied each other in embarrassed silence. No one coveted this thankless job.

"I might as well warn you," Seidenspinner added, "that looking after the cookhouse won't get anyone off doing picket duty. I can only free the cook in the daytime. At night he'll go out on patrol like everyone else."

That merely increased their reluctance. Then, all at once, Velten had a nauseating mental picture of Schnupphase or Tülle sticking their dirty hands in the food. Apart from that the prospect of not doing any daytime patrols attracted him. He took a pace forward.

"Sergeant, I think I can manage the cooking."

"You!" cried Seidenspinner in amazement. "But you don't look the least like a cook!"

"I've done quite a bit of cooking in my time. I think I'll manage."

Seidenspinner ran his eye over his squad once more and then gave his consent. Apparently he thought Velten the safest bet.

The company had requisitioned a number of two-wheeled carts for transporting equipment and personal kit to the various outposts. Before they left, Velten presented himself with the other cooks at the ration depot to draw ten days' rations on the strength of an indent showing each man's allowance of bread, meats, fats, cereals, sugar and cigarettes for that period. This at least meant that Company Headquarters could no longer cheat them out of what was due to them. The rations non-com moaned and groaned about shortages and weighed the rations with painstaking care. The cooks accused him of not keeping his scales in order. Then they found fault with

185

the weights. When he made an obscene retort they cursed back at him. Only a threat to call the sergeant-major subdued them.

"That lot," Velten told his comrades, frowning at the rations as they were being stacked on the cart, "is supposed to feed eighteen men for ten days."

Slinging their knapsacks and kitbags on top, they trudged off southwards behind the squeaking cart and the shaggy pony that pulled it. At the far end of the village, on the left-hand side of the road, stood an unusually imposing building—a former water-mill now run on steam. A small stream meandered past.

"A tributary of the Szczara," Stodolka told them. "It must wind around here somewhere."

"It really is too damned silly for words," said Velten. "We haven't the foggiest notion where they've stuck us."

"We must be in fen country," Stodolka remarked, pointing farther south where the highway was made of large baulks of timber and held together by broadheaded nails. To the right and left of the embankment there was nothing but swamp.

"When we get there, I must have a look at Seidenspinner's map," said Velten. "It gets me down not knowing where I am."

They came to a sawmill surrounded by a high wall and with a guard in the uniform of the Todt Organization standing outside.

Shortly afterwards the ground under their feet became firmer. Instead of marshes there were now ploughed fields and meadows to the right and left of them. The track plunged into a wood, becoming narrower and cutting deep into the ground. There was a sinister stillness. Seidenspinner held his machine-pistol ready for instant use and ordered the men with carbines to release their safety catches. Velten, Stodolka and the other machine-gunners thumbed back the safety catches of the pistols with which—to their great joy —they had been issued instead of carbines. As they emerged from the wood they saw that their path crossed a single-track railway running from north to south. To the left and right of them, some two kilometers away, the timber walls of outposts were visible.

"Kuleni," said their driver, pointing his whip at the gray, thatched dwellings. At an order from Seidenspinner they swung to the right and headed towards the southern outpost.

CHAPTER XI

THE PREVIOUS occupants had moved out the day before their arrival, so it did not take long to settle in. The outposts in this region were not numbered but named after their localities. Their own was called Kuleni Central.

From Seidenspinner's map Velten saw that they had to guard a stretch of railway running almost straight from Baranowicze in the north to Luniniec in the south, where it intersected with the line from Gomel in the east to Pinsk, Kobryń and Brest-Litowsk. That meant that they were in the northerly part of the vast Rokitno Marshes, which extend from the trough of land between White Russia and Wolyn almost to the northern spurs of the Carpathians and are cut transversely by the river Pripet. This impenetrable expanse of swamp and woodland concealed hordes of partisans in inaccessible hide-outs. There were many tales about the life they led. Whole armies of them were supposed to live in fortified camps amid the marshes and to maintain efficient standing patrols of mounted sentries.

Initially the outpost garrisons saw no evidence of the existence or efficacy of the guerrilla bands. Though it was now the end of March, a heavy fall of snow caused huge drifts to form along the railway. There was very little traffic: at most six to eight freight trains in the daytime and none at night.

Stodolka soon became the second most important man in the outpost. The local people were glad to work there. If they were not engaged by the company they got sent off to Lubaszewo to do forestry for the Organization Todt, which they hated. They told dreadful stories about "Djadja" Fritz, Uncle Fritz, the transportation chief, who kicked the men up the backside with his hobnailed boots and was alleged to tie women to trees and have them birched

187

across their naked buttocks. There was no risk of anything like that befalling them at Kuleni Central. On the contrary, they were very much attached to Stodolka, who was perfectly satisfied with their slow rate of work. The fortifications were never finished as long as Velten was there—a fact that was also due to the contradictory nature of the instructions they received. One day a visiting senior officer would decide that the walls were too high for proper vision. They would hardly have completed the job of sawing two or three feet off when along would come another officer who wanted the wall heightened and fitted with firing platforms.

Stodolka did not mind. He continued to fill up the workers' payroll, settle up with the company and pay out every ten days. In a moment of indiscretion induced by *samagonka* he made a confession to Velten. He was receiving regular emoluments from the peasants in the form of butter, eggs, bacon and schnapps, and was able to send at least one parcel home a week. The others were beginning to grouse about it. "The whole secret," Stodolka told him, "is in the wage sheets. Boys under fourteen and girls under eighteen get eleven pfennigs an hour. An adult worker gets up to thirty-six. The people need the money, and this is their only means of coming by it. On the other hand, a family man has got his own work to do on his patch of land, particularly now the spring sowing's starting. That's why many a man is glad to be able to stay at home and send his kids instead. He's even more grateful if I put down the hours worked in the adults' column. Who's to tell whether the work was done by the fathers or their youngsters?"

"So that's why there are always so many adolescents running around here!" said Velten. "Long live regulated corruption!" He raised his tumbler of egg-colored liquid.

"Peter," said Velten after a moment's thought, "you must do something for me, too. What about getting me one or two of your village beauties for my cookhouse?"

"You silly bastard," Stodolka retorted in his hard Eastern accent, "you don't think you'll get anywhere with them, do you? Even I can't do that. The Polack girls are too dirty and the Russians as chaste as nuns. Apart from that, both sorts have their national pride. Just listen to the way they spit 'Nemts—nix kultura' in your face."

"Can't think of anything else, can you, except sleeping with them?" Velten smiled, running his eye over the slim figure of his drinking companion. "D'you think I've no other worries? I just want a girl or two to peel spuds, scour pots and pans and keep the place clean."

"I'm all for it," said Stodolka, "but you'll have to talk to Franz. D'you think you can bring him around?"

"Franz" was Franz Seidenspinner, the non-com in charge. He was not popular, as he was severe to the men and strictly complied with company orders by having them out training or on working parties all day long. At the same time he set out to cultivate Velten, whose academic background clearly gave him reason for assuming that the two of them should have much in common. "I'm closer to you than you think," he had confided to Velten one day.

After much hemming and hawing, Seidenspinner finally con sented to let Velten employ a few girls in the cookhouse. What ultimately decided the regulation-conscious non-com in favor of the scheme was the realization that the release of men from cook-house fatigues would augment the number available for working parties.

Velten chose Lydia, Marusja and Bronja to help him with the cooking. The first was a podgy, vociferous, but intelligent young woman of about twenty. The second, Marusja, was a delightful creature of seventeen in the first bloom of womanhood, with dark blue, vivacious eyes, neatly parted black hair, a fresh complexion and strong white teeth. She was always cleanly dressed. She was Orthodox, whereas the other two were Catholic. Bronja was a half-starved orphan of about thirteen. She swiftly attached herself to Velten and anticipated his every wish. He soon got out of the habit of doing anything for himself in the way of boot-cleaning, darning or laundry. He endeavored to pick up a few phrases of Russian and Polish from the girls and liked to listen to them singing at their work. Even "Franz" would occasionally come to the cookhouse window and have Stodolka translate the words for him.

And so they lived for a few weeks in the isolation of this wooded marshland. Their existence was half military, half Wild West. The duties were not over-strenuous, as the outposts were only about three miles apart and there were no longer round-the-clock patrols as in the old sector.

So far no one had seen a trace of partisans, but they were there, all the same. One sensed it in the glances and whispered conversations of the local inhabitants. From his visits to the village Stodolka brought back stories of how the "people from the forest" had appeared to demand bread, butter, poultry and perhaps a sheep or pig, and then melted away into the darkness again. A certain Josef Sczycz had been terribly beaten up for refusing to co-operate.

The men at the outpost stretched fine wire across the paths leading through the swamp and linked each length to a tent-peg on which there was a fuse mechanism and a rocket. A sharp tug was enough to set it off, and the rocket in turn released a yellow flare. Whenever one shot skywards, they sprayed the spot with fire and then cautiously closed in on it—but never found anything. It was always an open question whether a wild animal or a human being was responsible.

At Easter they had a blow-out at Kuleni Central. Not far from Kuleni South there was a potato plot among the marshes. Being hard to get to, it had not been dug up the previous autumn, and the frozen, sweet-tasting potatoes attracted game from the swamps. Seidenspinner's "roughs" had begged him in vain to let them go out after wild pig: it would have been incompatible with his conception of soldierly behavior to consent to such a thing. The fellows down at Kuleni South, on the other hand, had bagged a big black boar a few days before, just as it was rooting up one of the succulent tubers from the damp earth, and no objection of Seidenspinner's could deter the non-com in charge from coming over on the Saturday with two of his men to present them with an enormous ham. "You poor buggers must have a holiday treat too," he explained pointedly. Seidenspinner was known throughout the company.

Velten duly roasted the piece of wild pig in the new pan and served it with sauerkraut recently drawn from Company Headquarters.

On April 20th—the Führer's birthday—there were promotions and citations. A few men at the outpost moved up to acting lance-corporal. Reichert, Berger and Velten were made privates first class. Their unit was no longer an independent battalion, but was now part of 711 L.-of-C. Brigade, which in turn belonged to 62 Division. Privates were henceforth to be known as grenadiers, and a company or battalion headquarters was now a "command post." The Zorn mob had become warlike.

Not long after that, they killed someone else. One day Stodolka was called to Outpost Kuleni North to act as interpreter. He was back again in a few hours. The burgomaster of a small settlement in the vicinity had been denounced by a local woman who claimed he was in league with the partisans. The Germans had arrested him and brought him to the outpost. In Stodolka's opinion the interrogation had produced nothing incriminating. The man himself regarded the denunciation as an act of vengeance. His story was that he had got drunk and forced his way into the house where the woman lived alone with her sister. He had made advances to them both, but without success. He admitted having been a bit violent—that was why they had sworn to get even with him. The man pointed out that his own barn had only recently been plundered by the partisans.

On telephoning to Mortensohn for instructions, the non-com in charge had been ordered to send the prisoner up to the company command post. Thereupon he had selected two men, taken them to one side and given them precise directions. That same evening villagers from Kuleni had found the peasant's body in the wood, just off the road. There were several bullet wounds in the base of the skull. The workers at their own outpost heard the news in next to no time, and it was from them that Stodolka learned of the sequel to his visit. According to him, their mood had swung right round.

When the picket from Kuleni North appeared that night, its members were closely questioned. Two of them admitted to being implicated. "Shot trying to escape," they stated.

"Don't talk such bloody nonsense!" Stodolka fumed. "You aren't going to tell me the man was trying to run away when you were armed. And how did you manage to hit him slap in the back of the neck? The wounds were black with powder!"

The last sentence was pure bluff, but it reduced the two men to an embarrassed silence. At last one of them, a tall, big-boned,

191

broad-chested East Prussian who had been smirking self-consciously and stepping uncertainly from one foot to the other, brought out the explanation Velten had been waiting to hear all along. His thick lips uttered it quite unashamedly: "Orders is orders." Nobody said anything after that: even Tülle forgot his silly, jarring laugh. The picket left without another word.

On Friday, April 28th, unexpected reinforcements arrived. A special train drew up in front of the outpost, and from it alighted twelve men under the command of a sergeant. An attack was anticipated on May 1st, as previous experience pointed to the likelihood of the partisans taking some action to mark the occasion. The reinforcements had brought two MG 34s and a captured Russian machine-gun with them. When Franz Seidenspinner saw the latter, there was no holding him, and a little later Velten, preparing the evening meal in the cookhouse, could hear him and one or two of the newcomers playing around with it outside. Suddenly the firing ceased. There was a lot of confused shouting, and heavy feet clumped across the threshold. Velten stuck his head out of his cookhouse to find Seidenspinner sagging between two men who had just dragged him inside. He was as white as a sheet and biting his lip. They carted him into his room and dumped him on the bed. The new sergeant was bringing up the rear and stuck his elbow in Velten's ribs as he passed.

"Your boss has shot himself in the leg. Not a bad effort, eh?"

Velten hastened into the room with the first-aid kit. Franz was sitting on his bed looking a picture of misery.

"I'm so ashamed," he whimpered. "I shall be court-martialed— I *want* to be court-martialed."

Velten tugged the boot off the injured foot, causing Seidenspinner to groan with pain. There was a hole in the toe where the bullet had entered, and another where it had come out of the hole. It had gone clean through the root of Franz's big toe and there was hardly any bleeding. Velten dabbed the spot with iodine and applied a dressing. It looked suspiciously like a self-inflicted wound, he reflected. Seidenspinner volunteered an account of the incident. It sounded like a self-indictment. He had laid the automatic weapon on the wooden parapet and—apparently having never heard any-

192

thing about recoil action—had quite happily pressed the trigger. The gun had rebounded on him and, his finger still being on the trigger, several shots had gone into the ground. One, however, had passed through Franz's foot.

"I'm sure to get court-martialed," he whined.

"You'll be hospitalized first, anyway," Velten told him.

He rang up Company Headquarters and reported that Sgt. Seidenspinner had been injured on firing practice.

The following afternoon Seidenspinner was taken to the regimental aid post in Honczary, where Battalion Headquarters were located. Stodolka had never experienced less trouble in requisitioning a horse and cart in the village.

Seidenspinner did not, as it turned out, have to face a court-martial. The injury was assumed to have been unintentional, and when it was found that a tendon had been severed he was packed off home.

The cart returned with a new incumbent that same evening—Corporal Kampe. He was to command the outpost temporarily until a sergeant became available. Kampe was a taciturn fellow who, apart from allocating the duties and taking his turn on patrol, took no interest in anything.

Nothing happened on May 1st, of course. Military emergencies tend to arise only when everyone is unprepared for them. The surest means of forestalling one is to plan on the basis that it is bound to occur. On the morning of May 2nd the reinforcements withdrew and the outpost settled down to a tranquil existence that would never have been possible under Franz. Stodolka interpreted at the barter deals between soldiers and civilians. Tülle fooled around with the girls. Schnupphase lay asleep on his bed. The new outpost commander sat in his cubbyhole reading a detective story. Berger and one or two others busied themselves laying out a vegetable garden near the outpost—they had obtained seeds for radishes, carrots and cabbages from the villagers—while Velten looked idly on, drawing the sharp, though already warm, spring air into his lungs.

"Seeing as you're the cook, you really ought to do a bit of planting yourself, you know, really you should," Berger sputtered in his nervous, jerky fashion.

"And I," Velten mimicked him, "am damned if I will, yes, damned indeed."

"Why not, then?" inquired Boberg, looking up from his work.

"Because I haven't the least inclination to sow what the Russians will reap," Velten retorted somewhat brusquely. Boberg laid down the bayonet he had been using to make little trenches for the seeds, and stood up. "What do you mean?"

There was something sinister about his tone and expression. But Velten preferred to ignore it and replied lightly:

"You know as well as I do that the Russians'll be here by the time that stuff comes up."

"Just listen to him!" said Boberg with a malevolence in his voice that would have put Velten on his guard much earlier had he been only a little more vigilant on this first day of spring. "You seem to know more about it than the Führer. We shall have to remember that. I've already had to remember a number of things. Very instructive it's been, living among you."

Velten turned away. He had no inclination to argue with this Boberg, who had a name for being cantankerous and quarrelsome. It was he they had found installed at the outpost as their advance party. Nobody had known him before, nor was anyone aware of his background. Damned nonsense, Velten thought, what the hell did the fellow imagine he was going to "remember"? To hell with him!

Velten clambered onto the wall and looked around him. Even this poverty-stricken country had its beauty. Though no greenery was to be seen as yet, the marshy meadows basking in the weak sunshine seemed to presage the blossom and fruit to come. Now and again the black bog water would sparkle in the interplay of cloud and sunlight. Over by the forest solemn pines and firs were aligned before the alders and elms, like a row of sentinels before a treasury into which the sun's rays still had to infuse the magic green gold of life. Farther east, on the far side of the silvery thread of railway track, the open marshes gradually became undergrowth and woodland. In the distance shimmered the roof of the Kuleni school building.

Plodding along the narrow path across the meadows he saw three men coming towards the outpost. Each of them was carrying

194

something. As they drew nearer he recognized the burgomaster and two other Poles he had seen on working parties at the outpost and attending the Easter party in the village. When the sentry had let them in, it turned out that they had brought four chickens, fifty eggs and a bulky slab of butter. The *szoltis,* as the burgomaster was called in Polish, or *starosta* in Russian, made a little speech. Stodolka translated. The villagers regarded the change of command as an occasion for expressing their good-neighborly sentiments. They sought, by various hints, to make it clear that they knew Kuleni Central had nothing to do with the shooting of the peasant. Apart from that, they wished to express their pleasure at the fact that there was now no impediment to barter trade between Poles and troops. Velten fetched the bottle of egg-yellow *samagonka* and poured out drinks all round. Glasses were clinked. It filled the Poles with awe that every man should have one to himself.

That day dinner was much later than usual. But there were no complaints. Velten boiled the four birds into a rich broth, then cut them up and fried the pieces in the pan. The men fell to with a will and blessed the shot that had banished Seidenspinner from the outpost.

The following morning, just as Velten had put the water on to boil for the breakfast coffee and was taking a turn outside in the fresh air, the sentry hailed him. "Hey," he called, "there's something wrong over there." He was pointing to where the men on the morning patrol had halted some three hundred yards away and were standing huddled around something. Full of curiosity, Velten ran over. The men were gathered in a semi-circle round Corporal Körnle, the Swabian and World War I veteran. He was scratching away with his bare hands at the soil under a rail.

The earth here was remarkably loose and had attracted the attention of Kampe, the non-com in charge of the picket, because it was of a lighter shade than that surrounding it. Before long Körnle had uncovered a wooden box, which he cautiously lifted out of its hole and set down on a sleeper. In the lid was a hole with a little iron nozzle protruding from it—the fuse. There could be no question about it: Körnle had found and lifted their first mine. For such an achievement Battalion Standing Orders prescribed a reward of two bottles of schnapps. Kampe told Velten to take the mine back to the outpost, as he wanted to check over the same stretch of track once again. There was always the chance they might find one or two more.

As Velten was warily raising the heavy box from the ground preparatory to carrying it home, someone behind him cried: "Don't make such a fuss, man! Nothing can go wrong now! Just stick it under your arm!" But he felt most uneasy about the whole business and refused to be rushed. He carried the object in both arms like a new-born babe, stepping slowly and with the utmost caution. Having reached the outpost, he gently deposited it on the floor of the commander's cubby-hole. Then he returned to the cookhouse to make the coffee.

When Kampe returned with the picket, he went straight to his room and began to tinker with the mine. After a while he came into the cookhouse and laid something on the table with elaborate care, as if he were handling a raw egg.

"There you are," he said. "That's the fuse."

As he inspected the device the room began to dance before Velten's eyes. He took a deep breath and staggered to a seat. The fuse consisted of the percussion cap of a Russian hand-grenade and a firing-pin held back by a spiral spring. Instead of a safety catch—this was what made Velten totter at the knees—there was a length of ordinary pencil lead. The mine had been planted in such a way that the upper end of the firing-pin came into contact with the underside of one of the rails. When a train passed overhead a depression of one millimeter was enough to push down the firing-pin and crush the flimsy graphite. This caused the spring to fly back and release the firing-pin, which duly snapped down on the percussion cap. Thereafter everything took its intended course.

Velten looked at Kampe.

"Delightful to think that my life was dependent on this tiny piece of lead, isn't it?" he grated. "What the hell did you mean by making me cart the goddam thing about like that?"

Kampe stared at the fuse in utter bewilderment.

"God, man, you don't think I've ever seen a mine before, do you? I haven't got the faintest idea how a thing like that works."

"Christ Almighty!" Velten ejaculated. "Then how the blazes could you go poking around at it like that? The whole outpost might have been blown sky-high!"

"Oh, well," Kampe murmured, "it all turned out all right in the end." He retired in some confusion. The box mine was later found to contain ten pounds of dynamite.

CHAPTER XII

ON MAY 5th, a Friday, Mortensohn unexpectedly turned up at the outpost in the middle of the morning. When the sentry reported the approach of the one-horse hunting-brake they all knew from previous visits, Körnle thought the reward for his mine-lifting exploit had come, but his hopes were swiftly disappointed. Even before Mortensohn entered the building, Corporal Mieses, a man everyone knew to be company cook, staggered in with his entire equipment—kitbag, pack, rifle, steel helmet and gas mask.

"Looks as if you're off to the wars," was Kampe's greeting.

Mieses pulled a face. "The Old Man's chucked me out. I'm coming to you in exchange for your cook."

Velten, emerging from the kitchen to see what was the matter, caught the last remark. "You must be nuts!" he roared.

Before he could say anything more, Mortensohn swept in, the inevitable riding-whip switching in his hand. "Come on!" he bawled at Velten. "Pack your things! We're off again in ten minutes! You're appointed company cook. I can't stand the sight of that pig Mieses any longer."

Mortensohn had called at the outpost once or twice before on inspection trips, and each time Velten had managed to produce something edible for him and his retinue, with the result that Mortensohn had not ceased, in his own unfriendly fashion, to praise Velten's food.

But Velten, who once or twice before had shown the company despot that he was not ready to bow to his every whim, had no intention of accepting the transfer without a murmur. So, standing to attention and looking straight into Mortensohn's angry eyes in the way he had been taught, he began to state his case:

"I request Herr Oberleutnant to let me stay at the outpost. I didn't take over the cooking here as a function but for reasons of comradeship. Apart from that, I go on patrol like everyone else. I would ask Herr Oberleutnant to bear in mind that a man's civil occupation is always taken into consideration when he is being selected for . . ."

He got no further. Mortensohn was already bawling at him.

"So you're conceited in the bargain, are you? The university man is too refined for the job, is he? I'll soon get rid of those ideas for you, believe me! No more back talk—I've given you an order! Pack your gear immediately!"

Velten realized that any further resistance was useless. He made an about-turn and went into the barrack-room. Mieses was in there telling his story. According to him the Old Man had been drunk again the day before yesterday, the resultant hangover being so frightful that Mieses had not been able to do anything right. The last straw had been when the supply of white bread had run out. "The few white loaves we get are for men with stomach-trouble," explained Mieses, "but he scoffs at the lot." "I'm replacing you!" the Old Man had shouted at the end of his tirade. "You can go out on patrol until you fall flat on your snout. Get off to the outpost!"

"You'll be doing the cooking here now, won't you?" Velten asked as he packed his things.

"Not likely," growled Mieses. "Besides, I don't know what the Old Man wouldn't do to me if he found I was the cook out here."

"Who's going to do it then?" Velten asked. "One of you'll have to take over the rations."

After much beating about the bush a certain Hegener, a man who had seldom come into prominence till then, agreed to do the job.

"You'll have to give him a hand to begin with," Velten told the ex-cook. "Hegener will just have to take over the rations on trust

198

now. You can check them between you, any way. Next delivery's on the ninth."

Outside Mortensohn had started shouting. With no time to take his leave, Velten grabbed his kit and raced out of the building. The Old Man was already sitting in the brake. Velten put his belongings next to the driver and, in response to a mute gesture, sat down by Mortensohn. The tracks were so poor and narrow in these parts that Mortensohn had had to leave his car at home and come in the brake instead. Now he was whistling quietly through his teeth as Velten thought over his chances of wangling out of his predicament. The vehicle rumbled along the side of the railway track and then turned across it into the wood. As they reached the spot where the peasant had been murdered, Velten peered over the side. Mortensohn, as touchy as ever, immediately sensed something.

"What's wrong?" he bellowed at Velten. "What are you staring at?"

"This is the place where a Russian peasant was shot a few days ago," said Velten quietly.

"You don't need to tell me," Mortensohn grinned unpleasantly. "I told them to. Got to get rid of the dirty scum. Far too many of that kind running around."

Velten risked one more question.

"What had he actually done wrong?"

"Shut your damn mouth!" snarled Mortensohn, now thoroughly provoked. "Who the hell d'you think you are? Do I have to justify my actions to you? Never heard such damned cheek!" He relapsed into silence. Then, quite suddenly, the words came hissing out, as if from a snake: "Just to put you wise, you intellectual big-shot, he'd done nothing at all. At any rate, nothing I know of. But"—Mortensohn was back in his native Berlin dialect now—"I had him finished off, d'you understand? Fin—ish—ed off. And if you don't like it, you only have to say so. Perhaps . . ." He cut himself off: "That's enough! Shut your trap!" Then he let his head sag forward and stared in front of him with a vacant, expressionless face.

When they arrived at the manor-house Parkowski, the sergeant-major, came out to meet Mortensohn and disappeared with him into his quarters. Velten made for the company office, where he

199

found the two clerks and the book-keeper standing in a group. They laughed as he came in. "Just in case you think," said a dark-haired, pallid lance-corporal who subsequently turned out to be a lawyer and, as an elder of the Lutheran Church, a theologian as well, "just in case you think you're going to be cook here, let me tell you now you're making a great mistake."

"God knows I don't want to," Velten replied. "But I'd like to know who's going to dissuade him. His mind's made up."

"Don't you believe it," said Rodewald, the book-keeper. "He got the idea in the middle of a hangover and the sergeant-major's this very moment busy talking him out of it. The point is Parkowski's dead scared of you sticking your nose in the rations. He's already been airing his fears to Kniebusch, the rations non-com. You were a lawyer, after all, and they can't be sure that you'll play ball and— what's more important—keep your mouth shut where it's necessary. It might occur to you to check the ration indents, for instance. Or you might play the lowest trick of all and let the stomach-cases have the white bread which, as everyone knows, the Lord really intended for the enfeebled stomachs of habitual drunkards."

They were laughing as Parkowski came in. Velten began to go through the formula of announcing his arrival: "Private Velten reports . . ."

"All right, all right," he said, "just listen. I've been talking to Herr Oberleutnant. He doesn't think you'd better be cook after all. You're an educated man and it might make a bad impression on the men. It's a different thing at the outpost. . . ."

"They're more companionable out there," Velten interrupted, once again unable to repress a civilian urge to answer back. " 'Did he not answer thus, the Father of the Companee?' " Parkowski looked somewhat taken aback, but made no attempt to censure this unsoldierly behavior. "You see, sir," Velten went on, "I told him all that once before in almost the very same words, but I simply got bawled out."

Parkowski's indulgent manner remained unshaken.

"I've talked everything over with the Lieutenant," he said. "We shall fetch Rötert over from Talminowicze to be cook. You'll stay here at Company Headquarters. We can't have you going straight back to the outpost now. Kindler, the man who's been runner between here and Battalion is sick. Spotted fever, so he won't be coming back. I'm putting you in his place and you can make your first trip this evening. Then every morning and evening. I haven't got anyone better or more reliable than you at present."

Looking very dignified, Parkowski left. They stared at each other in silent laughter.

"You see," said Rodewald, "everything's hunky-dory. The white bread's safe again. The rations can go on being fiddled!"

Velten's new job was a welcome change. At long last he had time to himself. He did not have to turn out in the mornings, stand guard or perform any other form of duty. Instead he went off on foot with a portfolio in his left hand and his rifle slung over his shoulder. After passing through the village he left the main road and took a track leading over the fields on the high ground to the left. By doing so he cut his journey down considerably. The village of Honczary was on the main road, and at the far end of it two highways and the Baranowicze-Luniniec railway line intersected. A shabby little station lay there—the same one at which they had detrained. On the far side of the point where the permanent way coming from the southeast cut the road from Niedzwiedzica lay the manor-house which under the martial title of "Battalion Command Post" was now helping to make world history. The estate belonged to a lawyer from Baranowicze, and his wife and daughters lived in the manor-house. One of the girls—a pale, thin, overgrown creature with sad eyes who occasionally flitted up and down the steps—could often be heard playing the piano. On his very first visit Velten found Martin Scholtz outside the main gate. He had been transferred to Battalion Headquarters exclusively for guard duty and happened to be on duty at the time. This monotonous form of military service had not sufficed to undermine his spirit, however.

When he got back from his first trip that Friday evening, Velten handed in the portfolio with its contents at the company office. The clerks sat smoking behind their desks.

"You've actually got quite a nice quiet set-up here," Velten remarked.

201

"Yes, it's peaceful enough when Bruno's sleeping," replied Uhlig, the theological expert. "But when he's on the rampage . . ."

They referred to Mortensohn by Christian name only. It seemed to make him less terrifying.

"What's he like then?" asked Velten.

"Just wait till tomorrow, my dear fellow. He goes on a binge every Saturday, so you can expect something to happen!"

"And in what form are we apt to get it?" Velten inquired.

"That depends on his mood and the degree of intoxication," Uhlig told him. "Either he turns out the whole crowd of us in the middle of the night and keeps us doubling round the drill ground and practicing the prone position or indulging in other forms of fun and games. Or else he gives the men a break and turns his attention to other objects. Once he smashed up part of the office furniture, another time he took pot shots with his pistol at that puppy belonging to old Stefan, the priest's brother. The poor little wretch has been lame ever since. Last Saturday things were quite peaceful—till he turned up just before dawn. There was a light in the building where the civilians are. Maruszka, the girl who feeds the poultry in the mornings, was getting washed. Our Bruno pulled out his pistol and put a shot through the window. Maruszka yelled her head off, but she wasn't touched. There was just a hole in the pane and another in the wash-basin."

It became clear to Velten that the entire company was afraid of Saturday. It was like a nightmare. That evening they all settled down at an early hour.

Velten slept badly, tormented by bad dreams. The gloomy and disturbing images of those first two days at Company Headquarters crowded like phantoms into his slumbers. He was soaked with sweat when a violent crash awoke him. As he struggled into a sitting position he heard the trample of approaching feet outside: the door was wrenched open and the guard commander burst in shouting to them all to stand to. Then there was another crash, and they jumped up from their mattresses and dived into their trousers.

"Those are hand grenades!" someone shouted. "Partisans!" cried another.

"Balls," said a quiet voice, "the Old Man's tight." They grabbed their rifles and ran outside, buckling on their belts as they went.

The sky was already gray. Velten took a quick look at his watch: Ten past four. The sergeant-major was already there: "Come on!" he was shouting. "Form up smartly in two ranks!" They lined up in the empty space between the entrance to the manor and the building where a shepherd used to live, a wooden hut with a steep thatched roof now serving as a guard-room. Only then did Velten perceive his company commander standing before them.

Velten was far from being a YMCA type. He himself was by no means proof against the temptations of alcohol. In civil life he had witnessed drunken excesses of the most evil kind and since then he had seen most forms of intoxication in conjunction with military uniform. But what he saw now was something uniquely bestial. It was more than drunkenness. It was a case of a sick brain poisoned by alcohol and a consciousness of the authority of an officer's epaulettes. The man now standing in front of them was drunk with power as well as schnapps. This was what Nero must have looked like as he watched Rome burn. This was what a sexual maniac must look like before he plunges his knife into the twitching belly of his unsuspecting prey, exploiting the rapture of the moment and the submission of the doomed woman. Frenzy and power and the helpless surrender of a victim—such are the agents needed to turn the human countenance into a mask of deviltry.

Mortensohn was still standing before them. His rumpled cap was tilted backwards, and below its peak his sweat-dampened hair stuck to his forehead. The skin over his protruding cheekbones was ashen. His thin lips were bloodless and white. His eyes, gleaming from their wolfish slits, glanced unsteadily up and down the ranks. He had lost his belt, and all his tunic buttons but one were undone. His legs, encased in their high boots, were planted well apart. In each hand he held a hand grenade of the long-handled type. Up till now he had not uttered a word, and his restless eyes were once again beginning to slither up and down the ranks like rats crawling through the darkness.

"Where are the clerks?" he screamed suddenly. "Do the dogs think they don't need to turn out? This time I'm going to show you all something, you swine!"

His voice was as shrill and penetrating as ever, but remarkably steady. His speech was free of any alcoholic thickness. But when

203

he turned towards the house Velten noticed that his movements were clumsy and sluggish.

"I'll sling a grenade in their bunk!" he bawled. Wedging one of the grenades between his thighs, he screwed off the top of the other and, letting the porcelain part drop into his palm, already had the fuse cord off. He swayed for a second, seemed to change his mind, and, wheeling to the left, pitched the missile among the shrubbery in front of the window looking out on the street. After the detonation the two clerks and the book-keeper came rushing out. They were unhurt. Only the window-panes were shattered.

The three men from the company office formed up on the right. Mortensohn turned to face his company again. He still had one grenade in his hand.

"Uhlig!" he roared. "Come out here! Stand by me!"

Now the bleary, pale face of the clerk, as well as the depraved face of the drunkard, faced the crowd of soldiers. Mortensohn spoke again. "Well, express an opinion, Uhlig. What's your impression of this bunch? What do they look like?"

Uhlig stared straight in front of him and did not say a word. "I'm asking your opinion!" Mortensohn shouted. "What does the outfit in front of you look like?"

No answer. Then men gazed fearfully at their company commander. What would come now? The drunkard seemed to become a shade less sure of himself. He called to the book-keeper. "Rodewald, stand next to the clerk! The bastard's still asleep." The book-keeper obeyed. Then the same question was repeated: "Come on, I want to know what they look like!" Rodewald clamped his teeth together so hard that his cheek muscles contracted, but he did not utter a word. Then Mortensohn caught sight of his driver. "Ebbecke!" he screamed. "Come here!" Ebbecke took up his position next to the other two. "Well, Ebbecke," Mortensohn almost purred, "now *you* tell me what they look like."

They could see the driver's plump, good-natured face working. It was clear that his sense of comradeship and his desire to do the same as the other two were competing with his fear of his master. "Well," the other screamed at him, swinging the grenade and peering into his face, "are you going to tell me?" The poor fellow groped desperately for some means of satisfying his drunken tormentor

204

without betraying his comrades. At last his lips stammered out an answer: "They look sleepy."

This reduced Mortensohn to a state of frenzy. His voice cracked into a hoarse screech. "Sleepy, you call it, sleepy! You mean they're a herd of pigs! Think you're soldiers, you stinking sows? Think you're soldiers? You make me spew! You're a lot of swine, goddam, stinking swine!"

He repeated the curse three or four times more. Then he seemed to be reflecting. The poisonous leer reappeared on his face, a look full of contempt, hatred and unbridled rage. Suddenly he became quiet. He spoke almost in an undertone, but loud enough for everyone to understand.

"D'you know what I'm going to do with you now?"

He raised the second hand-grenade, regarding them almost tenderly.

"I'm going to chuck this grenade among you." His repulsive grin passed over each of them in turn. They held their breath. He won't dare, thought Velten. What can we do? Shoot him down? Attack him in self-defense? Get him court-martialed? Then he heard the screech of Mortensohn's voice again.

"Look out, you dogs, it's coming!"

Velten saw that he had already unscrewed the cap and was holding the china bead on the fuse cord between two fingers of his left hand. The entire company might have been a single man, so tautly did they watch his every movement. Would he do it? Would he? Mortensohn said nothing more. He stared into the ranks, the mean, vicious grin distorting his features. Then . . . the whole crowd of them darted in all directions as they saw that Mortensohn had ripped out the cord. Velten just had time to see the bulky sergeant-major vault with unexpected agility into an empty barrel before he flung himself prone on the ground like the rest. He heard the grenade bounce, scrape along for a few feet and strike something, and then, as an almost merciful release, came an ear-splitting explosion.

A deathly silence descended on the courtyard. Velten jumped up with his comrades. Faces crowded to the windows of the upper story where the Poles lived. Mortensohn was standing uninjured in front of the main gate, his legs well apart and a vacant stare on his

205

face. Nobody gave any orders. But as they stood there speechless a faint moan was heard. Only then did they see that one man had failed to get up again. Five paces from Velten lay the company gardener, groaning as he rolled from side to side. Mortensohn bounded over to him, grabbed his shoulders and dragged him to his feet. "Get up!" he shouted. "Get up, Langner! What d'you think you're doing? There's nothing wrong!"

They hauled Langner indoors, with Mortensohn cursing along behind. When they got him on the bed of one of the clerks in the company office and pulled his trousers down they found the damage: the fellow's abdomen and thigh were smeared with blood. Mortensohn remained motionless, staring down at the groaning man. He still did not say anything when the corpulent sergeant-major, who had meanwhile clambered out of his barrel finally pulled himself together and took charge.

"Off you go!" he bawled at Ebbecke. "Take the car to Battalion Headquarters and get the medical officer!"

Ebbecke left at the double. As they heard him start up and drive off, Parkowski turned to Mortensohn:

"I'm reporting the incident to Mr. Brandstätter and having you placed under arrest."

Mortensohn made no reply, but continued to stare into space.

Parkowski left as fast as his legs could carry his fat body. The other men stood around like a lot of frightened hens. Velten felt a burning shame at what had happened and even more at his own behavior. How was such a thing possible? Why had not anyone, most of all he himself, screwed up the courage to shoot the drunken beast down before he could commit this maniacal act? He choked at the very thought of it. He could have torn his tunic off and ripped it to shreds. But he did nothing. Neither did any other member of that miserable bunch of conscripts.

What a stupid herd of pigs! thought Velten . . . That was right —a herd of pigs to which he himself belonged. They really were being turned into pigs as time went on.

At last the medical officer arrived. He was pale and hollow-eyed, obviously suffering from a hangover. All the same, the hand that opened his instrument bag was steady enough. They knew from Neugebauer, the medical orderly, that the doctor had a special remedy on hand which he took if ever suddenly needed when he was drunk.

"Morning, Bruno," he said. "Seem to have been having a bit of trouble here, eh?"

Mortensohn shrugged his shoulders and twisted his features into a grimace. "Only chucked a grenade among them," he said with a nod towards Langner. "He didn't get down fast enough. Not a properly trained soldier. Oh well, y'know what to do."

This seemed to shake the doctor but he said nothing. When Ebbecke had brought him a bowl of water, he took off his tunic and rolled up his sleeves. Then, having poured a disinfectant into the bowl, he washed his hands.

"Don't make such a fuss," he growled when his examination drew a half-suppressed yelp from Langner. "Scrotum torn open," he announced in even tones. Velten and Uhlig threw each other a look, but the others had not understood.

The men stared at the floor. Langner looked at the medic in silence, but his eyes were dilated with fear.

After finding that Langner had another splinter in his left ankle-bone, he gave him an anti-tetanus injection and some morphia and bandaged him up.

Before he had finished, 2nd-Lieut. Brandstätter arrived with Parkowski. The scout platoon was quartered in the village, and as it did not happen to have been out that night Parkowski had found the subaltern straight away.

Lieutenant Brandstätter was impeccably turned out, with boots gleaming and a pistol at his hip. His manner, though restrained and correct, was resolute. With a perfunctory salute he stepped up to Mortensohn and the doctor just as the latter was rising from the wounded man's bed. Mortensohn stared at him with glazed eyes. The doctor's face reflected his embarrassment at the painfulness of the situation.

"Sergeant-Major Parkowski asserts you threw a hand-grenade among your men and injured one of them," he said crisply, directing a keen look at Mortensohn. "May I ask whether you agree with that?"

Mortensohn first stared at the tips of his boots, then his gaze turned to the doctor. The men followed the scene with bated breath.

into the yard. Even before it stopped, the door opened and Mortensohn, the man they all believed to be finished, jumped out. Standing straddled-legged among the gaping men as they crowded round the car, he smacked his bulging pistol holster in an unmistakable gesture.

"What are you all standing around here for?" he demanded hoarsely. "Get back in the barrack-room, you scum! And I'll trouble you for a decent salute! . . . Parkowski!"

"Sir!" The sergeant-major stood as submissive and obsequious as ever before his master.

"Step along with me. I've a little bone to pick with you." He had already disappeared into the house. The fat warrant officer followed, puffing in his haste to obey.

The men stood there petrified. Then Ebbecke, who had been putting the car away, came in to face their barrage of questions. What had happened? What had he brought Mortensohn back for? And how did the man come to be armed and more insulting than ever? Where was Brandstätter, their savior and liberator?

"He got out in the village," Ebbecke told them with an omniscient air. "Too browned off to sit in the car with the Old Man for another minute."

"Now just start at the beginning and tell us exactly what happened," said Velten.

Ebbecke took a deep breath. "Well, fellows, you really ought to've seen it. Brandstätter wanted to go straight in and wake up Zorn, see. But the doctor was quicker off the mark and turned out the Adjutant, that tall fair chap. I'd been driving all three of them last night. God, they had some time I can tell you. They'd . . ."

"Now just stick to the story," Velten urged. "What happened when the Adjutant came?"

"Well, he was still a bit pickled, but he could stand up all right. God, you should've heard the rumpus they kicked up out in the yard. First Brandstätter said his piece. Wanted to speak to the Commanding Officer right away, he says. Nothing doing, says young Paul. Wouldn't dream of waking him just for a thing like that. Captain Zorn's had a strenuous night, he says. I'll say he had, too," Ebbecke informed them. "I know his orderly, and he says he's al-

210

ways in a bad mood whenever he's had any mail from home. Sends out for a supply of schnapps right away. . . ."

"Go on, go on!" one of them shouted impatiently.

"Well," continued Ebbecke with the eloquence of one completely in the know, "young Paul there being Bruno's pal, seeing as they're always boozing together, he says he ain't going to wake Zorn. Reckoned there'd be time enough for reporting this here thing when the Captain came on duty again. Brandstätter couldn't do anything about it. Then the Adjutant suddenly becomes all serious and official like. 'What's your idea exactly,' he says. 'What right have you as a second lieutenant to arrest a full lieutenant?' . . . Just fancy."

Ebbecke paused impressively. The men looked at each other. That was true enough, they reflected. A second lieutenant couldn't arrest . . .

Ebbecke had resumed his narrative.

"Brandstätter suddenly comes over all quiet. That's how it is in the Army, see? He's got no right to arrest Bruno. May get punished for it, for all we know!"

Velten's civilian sense of reason suddenly asserted itself. "Don't talk such tripe, man," he said. "If that were so, Brandstätter would have to stand by and watch Bruno bump us off one by one simply because he's a junior rank. If you ask me . . ."

"Nobody's asking you anything," said one of the older lance-corporals. "You haven't seen enough service to know what goes on. An officer can only be arrested by somebody of equal or senior rank. Brandstätter's not got no right to."

"He's seen that in the meantime," said Ebbecke, taking up the thread. "He gave Bruno his pistol back on the Q.T. You can just imagine Bruno's smirking grin."

Yes, they had driven home again, this time with Mortensohn sitting next to the driver and Brandstätter at the back. Without saying a word he had made the driver stop outside his quarters. With a sneer and exaggerated politeness Mortensohn had made room for him to get out. Brandstätter had walked away without saluting.

"What'll happen now?" It was Velten who asked the question.

"That's clear enough," replied the lance-corporal who had pre-

211

viously distinguished himself with his knowledge of military procedure. "The Adjutant tells the CO. The CO comes over here himself to arrest the Old Man. The thing's just been put off for a while, but it's got to be done on account of military discipline."

This seemed to be what most of them thought. Only Ebbecke shook his head doubtfully.

When the gray, box-shaped vehicle with the red cross on it arrived and the two orderlies were lifting the stretcher bearing a mute and motionless Langner inside, Velten pushed his way to the front.

"Langner," he called before the doors closed. "You know you've got to put in a report, don't you? We'll all back you up!" Langner nodded dumbly.

"Put it in, d'you hear?" Velten called once again. He had a dark presentiment that the affair was not going to run so smoothly.

"You don't need to act so important," said the lance-corporal who had previously displayed such profound knowledge of everything military. "It'll all take its own course. There's order in the Army, thank God!"

Initially things seemed to take a very quiet course indeed. When Velten got to the battalion orderly room the next morning, everyone was already aware of the incident, the battalion sentries having already picked up a certain amount of information from Ebbecke. Velten gave the clerks an exact account.

"Well," he asked anxiously when he had finished, "what now?"

Well, they told him, the Captain was still sleeping and knew nothing yet. Even 2nd-Lieut. Schwinger, the Adjutant, was also still sleeping it off. The same applied to the doctor. One simply had to wait, one usually did in the Army.

Back at Company Headquarters everything remained peaceful. They spent a nice, quiet Sunday. In the afternoon the sergeant-major drove out in the car to see staff-sergeant Kowalski; and Ebbecke later reported that Stüring, an unpleasant, officious fellow whom Mortensohn had recently inflicted on the old outpost commander in a mood of drunken arbitrariness, had been transferred to the post at Talminowicze and dispatched forthwith.

Uhlig and Rodewald glanced at each other meaningly. "Parkow-

212

ski's swinging the smoothing-iron," said Uhlig, making the appropriate movement with his arm.

"There's plenty to iron out this time," the second clerk replied. "They won't pull it off!"

"And Langner's putting in a report," Velten added with conviction. "I particularly impressed it on him. Apart from that, there's still Brandstätter."

Uhlig's face remained expressionless. "We can only wait and go on drinking tea," he said. "I've seen pigs fly in the Army."

When Velten went to battalion again in the evening there was almost no change. 2nd-Lieut. Schwinger had had a long interview with Zorn. The doctor had been called in as well. Otherwise it was a case of All Quiet on the Eastern Front.

About eight o'clock Schwinger rang up from battalion and asked to speak to the company commander. Mortensohn, who had not emerged from his bunk all day, shot into the office in his shirt-sleeves. Having thrown out the clerks, he had a long talk with his drinking companion. The stolid company telephonist, who was in any case regarded as a member of the Mortensohn-Parkowski clique, could not be persuaded to reveal what they had said. He had not listened, he maintained. Bruno was whistling cheerfully as he came out of the company office. He told Ebbecke to get the car out and, having shaved and put on a clean uniform, came out of the house with his riding-crop switching against his shining boots and swung himself into his seat.

He returned late in the evening—only slightly lit, the sentry told them the next day. Nothing happened. Except that the office staff, under Parkowski's direction, worked out an alarm plan for the Company. Presumably it had at last dawned on someone that Mortensohn's nocturnal check-ups were devoid of all reason as long as the sergeant-major did nothing more about it than line up the men in two ranks as an obliging target for Mortensohn's hand-grenades. From now on, everyone had a post allocated to him in case of an emergency. Velten became No. 1 on the light machine-gun and had to take up his position at the southern exit from the courtyard. Mortensohn actually held an exercise the very day after the alarm orders were posted. He was quite sober and issued his instructions in true training-ground style. Whenever he pressed anyone's heels

213

down to correct his position he made a point of formally asking the man's permission.

The men cursed to themselves. Instead of being arrested by Zorn, their grenade-thrower was making them wallow in the mud and yanking their legs together with a murmured sneer of "By your leave."

The next surprise was for Velten. When he entered the battalion orderly room the morning after the alarm practice, the chief clerk, a short, dark-haired corporal whose sallow complexion and strong beard combined to give him a perpetually bluish and unshaven look, received him with mock solemnity. By profession a lawyer and in civil life a member of the Frankfurt-on-Oder judiciary, he took a delight in exchanging professional confidences with Velten in a stilted form of language which bore a remarkable contrast to the usual parlance of soldiers.

"Behold, my pet," he said in the mockingly affectionate form of address by which Mortensohn was known all over the battalion, "what have I here?"

He was holding out his up-turned palm, in which there lay a little blue stamp perforated round the edge like a postage stamp. Velten gazed at his colleague uncomprehendingly.

"That," said the corporal impressively, "is a leave stamp." Velten regarded the little piece of paper in respectful amazement. Leave was almost unknown in the company. According to a recently pro-mulgated regulation no member of the Wehrmacht could board a leave train—his sole means of getting back to the Fatherland—without having one of these leave stamps stuck on his pass or rail-road ticket. Gossip had it that no more would be available for some considerable time to come.

"It surprises you, does it not, my pet?" intoned the clerk. "The Herr Battalion Commander has been pleased to grant some home leave to the deserving commander of our scout platoon, 2nd-Lieut. Brandstätter, in view of the exhausting nature of his work and—as certain recent happenings have shown—the effect this has had on his nerves."

Velten looked thunderstruck. The other clerks merely grinned. "Yes," one of them said, "to cut a long story short: Brandstätter has been put on the skids. We hadn't got a single leave stamp in the battalion. The Old Man actually drove over to Siniawka to scrounge one from the next battalion just so that he could send Brandstätter home."

The chief clerk took up the tale again. "The Herr Leutnant has been granted three weeks' leave. But when he gets back there'll be a travel warrant waiting for him for a course at the leadership school in Lida." The clerk put the leave pass, railroad ticket and stamp into an envelope and handed it to Velten with the other mail. The only officer who knew of the affair and did not belong to the clique was thereby eliminated. Poor old Langner, what would become of his report now? "Has Langner actually put in a report yet?" Velten inquired. "Nothing has been heard yet," the juristic non-com replied. "But tomorrow the Herr Battalion Commander is to visit Langner in the hospital at Baranowicze. The Herr Captain is much exercised about the poor fellow's condition."

The news of Brandstätter's furlough hit Company Headquarters like a bombshell. The subaltern left at once, refraining from any comment on his unexpected good luck. His successor, 2nd-Lieut. Schwarz, had just recovered from trench fever, and after an interview with the captain had—wonder of wonders!—decided to forgo his sick-leave.

What would Langner do now? That was the question going through the entire company. Could a man so ill-used as he even consider giving up his right to disciplinary redress? No, Langner would put in his report and Mortensohn would be court-martialed. Then they would at last be rid of the monster.

The *dénouement* came a few days later. When Velten entered the orderly room at battalion, the clerks chanted him a piece of rhyming doggerel, one of them beating out the rhythm on the desk with a ruler. Hashed-up on the disreputable model of "Three German Officers Crossed the Rhine," it began with the words:

> The landlord's wife she had a son
> In an L.-of-C. battalion . . .

and went on to recount in drastic terms the calamity which befell the said son "when a hand-grenade got chucked . . ."

"You seem to be having a lot of fun at poor Langner's expense," said Velten in some astonishment.

"Indeed we are," the chief clerk replied in impressive tones. "Justice has been done. The guilty party is to be punished, the innocent promoted." He rose to his feet, took up a sheet of paper and solemnly read out the following order:

> I hereby punish Lieut. Bruno Mortensohn with five days' confinement to quarters for throwing a hand-grenade in a moment of justified agitation during an alarm exercise and thereby injuring a man.
>
> In the Field   (*signed*) ZORN
> May 12th, 1944   Capt. and Bn. Comd.

There was complete silence in the orderly room. "What about Langner?" Velten finally inquired.

"Oh, yes, Lance-Corporal Langner," said the clerk.

"What do you mean?" Velten demanded. "I thought he was a Private First Class—or isn't he?"

"The Herr Captain and Battalion Commander has been pleased to promote Langner lance-corporal. That, as Langner is well aware, is no mean advancement. Lance-corporal is the lowest non-commissioned rank to draw a salary as opposed to pay, so Langner has immediately compensated for the loss to his virile faculties by improving his financial position."

"Having decided that a salary is well worth a testicle," the clerk went on with a grin, "Langner gave his word that he wouldn't put in a report. Over and above the salary the Old Man guaranteed him an immediate home assignment. What more can the heart desire?"

Velten bit his lip. "All right—we'll put the report in, then," he said angrily. "Zorn must be made to take a Summary of Evidence so that the swine gets court-martialed."

"You must have had a bad night," observed the juristically minded clerk mildly. "If the main person involved lets the matter drop, what good is a report from you going to do? Do you think any cock is going to crow for your uncrushed eggs when Herr Lance-Corporal Langner doesn't want his damaged one avenged?"

"So we just wait till the fiend ruins the lot of us?" said Velten bitterly.

216

"Not at all, my dear chap. Zorn has already ordered Morten-sohn's transfer to No. 4 Company. Your new skipper is Quandt. But first of all Bruno's got to do his five days' atonement with you —for disciplinary reasons!"

And so it turned out. The now salaried Lance-Corporal Langner went back to his native Saxony on sick-leave and from there to his regimental depot. 2nd-Lieut. Brandstätter was not seen again. Mortensohn cheerfully settled down to his period of "punishment," shutting himself in his quarters with an imposing array of schnapps bottles. He did not remain alone, however. A buxom wench put in an immediate appearance. The devil alone could tell where the clique of topers had dug up that Polish whore. By her screeching when Bruno beat her, and by their combined groaning when he was otherwise engaged with her, the troops were able to gauge the mood of the moment. Velten saw her once when she and Bruno came out to take the air. She was a bedworthy wench of about twenty with an untidy shock of thick brown hair. Her bulging bosom threatened to burst the buttons of the brightly colored cardigan she was wearing. A skirt of taffeta was stretched across her hips, making a few wrinkles over her belly. Her nose was short and thick, with wide nostrils, and her dark-red lips were parted. She stared at Velten provocatively.

Velten turned away. Disgust, shame and rage surged up inside him, making it seem like a salvation to be able to leave Company Headquarters before Mortensohn's five days of whoring were up. Bernd Eichberg was back from leave and had listened to Velten's account of the whole affair with much shaking of the head. Then he had gone to the sergeant-major and talked him into letting Velten go back to the central outpost at Kuleni. The most gratifying thing about this was that Eichberg was going there too. In the meantime a new commander for the outpost had arrived. It seemed that the powers that be had finally got around to the idea of teaching the outpost troops something about land-mines, as Kampe was going to Minsk on a course and Eichberg was to relieve him as deputy commander of the outpost. They were just in time to return there with the ten-day ration delivery.

217

CHAPTER XIII

To THE MEN's great satisfaction Velten took over the cooking once more. His replacement had not been a success. At the outpost the peasants were still dismantling and re-assembling the walls under Stodolka's direction. Lydia, Maruszka and Bronja, whom he found sitting in the kitchen, welcomed him with shrieks and giggles. It was a tremendous relief to Velten not to see any more officers' epaulettes around. Sergeant Perske, the new non-com in charge, had come to the outpost from the scout platoon. The group also included a new man who had joined during Velten's absence. He was a Thuringian from Rudolstadt called Hermann Aue. Initially Velten had treated him with great suspicion, for Aue wore the golden badge of an Old Fighter of the Nazi Party. These qualms were soon dispelled. Stodolka reported that Boberg, the man with whom Velten had fallen out over the vegetable garden, had approached Aue and revealed himself as an agent of the SD—Himmler's "thought police." His idea was to submit the same morale reports from the field as he had previously done at home. "And," he had added significantly, "the most important thing is to report suspicious occurrences."

Aue had wanted to know how anything suspicious could possibly happen where they were now. That had been Boberg's cue to relate his experience with Velten. "A clear case of defeatism!" he averred. "Borders on an attempt to incite members of the armed forces!" Should he inform the SD or report the case direct to Company Headquarters? "Man," Aue had retorted grimly, "if you think you can attach yourself to my golden sheet-anchor, you're making a big mistake. I'll smash every bone in your body if you start dirty games of that kind here." The crestfallen Boberg had taken one look at the

218

Old Fighter's broad shoulders and barrel-like chest and never raised the subject again.

Sergeant Perske was, in his own words, damn glad to be away from the scout platoon. It was a dog's life trailing partisans through forest and swamp, for they were dangerously well versed in the most treacherous refinements of guerrilla warfare. Both sides fought with low cunning and pitiless cruelty, and the platoon often came upon the naked and desecrated corpses of butchered Germans. Once, when raiding a fortified camp in the depths of the forest, they had discovered a whole squad of filthy, verminous, demoralized women —female auxiliaries of the Wehrmacht who had fallen into the hands of the partisans over a year before when traveling by road. Some of them were nursing babies and others were pregnant. The reaction of the German troops—above all the SS—had been frightful. On the other hand, Brandstätter, according to Perske, had always set his face most energetically against any kind of excesses.

They were not to have many more opportunities for these "kitchen tea-parties," as Stodolka called them. Things began to warm up, both in the world at large and at Kuleni. The first indications of this were rumors picked up by Stodolka in the village to the effect that the "forest people" were getting lively again and beginning to lay in stores on a considerable scale. Chicken after chicken, sheep after sheep, vanished from the barns. Partisans would appear at night to demand the peasants' last pots and pans. Then, one evening, an unusual din was heard. From the direction of the level crossing came suppressed shouts, the grating creak of cartwheels and the jingle and crunching of harness and horses' hooves. It went on uninterruptedly for a good two hours in the pitch darkness. There was no sign of the night patrol from Kuleni North.

"Why don't a few of us make our way over there and see what's going on?" Velten suggested.

"You won't do any such thing," Perske told him. "I'm not risking a single man. This is Kuleni North's worry."

At last, more than half an hour after the row had died away, the picket arrived—at the double.

"Guess what we've just seen!" gasped their leader, fighting for breath. "They been pulling across the railway . . . from East to West . . . one column after another with horses, oxen and cows.

219

They even had field kitchens and bakeries. Several of them were on horseback, and there were field guns, too. There were women of all ages in trousers and skirts."

"And what did you do about it?" someone asked.

"Why, we hid in the ditch. What could we do against odds like that? We were only glad they didn't spot us."

When Velten took his usual party to draw rations from Niedzwiedzica next morning, they saw various signs of the nocturnal trek. The soft earth of the cart track was deeply rutted, and in one place a wagon with a broken rear wheel had been jettisoned on the field at the side. The tracks led over the main road, gradually becoming fainter and finally losing themselves in the forest.

At the company command post Velten was given special supplies over and above the customary ten-day supplies: emergency food in anticipation of the outposts being cut off from their normal source of supply.

The men back at the outpost were annoyed at the sight of the preserves. So they were back on tinned meat again. Stodolka's only response to Velten's urgent plea for fresh meat from the peasants was to shrug his shoulders. Their generosity had flagged off recently, it seemed. There was now a perceptible reserve in the air. The villagers realized that something was afoot. Might Kuleni not change its occupiers in the near future? At the outpost the possibilities of hunting for fresh meat came under discussion. Should they sit up for pig? Other worries soon pushed the food question into the background. The woods and thicket around the outpost began to liven up—and not with game, either. At first there was occasional sniping at twilight. One day the outpost would come under fire from the west and the next from the east: always from a single rifleman. The outpost's answer was to empty one or two machine-gun belts into the forest. Then silence would descend again.

One night, when the new moon was hidden by low clouds and Perske was out with a picket, pandemonium broke loose. Velten sprang out of bed and yanked his trousers on. Without giving himself time to put on his tunic and belt he made for the armory to get the machine-gun out. Stodolka arrived at the same moment and grabbed the ammunition boxes. The rest of them poured out of the big dormitory hut. Shots came whining in at the outpost from every

220

direction. While Velten and Stodolka set up their LMG on one platform, Berger raced with his to the other, his No. 2 close behind. The others distributed themselves around the wall. It had just occurred to Velten that Reichert, the only man who knew how to work their Russian machine-gun, was out on patrol with Perske when he heard a shout from Wandrey, who as senior lance-corporal took over the outpost in its commander's absence: "Bosselmann, Villwock, Hegener—get round the back and give some assistance!"

"Round the back" meant up on the wall at the rear of the building, where the Russian weapon was mounted. As the three men thus addressed jumped down from their firing positions to obey, the whining tones of the moronic Villwock were heard.

"Thank God we've got Wandrey here," he said. "We'd be done for if we hadn't!"

"Listen to the silly bastard!" whispered Stodolka.

"That's the Führer principle," Velten rejoined.

Wandrey was a decent but not very brilliant construction worker from Berlin. Bernd Eichberg had been ordered away only a few days after Velten's return to the outpost.

By now they were under fire from all sides and could make out both the cracks of rifles and the bark of Russian machine-pistols, which sounded rather more muffled than their German counterpart. They estimated the range at between fifty and sixty yards and pumped burst after burst at the spots where they saw the muzzle-flashes of the enemy's weapons. Velten brought his whole weight to bear against the butt of the LMG and nestled it into the space between his shoulder and cheek, just as he had learned on the range. He marveled at his own calmness and simultaneously cursed the situation in which he found himself. The *bick, bick, bick* of enemy bullets slugging into the soft wood of the palisade became more and more frequent.

"Hell!" Stodolka whispered, tugging at Velten's arm, "they're finding their range. Let's get out of this or we'll get hit."

Clambering over the low gate with the barbed-wire entanglement in front, they made a dash for the railway embankment and threw themselves down behind it. On their left they were covered by the wall. This time Stodolka did the firing and Velten fed him the cartridge belt.

221

All at once they had the impression that the enemy fire was subsiding. To the left of the outpost little white streaks of flame were bobbing up over the rails. One after another: perhaps thirty in all. After each flash there was a bang which momentarily drowned the sound of firing. Finally even this came to an end, and as the enemy side went quiet, Wandrey ordered his men to stop.

The next morning they discovered the reason for the pretty flashes on the railway. The partisans had blown up about 100 yards of track by affixing small charges to the rails.

A breakdown train soon arrived from Baranowicze, and the rails were repaired in no time. But there was no peace the next night, either. Like the last, it was dark and clouded over. From the top of the fortification, Perske, Aue, Körnle and Velten watched a picket led by Wandrey melt away, man by man, into the soggy blackness.

The four men peered out into the night. A cool breeze was blowing in from the marshes, and Velten pushed his cap back to let the night air caress his brow. He vaulted down from the platform, went over to the well and let the pail rattle down on its chain. The windlass creaked and groaned in its bed as he wound the pail up again, overflowing the brim. Closing both hands to pull it towards him, he propped it on the brick wall and began to pour the cool water down his throat, sprinkling his arms and face as he did so.

"Have you gone crazy?" Perske called to him. "Filling yourself up with typhus like that!"

It was strictly forbidden to drink well-water.

"Ach," said Velten with a deprecating sigh, "I've drunk the stuff as long as I've been in this stinking country. It agrees with me just like Munich beer."

"Anyone'd think you were out to catch spotted fever and get yourself sent home on sick-leave," growled Perske. "That's almost as bad as a self-inflicted wound, my lad."

"The problem there," Velten retorted, "is how to get the wound. What about chucking a few hand-grenades around, Sergeant? Surely you wouldn't mind risking a few days in the cells to fix your chaps up with some home leave . . ."

Perske was in a bad mood. "That's all I want to hear of that nonsense, Velten!" he shouted. "You've shot your mouth off far

222

too much about that business already. It's got to be forgotten some time like anything else!"

"You know you don't really think that," Velten returned.

The words were hardly out of his mouth when they heard shots from the southern end of the sector, in the direction the picket had taken. A few rifles cracked, and then a machine-gun started up. Somewhere rifles answered the fire.

"There's something brewing out there," said Perske anxiously. "We'd better . . ."

He stopped abruptly as they all raised their heads. Down the track, where the picket must now be shooting it out with an unseen enemy, a red Very light was sailing skywards. The tree tops were a weird sight in the crimson glare. One red signified danger. Now a second one was on its way up! The four men looked at each other. Two reds meant *Come to my help immediately."*

"Right!" shouted Perske, springing down and making for the main building. "Who's coming along? Every man take a couple of sticks and egg grenades!"

"Wait a minute!" Körnle called. "You'll have to stay here. If we get worked over again like last night, there'll have to be someone dependable in charge here."

Perske swore under his breath, but saw the point. He put Körnle in command of the relief party. Aue, Velten and Knaus volunteered to accompany him. The others—apart from Stodolka and Berger, who had already been detailed to stay behind and man the LMG—remained silent.

"Schnupphase will go too," Perske ordered, having cast a last glance round the remaining men.

"Me of all people!" whined the old pimp, looking down at his knock-knees.

"Yes, you!" Perske snapped. "I've watched your games long enough. All right, get ready to move off! And watch your step," he told Körnle. "Make contact with Wandrey and see that you all get back here together. If there's no other way out, try to get through to Kuleni South."

The five men set off, and the sentry pushed the barbed-wire barrier into place behind them. Bent half-double, they made their way down the railway track in single file. Suddenly they all froze

223

in their tracks. To the south yet another Very light was rising—this time a yellow one. It was closely followed by a second of the same color.

"Down!" Körnle yelled. In a second they were all down from the embankment, lying flat on their bellies against the sloping earth. There was one exception. Schnupphase. He remained rooted to the spot, trailing his carbine so that the muzzle almost scraped the ground, and staring in knock-kneed stupidity at his recumbent comrades.

"You blithering idiot!" Velten roared at him. "Get down or you'll be a goner in two seconds!"

The other tumbled awkwardly down from the permanent way and came to rest beside Velten. "Listen you," he hissed with suppressed rage, "if you start on me again . . ."

He got no further. A whistling stream of steel raked through the air a few inches above his head. They could tell by the tracers— one in every five cartridges of the ammunition belt—that the bullets were almost skimming the rails. The picket's machine-gun was raking the track, having previously given the prescribed warning signal of two yellow Very lights.

"They must be raving mad!" roared Körnle from his place next to Velten. "First they drag us out of the post and then fire straight at us!"

Velten made no reply. He jammed himself even closer to the sloping surface of the shallow embankment, making himself as flat as was humanly possible. He held his forearms before his face, squinting through his fingers at the tracers overhead. He was sure he could feel a cool draught set up by the bullets tearing past him. What if one of the damned things were to ricochet off a rail and split his skull open? He burrowed deeper still into the short, prickly grass. What a damn fool he was! What ever had made him come along? Curiosity? Indifference? Perske's ridiculous talk?

"I'll beat that Wandrey to a frazzle," Körnle swore, "the stupid bastard." He added a well-known Swabian curse-word which appeared to relieve his feelings considerably. More coolly, he went on: "We'll have to crawl back to the post—pass the word on!"

But before Velten could repeat the instruction to his left-hand

224

neighbor there was a fresh development. The outpost had opened up now, too. Berger and Stodolka were firing bursts along the railway with their LMG. Now there were two streams of lead flying along the track in opposite directions.

"Well, I'll be damned!" Körnle bawled in complete frustration. "Now *they've* gone whackey too!"

The fire from the outpost grew hotter. Rifle shots could be heard between the bursts from the automatic weapon. The picket fired on indefatigably. The five men in between lay as flat as pancakes against the shallow bank. Just here there was not so much as a bush or a fold in the ground to offer any cover.

A puff of wind chose this moment to brush the clouds away from the half moon. Velten took a cautious look to his right. On the far side of Körnle lay Knaus with legs well apart; behind him was Aue.

All of a sudden Knaus rolled over and screamed. Then, still writhing, he toppled onto his side. Körnle nudged Velten: "Listen —d'you hear? They're firing from the wood!" It was quite true: a machine-pistol was firing at them from behind. They were between three fires now. However, there seemed to be only one machine-pistol.

All at once Körnle was calm, self-possessed and firm.

"We must get back to the post," he announced loudly enough for all to hear him. "Otherwise we'll all go to the devil." He gave Knaus a nudge: "Can you walk?" he asked. The other merely writhed more than ever and murmured something incomprehensible.

"Listen," said Körnle, "I'm going to run towards the post and shout to them to stop shooting. If we stay here we're in for it."

Suddenly Schnupphase raised his head. "Now then," he said, his voice for the first time free of hoarseness, "just you stay here. Let me go. I'm in the shit anyway!"

Before anyone could say a word the old pimp was on his feet. They had a final glimpse of the bent back and crooked legs. And then he was gone. He went unarmed, waving his hands above his head.

"Give over, give over!" they heard him bawling.

" 'Cease firing!' is what the fool's supposed to shout," Körnle had time to say. Then Schnupphase's yells were abruptly cut off.

With the same suddenness the machine-gun at the outpost fell silent. The rifles followed suit, and a few seconds later the picket also stopped firing.

"I'll kill the dog when he comes home," Körnle snarled, his thoughts still on Wandrey.

The lone partisan with the machine-pistol continued to loose off behind them, but the moon had gone in again and he had no chance of hitting anything in the darkness.

Velten crawled over to Knaus. Blood was seeping through his trousers. He was groaning and his teeth were chattering. They lifted him cautiously. Then, when Körnle had grasped him under the back, the other two lifted him on to the burly Swabian's shoulders.

Three hundred yards from the outpost they came upon three men from the garrison standing by Schnupphase's dead body. He was lying on his back, his hands and legs outstretched.

"Ooh, no!" they heard Tülle cry, braying with moronic laughter, "I can't touch that old corpse. It'll make me sick!"

"Belt him one with the butt of your rifle, Victor!" Körnle gasped under the weight of his wounded fellow Swabian. "The dirty, stupid sod!" In the end four men took hold of the body and lugged it along between them.

At the outpost they laid the dead Schnupphase on the wooden platform which ran round the inside of the stockade. Knaus they carried into the dormitory. When they had slipped off his trousers and laid him face-down on his cot, it turned out that one bullet had lodged in his right buttock and another had made a bloody pulp of the organ whose efficacy had been such a source of pride to its owner. Velten began to feel there must be a hoodoo on the unit in this respect.

They bandaged up the wounded man as best they could. Velten gave him a few anodyne tablets from the medicine chest while Perske telephoned to the medical corporal. The latter promised to come at daybreak, as he could only get there by leapfrogging through the various pickets.

Then the agitated Körnle flew at Perske. What the hell did he mean by bringing the railway line under fire just after he had sent the picket down it? Perske in turn demanded what else he could have done but give supporting fire to the picket after it had signaled a request to that effect. He had naturally assumed that Körnle and his men were under cover.

"Some cover," remarked Körnle bitterly. "Just you try taking cover on that bare embankment where the wood's all been hacked down!"

When a completely unscathed Wandrey arrived back with his picket, Perske and Körnle went for him in unison, but they were quite unable to establish what the exact trouble had been. The picket, it seemed, had been shot at and got the impression that the enemy was there in strength. But what Wandrey had thought he was doing when he called for support and then brought the track under fire remained an unsolved mystery.

Perske cursed. "Well," he demanded, "what the devil am I to report about this little shambles?"

"There won't be all that much trouble," Velten assured him. "It's perfectly in accord with unit tradition to kill each other off by our own blasted stupidity."

Just after dawn the medical corporal arrived with the picket from Kuleni North. They brought a stretcher with them, and, after putting Knaus to sleep with an injection, carted him away.

At the forest edge, behind the outpost, they dug a grave and lowered Schnupphase's remains inside. Körnle nailed two strips of wood together into a rough cross, and on this they hung the dead man's tin hat. Thus did the war bring one wasted life to an end whose dignity no one could question.

Shortly after Capt. Zorn was recalled to the Reich, a Major Schäfer became battalion commander and had Perske moved up to the orderly room. In exchange for Perske the outpost got Staff-Sergeant Trollberg.

Fritz Trollberg, known throughout the company as "Fritze," brought a deputy with him: Cpl. Anton Zaremba, a tubby, cheerful-looking Upper Silesian. Fritze himself was a haggard fellow in his fifties, with an unhealthy pallor and sparse fair hair which was going gray. Don Quixote and Sancho Panza, thought Velten, as he showed the bizarre couple into the outpost commander's cubbyhole. Hitherto Trollberg had not been entrusted with an outpost but had hung around the company command post and taken a picket

out on patrol now and again. Apart from being pathologically nervous, he was excessively zealous and utterly incompetent. Out of a
perpetual fear of losing the authority he imagined himself to have
over the men, he affected a formidable manner in an attempt to
impress people. It earned him nothing but mockery, scorn and open
resistance. To break this he had neither the capacity nor the courage.

"Him as 'our Führer'!" said Velten to Stodolka when the dreary
fellow had disappeared into his room. "The next thing'll be Villwock shouting 'How lucky we are to have Fritze here.' "

The following morning Fritze caught sight of the girls in Velten's
cookhouse. He gave each of them a thorough once-over. In the end
his gaze came to rest on the flabby Lydia, and a pale flush spread
over his hollow cheeks. He returned to his room. After a while he
sent for Velten. It was Fritze's desire that the "plump one" should
clean his bunk.

"Lydia, kemnata kommandant pamitj," said Velten, drawing on
his jumble of Russian, Polish and White Ruthenian. He took a
broom and duster and made sweeping movements as he said it.
Lydia rose to her feet languidly enough, but her eyes shone with
pride and the round holes in her thick nose distended. When she
was outside, the other two giggled to each other, and Velten caught
words like *bled* (witch) and *kurwa* (whore).

But the envy or joy of the two village beauties at being thus
passed over was of short duration. In a matter of seconds there was
an uproar in the outpost commander's room, followed by the sound
of two sharp smacks. The door was wrenched open and Lydia
rushed out. Her hair was awry and her face crimson, and she was
screeching something that sounded like *swinia* and *chort palassatij*.

Fritze lurched out close on her heels with two circular patches
glowing on his face. Maruszka and Bronja watched the scene wide-
eyed.

Fritze tried to pacify the weeping Lydia, who, having squeezed
herself into a corner between the wall and the table, was now howling the roof down.

Velten tore open the window.

"Peter!" he yelled to Stodolka, "come in here, will you?"

228

When Stodolka had joined them, he rapidly proceeded to explain:

"Our 'Djadja' Fritz tried to make a pass at Lydia. Now make the stupid wench realize that nothing has happened to her and that nothing's going to happen as long as we're here."

While Stodolka was doing his best with the sobbing Lydia, Velten wheeled on Fritze. "As for you," he said with quiet deliberation, "what d'you mean by upsetting my girls? After the whole damn outpost has managed to leave them alone all this time, a clapped-out old goat like you has to come along and start dribbling over them!"

Trollberg was seized with a neurasthenic twitching. His narrow upper lip began to tremble under its blond toothbrush mustache.

"How dare you!" he stuttered. "I've never known such impudence! I'll report you, you, you . . ." He could not find the word and fought for breath.

It was Stodolka who finally saved the situation. He went out and returned with a bottle of egg schnapps. All three of them drank one. When the girls were invited to join them, Maruszka and Bronja surprised Velten by refusing, while Lydia, a crafty smile already peeping through the tearstains, downed hers with alacrity.

"What an unpredictable bunch they are!" remarked Velten with a despairing shake of the head. Stodolka was on the point of launching into a disquisition on the emotional life of the Slavs when Fritze forestalled him by suddenly becoming conversational. He seemed to have forgotten the altercation and was obviously feeling an urge to show himself in a favorable light. He began talking about his job in civil life. He was a registrar of births and deaths in the borough of Prenzlauer Berg, a thickly populated part of North East Berlin. A registrar, according to Fritze, was a State functionary of considerable importance whose stewardship was the very life and health of the German people.

By the time Fritze had downed his third egg schnapps he was demonstrating how to administer a statutory declaration of personal and hereditary health to a young couple about to be married. With their right hands raised, they must stand before him and repeat the words: "I swear by Almighty God that to the best of my knowledge and belief . . ."

"But look here, Fritze," Velten interrupted, "that's all bullshit. All you're supposed to do is to have them sign a statutory declaration. You've got no authority to administer oaths."

"I know," Fritze agreed, "but it's more impressive this way."

After pouring down his fourth glassful, Fritze became progressively less impressive. He spoke of his scanty salary and his four children, two of whom were still at school. The remainder of the narrative trailed off into an incomprehensible babble.

"An inexpensive guest," Stodolka commented, tossing off Fritze's fifth glass of egg schnapps himself. Then they led the drooling outpost commander back to his cubby-hole and pitched him onto his bed.

It became a custom from that day onwards for one of the girls to clean Fritze's room. He made no more passes at them. Lydia did not appear again, the story being that she had moved to her aunt's in Niedzwiedzica. By this time the men, too, were demanding female assistance for their chores. Before long the entire building was being cleaned from top to bottom by women specially detached from the working parties for this purpose. Not a single private soldier washed his own shirts and socks or polished his own boots any longer. They even delegated the washing-up.

"All you need do now," observed Stodolka, "is to have them up here for weapon-cleaning."

Fritze let things drift their own way. He was quite content as long as he received a mess-tin heaped with food every midday. For all his wasted appearance he gorged himself continuously, but never put on weight. Velten was sorry for him and helped him to as much as he could without evoking complaints from the others.

From time to time, though, Fritze became energetic and sought to keep to the duty program laid down by the company. The good-humored Zaremba tried to talk him out of it but Fritze remained obdurate. One morning Stodolka called Velten out into the yard. Stodolka's ragged workers were holding their shrunken sides with helpless laughter. Fritze was making his squad practice "Saluting on the March, With and Without Caps, in Pairs." As if on the barrack square, he was standing on a raised patch of ground with his fists pressed into his lean flanks. The men were formed up in two ranks. "First pair—begin!" Fritze commanded in his jarring

230

voice. Off they stepped. Five paces from Fritze they jerked their heads to the left and raised their hands to their peaks. The same moment the next two, who had been marking time, did the same, and the process was repeated until they had all marched past Fritze. Then they went through it all the other way round, this time with him standing on their right. Now, however, they had to stick their caps between two tunic buttons and salute Fritze bareheaded "With the Right Arm Raised to Eye Level."

So far so good. But when Fritze announced that they would next march round in circles and sing songs something snapped. Lance-Corporal Mieses, the perpetually bad-tempered ex-cook, threw his cap on the ground and jumped on it.

"It's like being in a troop of trained monkeys!" he bawled. "D'you think you can kick us around in front of these lousy Polacks? If you don't quit, Fritze, we'll fix you."

The familiar crimson patches appeared on Fritze's face.

"Mieses," he screamed, "Lance-Corporal Mieses, I shall report you! That's refusal to obey an order in drill! That's threatening a superior! That's mutiny!"

At that moment the thick-sct figure of Zaremba appeared at the entrance gate of the palisade. He beckoned eagerly to the post commander and then ran up to him and addressed him in an undertone. Trembling with excitement Fritze disappeared without a word into the blockhouse.

"I'm taking charge," the plump Zaremba stated quietly. "There'll be a break to begin with. Atten-*shun!* Fall *out!*"

They broke ranks and gathered round the good-humored Silesian. It soon emerged why Zaremba had called the outpost commander to the telephone, thereby stifling the mutiny at birth. Company Headquarters had telephoned to say that the invasion had begun in the north of France. It had come at last—the great gamble for which the whole world had waited with bated breath.

The next thing they heard was that the handful of soldiers the company had been able to send on leave would not be returning. All Germany's resources were being drafted West to force a decision. The Eastern Front had become a theater of secondary importance. Kuleni Central lost Wandrey in this way. He had gone on leave when Fritze turned up with Zaremba.

231

The outpost commander became heroic. "Men," he said—he loved this robust turn of address—"Men, it's up to us to acquit ourselves like our comrades in France. Germany expects every soldier to do his duty from now on. I shall be at your head."

The next morning Fritze set out with the picket in the early morning mists. He had provided himself with a long staff rather like a fishing-rod. "Watch me, men," he said. "I strike the ground with this whenever we come to a suspicious spot. If it's a mine, I set off the fuse. The thing explodes and the train's saved. If I go up with it, I shall be dying for Führer, Nation and Reich. Verve's what we need, men, verve!"

And off they went. Like some water diviner Fritze made his way along the railway track, poking at sleepers, rails and gravel.

Velten watched them go, shaking his head sadly. Then he turned his attention to his job, as the morning coffee had to be ready by the time they returned. He also had to prepare the dinner for another man to cook. The ten-day ration issue was due again, and he had to be present in person. The ration non-com always tried to outwit the uninitiated.

When the picket came back its members were bickering among themselves. Velten heard Fritze's shrill voice and Körnle's gruff Swabian dialect. They really had found a suspicious spot, it seemed. Fritze had fiddled around there with his divining rod—"but warily and without spending too much time on it," as Körnle grinningly pointed out. Then the outpost commander had decided they ought to dig for it. But they had refused, contending that there was no mine there at all and that if Fritze thought there was he could damn well dig it for himself. Fritze hadn't done any digging either. Now he was babbling incessantly about refusal to comply with an order.

"Look, I'm coming up to headquarters with you," Körnle told him when the other members of the picket had settled down to sleep.

"What for?" asked Velten wonderingly. "Don't you want to have a rest after patrol?"

"Victor," said the Swabian, "I've no wish to be here when the train comes and that thing goes sky-high. I couldn't bear listening to that silly bastard Fritze!"

232

Velten looked into the wily Swabian's smiling face. "Is there really a mine there?"

"Of course there is," Körnle replied, filling his pipe with the utmost aplomb. "The spot looked just like that last one. I'll swallow a broom, handle and all, if there's not a mine underneath!"

"Why didn't you lift it, then?" Velten inquired.

"Schwätz nit so saudumm!" the Swabian retorted coarsely. "Don't you remember how the pigs did me out of my reward? Only giving me one bottle of schnapps instead of two? I've sworn never to take a risk again!" To this he added, in a softer tone: "You know yourself everything's lost, *gell,* Victor! Main thing now's to get home in one piece!"

As they emerged from the woods with their requisitioned farm cart and turned onto the track which led across the fields, they heard the snorting of the approaching freight train. Körnle gave Velten a nudge. They listened intently as the train came closer and then began to draw away into the distance. Körnle's face already bore a faint trace of disappointment. There it went! The four members of the ration party halted as one man and wheeled round in their tracks. A muffled clap of thunder boomed through the air, and over the forest a mushroom-shaped cloud of smoke started climbing skywards. The next moment the hiss of escaping steam reached their ears. At headquarters they learned that several cars of a supply train had been overturned. The breakdown train from Baranowicze was already on the scene.

Tremendous excitement reigned at headquarters about something quite different. Germany was retaliating at last. Since last night a miracle weapon had been bombarding the coastal districts of England. The name of this hush-hush wonder—V-1—implied that other secret weapons were on the way. The mood of the troops had changed like a flash when they heard the news. There you are, they told each other, the Führer was right again! He'd kept his word. He'd promised all along that they'd get their own back—and now it had happened! Now everything was bound to turn out all right— everything!

On arriving back at Kuleni Central they found everybody in the best of spirits. The reason, however, was not the V-1, of which news had meanwhile come through by telephone, but the mine! At first Körnle could only gape when he learned the cause of their jubilation—then he clapped his hand on his thigh and roared with delight.

What had happened? The mine which Körnle had mischievously refrained from lifting had derailed one car loaded with excellent seed potatoes and another with all kinds of agricultural implements. Several cartloads of potatoes had already been removed to the outpost. They would make a delightful change after all the dry fare—noodles, millet and groats—now being issued.

The contents of the second car, however, were infinitely more valuable. As the peasants were taking the potatoes away in sacks, wheelbarrows and carts, Zaremba had a brain wave. He posted guards round it before the peasants could lay their hands on the farm tools.

"We can swap that stuff for all sorts of things," he explained with a knowing smile. They were all aware how short the indigenous population was of even the most primitive tools. Here were spades, picks, hammers and pliers in abundance. In the mind's delightful eye they were already turning into sheep, chickens, eggs and bacon.

With Stodolka's assistance Velten did actually succeed in bartering a certain amount of this wealth, thereby acquiring six hens, fifty eggs and several kilos of fat bacon. Then the peasants' eagerness suddenly abated. In due course it was found that the sentries had been running a barter business on their own account and undercutting Velten's official rate.

"What if someone comes along to salvage the freight?" Fritze Trollberg asked anxiously. No one could answer that one. In point of fact the problem was to be solved—quicker than Fritze imagined—by the war itself.

For the time being, however, the outpost of Kuleni Central seemed destined for a phase of feasting and carousing. Though Fritze, who guzzled enough for three, continued to look famine-stricken, his Sancho Panza of a second-in-command grew fatter from day to day. Their commander, visibly consumed by the responsibility of his post, accordingly resolved to make his own contribution to Total War. He acquired the habit of blowing unex-

234

pected blasts on his whistle when the men were flat on their beds after dinner and shouting "Stand to! Stand to!" as if he were Mortensohn himself. When they stumbled outside, cursing and groaning, he would have them mount the walls for half an hour and carry out aiming practice at a hypothetical enemy.

From time to time Fritze held his field days on the assumption that part of the garrison was out on patrol and the remainder had died heroes' deaths. This made the struggle of the surviving troops harder and the situation confronting the Military Mind even more complex—particularly when Fritze was unable to distinguish between those involved in the exercise and those who, in his own words, "weren't really there."

"Stodolka!" Fritze yelled on one such occasion. "Why are you standing around by the well without a weapon? Get over to the LMG!"

"But, Fritze," Stodolka protested, "I'm not supposed to be there."

Fritze put both hands to his head. "Oh, I can't stand this any longer. Look men, just listen. Anyone who's not supposed to be there is to go indoors and not hold up the operations!"

At times Fritze's silly games became intolerable. One night he was in charge of the first picket. As luck would have it, Velten was on it, too. When they reached the middle of their sector, where the two empty freight cars stood beside the track, he called a halt.

"Now just listen, men," said Fritze, "I've thought out a stratagem. No more bandits are turning up these days. Therefore we must tempt them out and shoot them down. Pay close attention, then, men: three of you will get into position with the LMG by the permanent way, and the other two will stay with me here. We'll walk up and down and talk in loud voices. The bandits'll be lured by the conversation. They'll come nearer, try to take us prisoner—and you'll shoot 'em down from your ambush!"

They studied the poor fellow in silence. Only Tülle's silly laugh brayed out into the silence of the night.

"That's the style," said Fritze approvingly. "If he laughs like that, they'll come all the quicker."

He remained up by the cars with Stodolka and Tülle. Velten, Berger and Mamler got down in the ditch.

When Stodolka and Tülle had taken their places in the ditch and the other three had joined Fritze, the lunatic started to discuss the military situation.

"Just think, men," quoth Fritze, "in the West victory is ours. The Führer has allowed the enemy to land so as to encircle and annihilate him. Soon he'll be doing the same thing in the East. Two million Russians must be encircled and annihilated."

There was no end to the flow of verbiage. Velten leaned exhaustedly against the door of one of the cars. He couldn't stick this out, he told himself. He simply couldn't. Suddenly he straightened up. To hell with it, he wasn't here to join in such damned tomfoolery! At that moment the semi-imbecility of this one man seemed to him to embody the general folly of the war as a whole.

With a jerk he pulled himself together. "Well, good night all," he said loudly, deliberately breaking into Fritze's incoherent twaddle. Turning away, he dug his hands into his trouser pockets and marched off in the direction of the outpost.

His step was springy as he strode through the glittering moonlight. His whole body shared in the rhythm of his gait. He no longer thought of the outpost commander and his silly nonsense.

He did not come to himself again until a challenge rang out from the outpost.

"Halt! Wer da?"

"It's me, Karl," said Velten as he recognized Körnle, the Swabian.

The other pushed the gate open. "What's up?"

"Nothing at all," said Velten. "I just cleared off. Want some sleep." He was feeling that overpowering sleepiness once more.

"I'll tell you something, Karl," said Velten, resting his hand on the other's shoulder. "Imagine you've got a glass of water, a glass filled right up to the brim. You need one more drop, just one more tiny drop. The moment that drop gets added, Karl, the whole glass spills over." He yawned capaciously. Then, for three seconds, he closed his eyes happily and opened them again to conclude: "Well, I've had my drop. Out there just now. The glass was too full. 'Night, Karl! I'm turning in."

Leaving the Swabian to his astonished thoughts, he went indoors, turned into his cubby-hole, tore off his clothes and threw himself

236

on his bunk in his underclothes. With a feeling of deliverance he stretched himself out under the blanket and fell immediately asleep.

He was jarred out of his slumbers by the violent opening of a door.

"Velten," he heard Fritze's shrill voice cry, "you'd better consider very carefully what you're going to tell the court-martial!"

Then the door crashed to again. He heard Fritze groping into the next room.

CHAPTER XIV

EICHBERG and Velten shook hands joyfully. They had met at the Niedzwiedzica manor-house where the company command post was situated. Eichberg was back from his mine course, and Velten was assigned to Company Headquarters. He had arrived with the regular ration party.

"Yes," Velten was saying with a faint smile, "the Herr Captain wants me up here to investigate my suitability for a commission. . . ."

Eichberg gave him a searching look:

"Well, how d'you like the idea of becoming an officer?"

"Don't be stupid, Bernd," Velten pleaded. "You know quite well that I'll never be one. Even if I wanted to."

The long-awaited Russian offensive had just started, on the anniversary of Germany's invasion of her treaty partner of 1939. In both East and West flames were licking at the ramparts of the Fortress of Europe.

"Think I've gone mad?" Velten went on. "Now the end's in sight I've less reason than ever to rise above the level of the common soldiery. But there was no way out. The new commander came out to the outpost with Quandt to get to know the area. Just think of it: Zorn never saw an outpost all the time he was here! Well, then

237

they started. Said I was an intellectual, and now everyone's needed. I obviously had to become an officer. Provided I had the aptitude. That's what fat boy Quandt's supposed to find out now," Velten concluded with a grin.

Eichberg pondered. "What if they send you to officers' school before it's all over?" he asked doubtfully.

"Ach, these people here don't decide that all by themselves," Velten replied, "and it's known up at the top that I'm not ideologically suitable."

They sauntered up and down the spacious courtyard. "Incidentally," Velten remarked, "I was glad to get away from Kuleni. It wasn't pleasant there any longer. All sorts of trouble."

Eichberg's reaction to all that Velten told him was a little puzzling. While the latter was affected most of all by the humiliation the incidents brought on his own head and was filled by a neurotic fury only rendered worse by the weeks of sleep he had missed, Eichberg found the tale immensely saddening.

Velten made to wave aside what he knew was coming now. All Eichberg's thoughts and perceptions were closely bound up with the religious faith from which he drew his strength and serenity amid all this chaos. But there was something of the zealot in his make-up, too. Often he had tried not merely to put forward the view of a believer but to proselytize as well.

This bothered Velten. "Do me one favor, Bernd," he said, "don't preach me any sermons here, for God's sake—least of all in that uniform with the swastika on your chest!"

"God's sake," Eichberg returned emphatically, "is the very reason why I should preach them." He gazed at Velten in frank affection: "I shall go on reminding you about it. You'll come round some time."

The days that followed brought further confusion. Despite the bewildering news that filtered through from the central front about the great battle now developing around Bobruisk, the visit of a Strength Through Joy concert party was announced. One afternoon before patrol time the men were marshaled into the village's long whitewashed schoolroom. They sat on low benches without armrests, the captain, sergeant-major and clerks being accommodated on chairs at the front. The show began by three men executing some

238

gruesome music on the fiddle, piano-accordion and trumpet. Then one of them performed one or two elementary card tricks. Next a thin young lady in triangular panties and brassière went through the contortions of an acrobatic dance, preserving an arrogant mien throughout. Then came a heavily painted vocalist in her forties who sang the inevitable "Lili Marlene" and a few cheeky music-hall hits in a rather reedy voice. The whole performance was staged by a well-filled lady the wrong side of middle age who alternated between patriotic declamations and indecent anecdotes. She possessed a most impressive behind, and with every movement raised her black taffeta skirt to reveal two fingers' breadth of faded blue petticoat.

The men were wild with enthusiasm. But their eyes softened with melancholy as the reedy soprano quavered through the song of the soldier's wife who sings her warrior the refrain:

> Mach' dir um mich doch bittäh keine Sorgen:
> Ich bin dir treu, das weisst du ganz ge-nau.
> Wie's gestern war, so ist es heut' und morgen:
> Ich bin doch schliesslich deine Frau!

When it was over the three male performers disappeared to their quarters. The arrogant blonde acrobat climbed into the car of an officer who had come to meet her from Baranowicze, and drove off without a word. The troops stood their guards and sallied forth on patrol. The company commander whisked away the fat mistress of ceremonies and the painted soprano to entertain them at supper in his quarters.

Turbulent days followed the departure of the concert party. Soviet aircraft began flying over the area, the characteristic noise of their engines winning them the name of "coffee-grinders" among the troops. They only came in the hours of darkness and dropped little illuminated parachutes over the forest—obviously food supplies, ammunition and instructions for the partisans. From time to time the thunder of distant gunfire could be heard.

Then came the first signs of the incipient retreat. Odd vehicles belonging to field bakeries and other supply units rested up in the village for a night. "Cut off at Bobruisk," their drivers explained laconically. They volunteered no further information, but hastened to get back on the road again at first light.

239

One day the fall of Sluck was reported, and exhausted-looking troops came down the road, moving west in passable order. On the side of one of their trucks someone had chalked "First stop Berlin!" None of the officers seemed to have noticed this defeatism.

After that a whole brigade of Hungarian cavalry passed through. They came from Kleck, some twenty-five miles northeast of Niedzwiedzica.

Company Headquarters began to get uneasy. That night, for the very first time, no more pickets were sent out. Instead, Capt. Quandt mustered them out to announce that they would be moving in the next day or two. He ordered all kitbags to be packed and stacked in the main courtyard, where a truck collected them half an hour later. From now on they had only their knapsacks.

"I want to see lots of aggressive spirit!" Quandt concluded, with an energetic jerk of his graying head. Where they were to go from here, however, not even the clerks knew.

The next morning everything was quiet. Only the local inhabitants stood conversing in excited little groups in front of their homes. Rötert, the cook, was suddenly the possessor of a slaughtered horse, of which he distributed raw, hacked-off pieces to all comers. Velten acquired a piece of rib. He stripped off a few lumps of meat with his bayonet, put them through a mincer lent him by Rötert together with some onion stalks from the manor-house garden, and fried rissoles for Eichberg and himself in a saucepan lid. The remnants of the meat he gave to a barefooted village boy, who scampered away delighted with his spoil.

Hardly had they finished frying their horsemeat hamburgers when the alarm was sounded. They stuffed the fatty fare into their mess tins and ran to the courtyard, where they found a few open trucks already loaded with troops. These soon moved off through the front gate. Peeping over the tailboard of the last vehicle Velten espied Martin Scholtz, a smile of patient submissiveness on his face. That was the last he ever saw of him.

Quandt called out the rest of the company and notified them that they would be evacuated the same day. Only three men were to remain behind for special duty. After adding something about this being a "most vital commitment" involving a "chance to win the Knight's Cross," he gave an order.

240

"Lance-Corporals Malchow and Benzinger, Grenadier Velten—two paces forward march!"

Himself of all people, thought Velten. Now Quandt was doing his damnedest to turn him into a hero! But he was already standing out in front with the other two. The sergeant-major marched the rest of the company away without Velten being able to exchange so much as a glance with Eichberg.

The captain took the three heroes into the office, which was now completely bare.

"Right now," said Quandt, making a visible effort to appear military, "you three are to form a suicide squad. Benzinger will be in charge."

"Jawohl, Herr Hauptmann!" yelled the man thus addressed, taking a pace forward and clicking the heels of his jackboots together. Benzinger was one of the two candidates for a reservist commission. He was loathed throughout the unit on account of his exaggerated smartness and already felt himself every inch an officer.

"You two," said Quandt, meaning Benzinger and Velten, "will be able to prove whether you are fit to be officers. I've detailed Malchow to go as well, because he's seen service at the front."

The other lance-corporal was a quiet, stolid Mecklenburger. He wore the red ribbon of the "Frozen Meat" medal and, never having had much to say for himself, had not previously come to Velten's notice.

Even now he was as phlegmatic as ever.

The captain was speaking again: "You know the bridge at the southern exit of the village, where the highway leads south through the swamps? Well, the sappers have mined it. In all probability the Russian tanks will come that way. What you have to do is to set the fuses and then lie up in the mill this side of the bridge. As soon as the first two or three tanks are across you'll blow the bridge."

He paused impressively and looked at each man in turn.

Out came the strident Benzinger's inevitable repetition of the order.

"Jawohl, Herr Hauptmann: set fuses—lie up in mill. Blow bridge as soon as armored spearheads are across!"

And what, Velten wondered, his eyes still on his commander, would become of them after that?

241

Quandt seemed to divine his thoughts. "Oh, yes," he continued somewhat uncertainly, "and then you'll have to see about making yourself scarce in the resultant confusion. You'll crawl away and make for the Battalion Command Post at Honczary."

"Jawohl, Herr Hauptmann," bellowed Benzinger. "Crawl away and report to Battalion Command Post!"

Quandt silenced him with a weary wave of the hand: "You'll get through all right. Good luck to you. You have a tactically important task to do. For all we know, it may be of strategic importance. Do your job well!"

With that he went out to his waiting car and drove off towards Honczary in the north.

The three men walked down the dusty village street. The July evening was dry and hot. Malchow and Velten carried the weighty demolition set, Benzinger the responsibility. When they got to the mill they found a Tiger tank standing at an angle to the street, under the protruding roof of the barn. Two troopers in the black uniform of the Panzer Corps were at work on it with monkey wrenches. They were supervised by a slight, fair-haired second-lieutenant of no more than twenty who drew at his cigarette with ill-concealed nervousness.

Benzinger marched up to the officer, saluted ostentatiously and stated his mission in a series of clipped phrases.

"As far as I'm concerned," the subaltern told him with the suspicion of a grin, "you can blow the whole damn place sky high. We're off as soon as this crate's repaired." He turned to his men who were still toiling feverishly with streaming faces: "Come on, you guys. Get that fixed as fast as you can!"

At that moment they heard the sound of an approaching car. It pulled up in a cloud of dust in front of the mill and a major jumped out. The subaltern reported his name and unit, stating that his tank had been damaged in such and such an engagement.

"And you?" the major asked with a questioning look at the three infantrymen from the Zorn battalion. Benzinger snapped his heels together and stated his business. Velten caught the panzer subaltern's fleeting grin.

"So that's who you are? I know all about you," said the major.

242

Turning to the tank officer, he ordered: "You'll take up a position here and cover the demolition squad's withdrawal!"

"Damn it, sir," his junior ejaculated, "my vehicle won't maneuver! The reverse gear's broken!"

"No contradictions!" the major warned him sharply. "I'm operational commander of this area. All available troops are under my command!" All available troops, Velten reflected. One busted tank and three men from the Zorn outfit!

The major returned their salutes perfunctorily, got back into his car and sped away. The subaltern beckoned to his crew, and the three of them disappeared into the mill.

The three members of the demolition squad looked at each other. "Well," said Benzinger, "we'd better set the fuses and get everything ready." His voice was suddenly far less confident than it had been a few moments ago when he was addressing the major.

"Oh, well," Malchow said quietly, opening his mouth for the first time, "I don't suppose you two know much about it. You'd better let me handle that."

"I must be present," Benzinger declared, all officious once again, "I bear the responsibility."

"In that case," Velten remarked, "there won't be anything for me to do for the time being. You don't mind if I go along to the village for half an hour, I suppose? I may be able to scrounge a few eggs."

Benzinger agreed. "Be back in half an hour, though."

Velten dumped his equipment by the tank and sauntered off. Along the village street he came upon a group of ragged women chattering excitedly to one another. One of the younger ones, slightly better dressed than the rest, came up to him.

"I'm a refugee from Kleck," she said in German with a harsh Eastern accent. "We are so frightened. When are the Russians coming?"

Velten shrugged his shoulders. "I know as much about it as you do!" He pushed her to one side and walked on. A car with two Ack-Ack officers inside drew up beside him. A second-lieutenant beckoned to him. "What did that woman want?"

"Wanted to know when the Russians were coming," Velten replied. "I wouldn't mind knowing that myself."

243

"Give no information to civilians," the subaltern told him importantly. "The countryside's swarming with spies!" Then the car drove on.

Suddenly Velten felt a boundless longing for human warmth. Something had aroused his senses. Was it the voice of the young woman who had just accosted him? Or did the proximity of danger awake in him a yearning for contact with a warm, living being?

He cut across the street and made for the home of a young woman whose slim build and finer features placed her in a category apart from the local run of womenfolk. The medical corporal had told him, with many knowing looks, how he had cured the red-headed Xenia of a fever with a few pills and then, casting the danger of infection to the winds, enjoyed a very natural reward. The thought of it sent a prickle of lust chasing over Velten's skin.

Hardly aware of having pushed the door open, he found himself standing in the one and only room. The windows were tightly closed and it smelled badly. As the redhead stood gazing at him from the center of the room, there was no surprise in her dark brown eyes. She had often seen him: he was no stranger. She wore a freshly washed, white kerchief which exposed not a single strand of her hair. Velten knew that the medical corporal had shaved her head on account of the lice which communicated the fever. Her dark eyes smoldered in a narrow, pale face. She had no freckles, he noted in wonder. His gaze found its way down her body, taking in her tender throat, the curve of her breasts, her slender waist. He pictured the shape of her legs under her thin skirt, and saw her sun-burned, naked feet with their grubby but well-formed toes.

As her pale, narrow mouth broke into a startling smile, he felt his knees trembling with longing. He caught his breath and sat down on a chair by the window.

"Kislaya molokka?" she asked, the intoxicating smile still on her lips. Velten nodded dumbly. She knew that he liked sour milk.

While she was getting this refreshment Velten looked round the room. Only now did he notice a cradle with a sleeping infant in it suspended from the ceiling by a cord. Then he became aware of a ragged old man squatting in the corner by the Virgin Mary, appraising him with gloomy red-rimmed eyes. Velten looked away and studied the pots on the window-sill in which a few miserable flowers languished. How did one get rid of the old chap, he wondered. Or could they manage with the father—or whatever he was—still sitting there?

The redhead came back, placed an earthenware jug full of lumpy, curdled milk on the little table by the window and sat down facing her silent guest. She rested her arms before her and propped her chin on folded hands. Her sleeves were rolled up as far as the elbow, and the smooth pale skin looked cool and supple to the touch.

He was about to stand up, half crazed by the urge to touch the woman's cool, lissom body, when he froze in sudden alarm. She, too, shuddered convulsively. A column of heavy trucks was howling down the street, and one of them screeched to a stop in front of the house. Its towering mass overshadowed the low windows, leaving the room in semi-darkness.

Before Velten could make up his mind whether this turn of events was favorable to his intentions or not, he heard the tread of boots coming round to the door. A corporal in the Ack-Ack stepped in and cast a keen look around him. He seemed not to notice the shabby private sitting by the window. With a broad grin on his face he went up to Xenia and addressed her in the language of the country. She stood up, and in no time both of them had plunged into a jabber of talk of which Velten understood not a word. The redhead was a changed woman. She gave little shrieks of delight when the corporal produced a flat bottle of schnapps from his hip pocket. Even the old man in the corner began to giggle. No one took any further notice of Velten. He sensed how superfluous he had become. Unnoticed, and without a word of farewell, he sneaked quietly away.

When he reached the mill the tank was out of sight behind an enormous haystack. Only the barrel of its gun poked out. Malchow was throwing a few trusses of straw together beside the building. "Just the job for a good nap," he told them.

With officious pride Benzinger showed Velten the fuse wire which he, as the man responsible, would set off when the time came.

After Malchow had gone off for his own look round the village, Officer-Candidate Benzinger became confidential. Producing a bottle of schnapps from his pack, he declared that they must drink the German pledge of brotherhood and henceforth be on friendly terms.

"I must tell you about something that's causing me a great deal of worry," Benzinger remarked after a while. "In so doing I appeal to your comradeship and sense of duty." Dear God, thought Velten, were there still people like this in circulation?

"Shake on it, then, that you'll keep quiet about it whatever happens."

Velten groaned inaudibly. He held out his hand and felt the manly grip of the would-be officer.

"Just imagine, the captain told Egon Feld and me yesterday afternoon that he didn't believe in Final Victory any longer."

Benzinger paused and looked at his new friend expectantly. Velten thought rapidly. Was it a trap or was this character really as improbable as he behaved? He framed a cautious reply.

"Sometimes things look bad enough to make the best of us doubt."

Benzinger looked him full in the face. Then he shifted nearer.

"Good lord, man," he whispered, "you know yourself we mustn't lose. It'd be all up if we did. Think what it'd be like if they got us down as they did in 1918! It'll be even worse next time!"

He drove his fist into the straw. "I don't want us to lose!" he cried in strangled tones. "I don't want us to—do you hear? I want to live! I want to travel! I want a home—a wife and children! I refuse to go to the dogs!"

"Those are good reasons for wanting Final Victory, anyway," said Velten ironically. "Now I'm beginning to believe in it again." He had perceived that the other was safe enough. Just a hysterical little poseur—made courageous by a sheer panic of catastrophe. A yellow-belly.

They took another pull at the bottle and then several more.

Velten offered to stand the first guard, and Benzinger lay down in the straw. When it was quite dark Malchow returned from the village, cheerfully nonchalant.

"Hell!" he exclaimed when Velten urged him to get off to sleep, "you don't want to stand any guards! We can all hit the hay. We shall notice soon enough if Ivan comes. The Ack-Ack have got pickets out. They've *got* to keep alert with an orderly officer around. No bastard can check up on us. We can safely sleep!" Without further ado Malchow lay down in the straw and a few minutes later

246

was snoring rhythmically. Velten lay on his back and stared up into the black velvet of heaven. He was getting another bit of that holiday trip after all, he thought with a wry smile. Then he fell into a deep, dreamless sleep.

When he was roused by the cool of morning he saw that Benzinger was standing by the bridge. It turned out that he had wakened again and kept watch for the rest of the night without arousing the other two.

Velten and Malchow went to the wayside spring and took turns to splash cold water over their heads and bodies. Their teeth chattered as they rubbed themselves down. Malchow scrounged coffee from the Ack-Ack. As the three of them sat breakfasting in the straw, orders rang out along the column. The gun crews threw off the camouflage nets, and one by one the vehicles moved off in the direction of Honczary.

Soon the tank crew, who had slept in the mill, reappeared and set about extricating their vehicle from the straw. Then they clambered in and started up the engine. Officer-Candidate Benzinger rushed up to the subaltern.

"Herr Leutnant!" he called, "you're supposed to be covering us!"

"Like hell I am," the young man returned cheerfully. "We're off. You can tell your operational commander that we've been in touch with our own crowd over the air and been given other orders. That's if he ever shows up again, which I very much doubt!" He climbed onto the tank. "If you've got any sense you'll beat it too."

The tank began to move, setting up a tremendous din as it drew ponderously away in first gear. Malchow and Velten gazed after it enviously.

"I'm going through with my task until I'm recalled," announced Benzinger with a challenging look.

"Very well then," said Velten resignedly, "on we go—till Final Victory."

Malchow made no comment and threw himself lazily down in the straw.

They were quite alone now. The village seemed deserted. After half an hour of uneasy waiting they heard the thunder of big guns coming from the forest on the far side of the railway. As it gradually rose to a crescendo they were able to distinguish a sound which rose to a howl and then fell off to a dull thud. Malchow got to his feet and listened intently in the direction of the forest. Then he turned to the other two.

"That's a Stalin organ," he said quietly, but the skin around his nostrils had gone a shade paler. The Stalin organ—that legendary multi-barreled engine of war mounted on a self-propelled carriage! So it was Ivan himself now, no longer a mob of partisans. This time it was the Red Army with the fire-power of its artillery and the crushing superiority of its prodigious tanks. And it was all so near—just over the other side of the railway! Would they come over now—up the road and across the mined bridge? Damn it, thought Velten, why should he sit here and wait to be rubbed out? He looked at Officer-Candidate Benzinger.

"I'm going through with my job," the latter announced with bravado. Then all three of them started violently. From the direction of the forest came three consecutive explosions, and three gray pillars of smoke several miles apart rose into the air over the tree tops.

"That one's Talminowicze," Malchow pointed, "and that's Kuleni North and that's Kuleni Central. They've blown up the outposts. Must be getting pretty bad."

"I'm going through with it," Benzinger insisted. They waited another half-hour and listened to the thunder and howling drawing nearer.

"Where we've got three guns," Malchow told them, "Ivan's got a hundred. And they don't spend long ranging. They bracket one after the other on the same target." He fell silent and started to gather his kit together.

"Just wait and see how you feel when the T 34s and Josef Stalins are coming at you," he said, looking hard at Officer-Candidate Benzinger.

"I'm carrying out my task," he repeated. Suddenly Velten showed signs of animation. He nudged Benzinger and pointed down the village street. Three men were marching towards them. Yes, one of them was actually Bernd Eichberg. They shook hands.

"I've come to relieve you," said Eichberg. Even Benzinger cheered up at this. He showed Eichberg the mine and fuse set.

"Don't do anything daft, Bernd," said Velten.

248

Eichberg's teeth gleamed white in his tanned face. "Don't worry," he murmured. "You know I'm protected and what protects me. Before it gets too hot I'll be well away. We'll meet again at noon."

He went on to explain that the new company command post was next to the other road in Honczary on the other side of the railway. They ought really to have left for an unknown destination that morning, but Ivan had bombarded the station and set their train on fire. "All our stuff is shot to blazes," he told them with something approaching gratification. "There'll be nothing to slow us up next time we skedaddle!"

The three men who had been relieved picked up their belongings, shook hands with those remaining behind, and set off. They heard shells bursting quite close. Where Honczary lay, hidden from their vision by a curve in the road, smoke and flames were rising skywards. At that moment a number of gray figures emerged from the wood on their right and came running across the meadow towards the road.

"Russians!" screeched Benzinger. They took cover in the ditch.

"Rot!" said Malchow, springing up as the figures drew closer. "They're civilians."

They came straight up to the Germans, wailing dismally. They were a ragged bunch of local villagers.

"Honczary burning," they cried, men, women and children all trying to talk at once. "Doma y karowo! Our homes, our cows!"

The three men considered. To go through the village was impossible. Velten remembered the path through the fields he had regularly taken on his errands to Battalion Headquarters.

"I'll lead you round the village," he said. Even Benzinger had no desire to run into enemy artillery fire. They left the road and cut across the fields. From the other side they saw that the village below was a mass of smoke and flames into which shells were crumping with clockwork precision. Overhead, in the patches of azure sky between the white summer clouds, they could see one or two aircraft, too high for identification. Farther behind, towards the horizon, a burning machine dived earthwards, leaving a long trail of smoke in its wake. There were two—three—parachutes floating above it!

They reached the highway leading past Honczary station to the

249

East. They jumped down the bank onto the road, crossed it and took the track to the manor-house. The command post seemed deserted: there was no sentry at the main gate. In the courtyard stood a solitary car with its engine running. One door was open. Seated next to the driver, his booted feet resting on the ground and a map spread out on his knees, was an officer none of them knew. As they got closer they saw he was a captain.

"I'm Captain Sieber—your battalion commander since yesterday," he explained. "Major Schäfer had to take over another command at very short notice."

Benzinger gave the captain an account of the situation at the Niedzwiedzica bridge, concluding with the information that Talminowicze and Kuleni were burning.

"The situation's completely obscure," Velten heard the captain say. "My people have already pulled out. What's left of your company is holding the company command post. But Capt. Quandt has orders to disengage from the enemy. He and his crew are likely to come along the road any minute now."

"Herr Captain Quandt is at the command post?" cried Benzinger. "Then we must report back to him. May I ask Herr Captain to show me the route?"

"I suppose so," the new commander replied hesitantly. "Though they may have pulled out already. I gave orders to concentrate in the wood by the road, six miles to the west of here." He tapped the map with his finger. "I'm leaving now," he added.

Malchow cleared his throat noisily. Velten, too, had cottoned on to the fact that the weary battalion commander had no wish to force them to go forward again.

Benzinger turned round to his two men: "I'm reporting back to my chief!" The company command post, it appeared, was located on a farm some four miles down the road to the east, and then another five hundred yards along a sunken road.

The captain smiled and gave a tired wave of the hand.

"Best of luck to you," he said. He saluted again. The car rolled away.

As they were trudging away Malchow growled:

"We could have gone straight back to the rendezvous. Didn't you see what the captain was getting at?"

"I'm reporting back to our commander," Benzinger rejoined sharply. "You two can go to the rear if you want to!"

The little party fell silent. They were still on the path back to the main road when the enemy bombardment of Honczary stopped.

At the point where the highway and the main road intersected close to the station, three field-gray figures came into sight. It was Schrader, Talminowicze, and his two colleagues from Kuleni North and Kuleni South. They had been cut off while conferring with the company commander about the projected withdrawal. Now they wanted to get back to their outposts to guide the men back.

"Do you mean you don't know your posts are blown?" asked Velten. No, apparently they did not.

"Ivan's stopped firing now, anyway," Schrader remarked. "We'll try getting through along the railway. We've got to find out where our fellows are."

The three non-coms turned off to the right to follow the permanent way. The other three kept straight on along the road. Suddenly Velten halted. "Where's Fritze Trollberg then?" he called after the three sergeants. Schrader, the East Prussian, turned round: "That shitepoke has taken a powder," he shouted. "Cleared off on the quiet. Nobody knows how he did it!"

"Good old Fritze!" cried Velten. "Doesn't seem to be the fool I took him for!"

Shortly after that they met a farm-cart, jolting and rocking along the side of the road. Sternkopf, the old muddler who had sniped at the moon at Velten's first outpost and was now armory corporal, sat on his weapon chests threshing away with his whip at the shaggy little pony.

"Where're you going?" he yelled as he drew nearer. "We're supposed to be withdrawing. Meet in the wood by milestone 55!"

"I'm reporting back to the chief," Benzinger called.

"Best come along with me," said Sternkopf. The sweat stood out on his brow. "Who knows if you'll find any of them alive!"

"We're almost there," said Benzinger obstinately.

"Gee-up!" cried the old fellow, cracking the whip across his pony's back. They stepped to one side to let him pass and then continued on their way. A roaring sound overhead made them duck and look upwards. Sure enough, two, three, four aircraft were

251

banking steeply above the fields. They swooped so low that their identification marks were clearly visible. You could see the gunners squatting in their greenhouses.

"Our fliers!" Benzinger screamed proudly. "Our Luftwaffe's there! What did I tell you: we're going through to the chief—the position'll be held!"

"Look out!" called Malchow, taking only a fraction of a second to throw himself on his belly. The others swiftly followed his example. Over to the right, where the forest lined the fields five hundred yards away, a drab-colored monster emerged from the thicket and rumbled over the field in a wide curve, heading for the roadway. Another one, and then a third followed it out of the gloom.

"There's Ivan for you!" Malchow shouted. "Fine fix you got us in, haven't you, wanting to get through to your goddam commander!"

Benzinger made no reply. Neither did Velten, who was at that moment marveling at his own composure. Only a short time back he had been on the point of clearing off with Sternkopf to the rear. Only Benzinger's forced air of self-reliance had stopped him.

What happened next was over so quickly that they did not immediately grasp the sequence of events. The fighter-bombers had curved back towards them, and now they came in almost at ground level, firing at the earth-colored monsters with all their guns. The first tank stopped abruptly in a cloud of smoke and soil, a tongue of flame licking out of its interior. Clumps of earth flew into the air on all sides as the shells pumped into the ground. The second tank hove to a few yards farther on and lay there helpless. There was no sign of the crew. The third succeeded in escaping into the forest.

Velten and his companions jumped up and carried on at the double, heads well down.

"That," the would-be officer commented quite unnecessarily, "was our salvation. The Company would have been cut off in no time."

At last, on their right, they spotted the opening of a sunken road. They halted for a breather in the hollow. A few hundred yards farther along the lane opened out into a farm.

And there was the old crowd once again. A few men were busy loading a two-wheeled cart, and among them Velten noticed Willy

Specht and Alfons Schindler tearing packages of cigarettes out of a crate and filling their pockets to capacity. Out of their knapsacks the alluring necks of bottles protruded.

"The Old Man's opened up the canteen," called Willy with unconcealed exuberance, passing over a few handfuls of the spoil to Velten.

Capt. Quandt was standing by a barn at the back of the farmyard, haranguing his orderly with every sign of anger and agitation. Benzinger stepped proudly up to make his report, but did not come in for the commendation he had been anticipating. Quandt had other worries.

"Have you seen that fellow Ebbecke?" he bawled. "Where's he got to with my car? First he gets a puncture and now he's disappeared!"

Benzinger reported smartly that he had seen neither the vehicle nor its driver.

"The dog must have taken a powder when I was giving fire orders," fumed the fat, sweating company commander. "Come on, get weaving," he bawled to the men by the cart. "Anything you can't get on stays here. We move off in ten minutes!"

"By Herr Captain's leave," said the indefatigable militarist Benzinger, "I wish to inquire the whereabouts of Lance-Corporal Feld."

Quandt jerked his head impatiently. "They're all in position behind the farm. I'm giving the order to close any time now."

The three of them went round the building and found a row of riflemen lying under a hedge. Feld, who was the company's other candidate for a commission, proudly announced that an extended line of Soviet troops had tried to advance on their knoll from the woods. The assault had come to a standstill under the combined fire of rifles and LMGs. After that the Russians had retired. With binoculars it was possible to pick out a few bodies in earth-brown uniforms lying motionless at the forest edge.

"Own losses nil—enemy losses unknown," Egon Feld informed them impressively. Benzinger gave him an account of the Luftwaffe's victory over the enemy armored spearhead.

Then Parkowski, whom they had not seen so far, blew his whistle and gave an order to close. Velten ran back to the farmhouse. By the entrance crates of wine were stacked. Pouring the

253

coffee out of his flask, he picked up a bottle labeled "Serbian White Wine," knocked its neck off against the stone wall and poured away the splinters. The rest of the contents he decanted into his flask. After stowing two more bottles into his knapsack, he threw his pack on the cart. He never saw the pack again.

Finally, moving in small groups, the company reached the concentration point. A large number of troops were bivouacking there under cover of the trees. In addition to the men of the Zorn Battalion there were stragglers from every imaginable unit. Nearby the Ack-Ack regiment had taken up fresh positions along the fringe of the woods.

The three non-coms who had commanded the outposts were there. Fritze was still missing, but one or two soldiers were able to inform the fuming commander that they had seen him *and* the car—driving away with Ebbecke at the wheel and Fritze beside him. Quandt swore he would get both men court-martialed.

After a while Bernd Eichberg and his two men arrived. "Blown your bridge?" Velten inquired.

"Not me!" said Eichberg. "Not a single Russian tank turned up. Besides, there may still be some of our own folks on the other side."

"What did you clear off for, then?" said Velten.

"It looked as if none were coming. Do you think I wanted to be the last there till the Russians came?"

"Aren't you going to report to the chief?" Velten asked, thinking of Benzinger.

"Don't worry," said Eichberg. "The Old Man's forgotten that demolition job long ago. I'm not going to lead with my chin."

Velten took a look around him: Benzinger and Feld were sitting together a good distance away. "Bernd," Velten whispered, "there's bound to be an opportunity to give this outfit the slip before long. Wherever we finish up can't possibly be any worse than this."

They were soon on the move again. A dispatch rider from the Ack-Ack drove slowly along the road with an officer in his side-car blowing a whistle and yelling "Stellungswechsel!" They set off singly and in small groups, the fat Quandt groaning along in front. Gradually the highway became full of life. Other units were marching westwards, some in tolerable order, others in the same disarray as Quandt's motley little party. In addition there were motorized

254

columns which crowded the pedestrian troops to one side, forcing them to pick their way along the side of the road in Indian file. Preponderant in that jostling throng were the khaki uniform of Hungarians, many of them belonging to cavalry units.

At last, when it was just about midnight, they stopped in a village. And, miraculous sight, there was actually a field kitchen awaiting them! Like everyone else, Velten devoured his entire ration. There was bound to be something more in the morning!

The sergeant-major gathered the unit around him.

"We're going to rest up here till morning. No one's to leave the street! All of you lie down in the ditch!"

"I can see him sleeping in a ditch!" whispered Bernd Eichberg.

"That's where drunks belong—not us!" He tugged Velten away by the arm. No one noticed them steal away in the darkness of that moonless night.

There was not a soul about in the lonely village. Eventually they found a low barn, and Velten pushed open the door and flashed his light inside. Bale upon bale of straw confronted their delighted eyes. Like a flash they darted inside, carefully pulling the door shut behind them. In no time at all they had taken off their tunics and yanked their boots off their aching feet. Then they burrowed deep down into that crackling luxury.

Part Three

CHAPTER I

THE FOUR MEN dragged the chest across the railway lines. Now and again one of them would stumble, causing the others to curse. It was a dark, moonless night, and the station, in accordance with wartime regulations, was unlit. At last they attained their goal—an armored train standing in the farthest siding of the big marshaling yard. With much grunting and groaning they lifted their iron-bound burden to the level of the door. Simultaneously several pairs of hands reached down to help haul it inside.

The four men swung themselves up into the armored chamber, wiping the sweat from their brows as they waited for their breath to come back. In the large, feebly lit interior, with the embrasures in its armor-plating, stood another chest exactly like the first. On it squatted four private soldiers. The last four to arrive sat down on their own.

The after bulkhead of the compartment was fitted with a folding bench, now occupied by a second-lieutenant, a paymaster and two corporals. As the train moved slowly off, the lieutenant decided the time was ripe to enlighten his little party on the purpose of the mission for which they had been hastily assembled only a few hours before.

"Mal herhören!" he began, employing the peremptory formula current in the German armed forces for demanding the attention of subordinates. "Just so that you know how to behave and what you're responsible for from now on; those two chests hold the bullion of the Polish State Bank. They're worth millions of marks, understand? Our job is to hand them over safely to the Reichsbank in Breslau."

He paused here to give added emphasis to the words that followed.

"This trip is secret. You're to keep quiet about it, understand? Don't let me catch anyone shooting his mouth off!"

"Are we going straight through to Breslau?" one man inquired.

It was the end of November 1944. By that stage of the war it had become possible for a private to address an officer without being spoken to first. The lieutenant, moreover, answered the question.

"No, only to Skierniewice. By then we'll be out of the worst partisan areas and take the ordinary express to Breslau."

He turned to the paymaster. "We are getting reserved compartments, aren't we?"

"Provided it's been attended to in all this hurry," was the other's cautious reply.

Velten, who was one of the men on the chests, pricked up his ears at the mention of Skierniewice.

"That's the dump where the Army Group ordnance depot is," he told his neighbor. "Fixed myself up with new eyepieces for my respirator there not so long ago."

By now the whole vast expanse of Russia had been frittered away. Though Ivan had been halted on the Narew and Vistula, he already had two bridgeheads from which to threaten the western parts of Poland still occupied by the Wehrmacht. In the west the enemy stood at the gates of the Reich; and almost the whole of Italy was lost. In southeast and northern Europe extensive areas were still under German occupation, but these, too, would fall into the enemy's lap like ripe fruit as soon as the offensive was renewed on the Eastern and Western fronts and Germany's last resistance smashed.

However, no one allowed such fears of the future to worry him on that journey from Zyrardow to Skierniewice in the armored train. "If we're taking an express to Breslau," said Velten's companion, "there'll be nothing to stop us pushing off home tomorrow, will there?"

"Of course not. It means we'll have over a week's leave. They won't have the faintest idea how soon we got home!"

They were the clerks in the orderly room of the large and complicated organization which called itself Headquarters, Twenty-Ninth Army. Yes, Velten had landed on a staff after the vicissitudes of that eventful summer. This time, however, he was able to follow the curious working of military machinery from the inside—or, more precisely, from the underside. For now he did not belong, as in a faraway summer of happy-go-lucky blitzkrieg, to the outer circle of observers on the vessel's bridge. He was, so to speak, working with the stokers before the battleship's boilers. In short, he had become a driver on the staff of the Twenty-Ninth Army. He and Hans Arend had been detached from the Motor Transport Pool for this duty trip. As the other men on it were from the defense company, the two drivers naturally kept together.

After they had taken up quarters in Zyrardow, thirty miles south-west of Warsaw, in mid-August, life had become as humdrum as in any post. Then, quite suddenly, there had come the great boom of duty trips into the Reich. Machines were being transferred home-wards and vehicles beyond local repair had to be lifted back to army motor pools in Germany or even to their factories of origin. As accompanying personnel were needed for all these expeditions, the men found home-leaves coming their way.

When movement orders were issued, due allowance had to be made for actual duration of the rail trip, since freight trains took a considerable time to reach their destinations. It was clear that Velten and Arend had had a tremendous stroke of luck in this respect, as not a soul in the motor pool had any notion of the real purpose of the assignment. The party had merely received an order to "report to the Army Artillery Commander at 2200 hours." Staff-Sergeant Herschner, inferring from this that they were to "take some busted gun home," had had their papers made out for a freight-train trip. Now that they were to ride at top speed to Breslau and thence proceed at once on leave, they could tack every day allowed for travel onto their furlough. They concluded a solemn pact that neither of them would arrive back at the headquarters before the other, agreeing to settle the details at Breslau with the help of the time-tables. Arend's family had been bombed out of Cassel and lived in a Hessian village, whereas Velten was going to Berlin. This made him by far the most fortunate, as he would be home long before the rest.

"How did you manage to wangle yourself on this trip?" Arend inquired in some wonderment.

Velten grinned. "Don't go thinking I've got Herschner to thank for it. He bawled me out when he heard about it. I think I must be in the Old Man's good books. He detailed me to go."

The Old Man in this case was the Motor Transport Officer, Capt. Kessler, who regarded Velten as his own private acquisition. He had kept him in the Company when Herschner had wanted to pack the "high-brow" off again. Velten had told the captain the story of his military past and the Zorn mob, since when the powerful, squarely built Kessler, a man of the world who had been in business abroad for years and knew something about human nature, had to a certain extent taken him under his wing. It was through having told the commander how he had been whisked off with the Zorn mob without any draft leave that he was now setting a precedent for newcomers by enjoying the privilege of a duty trip back home.

"How long have you actually been with us?" asked Hans Arend.

"Since Wolkowysk," said Velten. He shifted a little closer. There was no need for the others to hear everything. "That's where the Old Man dug me out of the holding camp."

"Christ!" Kessler had bawled in his boozy, drill-ground voice when Velten stood before him in shirt-sleeves, ragged and emaciated. "What are you in civil life?"

"A lawyer."

Roars of laughter from Kessler. "Can't say you look much like one now! More like a country bumpkin on roller skates, if you ask me!" Kessler loved to use robust language. He had told Velten to fix himself up with a belt and tunic. The tunic had been supplied by the MPs in charge of the camp, but belts were not to be had. "You can scrounge one, can't you?" Kessler had bellowed, but Velten had not the impudence. Thereupon Kessler had stowed him and two others into the back of his Mercedes.

That was how Velten had found himself a new job—and he was inflexibly resolved not to lose it. It afforded him every prospect of remaining comfortably mobile for the rest of the war and of making that final trip back to the Fatherland on four wheels.

262

CHAPTER II

IN SKIERNIEWICE they discreetly tugged the two chests into a dark corner at the far end of the platform while the paymaster went to the transportation office. He returned with the news that there had been a hitch over their reservations. The lieutenant swore.

When the express came in, all the third-class compartments proved to be full. Most of the occupants—German civil employees of the Government-General traveling on duty—slumbered inelegantly with their feet on the seats. Quickly making up his mind, the lieutenant took over two adjoining second-class compartments and had one chest put into each. He, the paymaster and four men occupied one compartment and the two corporals and four men the other.

"What the hell do you think you're doing here?" yelled the sergeant of the train staff as he came to the compartment full of enlisted men. "Get out of the second class!"

"Next door," one of the corporals informed him with dignity, supported by the malicious grins of the privates, "you will find the leader of this detail. He will enlighten you."

The non-com slammed the door with a thunderous crash and made for the next compartment. After a while he came back and inspected each man's papers in sullen silence.

When they were alone again they began talking about the contents of the chests. One of the corporals was on the Army Artillery Commander's staff and claimed to know the precise origin of the bullion. According to him, two gunners had found the gold when rooting around in the ruined cellar of a doubtful tavern in a damaged part of Warsaw and had dutifully surrendered it to their unit. In recognition of their service a special leave had been granted them from the highest level.

263

Warsaw, as everyone knew, had become a gold-mine for German soldiers intent on picking up something for nothing. The motor transport pool had sent transport details into the ruined capital almost daily, and they would return loaded with loot—cratefuls of eggs from the communal refrigerators, sacks of sugar, rice and leguminous vegetables, jars of bottled fruit and items of furniture for offices and messes. And all this covered only the official procurements: it did not include what the troops appropriated on the side.

The morning after Velten joined the pool it moved from Wolkowysk to a village near Bialystok. The very day Kessler had picked him up, the "new boys" had been driven to the Army motor depot at Bialystok in a troop transporter called a "Kom." There Velten had been put in charge of a vehicle known in Wehrmacht parlance as a Kiz II and consisting of a chassis with a six-cylinder Wanderer engine on which was mounted an open box. The driver sat in a little driver's cabin with rattling window-panes.

As their Kom had been passing through Bialystok, a city thick with troops, Velten had received a nasty jar at one of the street crossings. There, pensively irresolute, had stood, of all people, Willy Specht, studying a sign-board bearing a black arrow and the legend 711 L-of-C Concentration Area. Velten had determined there and then not to avail himself of the helpful sign-post.

Each man had then driven back independently in his newly acquired vehicle. Once again Velten had reveled in the wild improbability of this new adventure. Here he was, all on his own, spinning through the gathering darkness at the wheel of an unfamiliar vehicle, unarmed, beltless and without the least scrap of paper in his pocket to identify him. Once or twice he was tempted to turn about and join the stream of traffic heading west, and then, reflecting that Bernd Eichberg's prognostication of final collapse was probably premature, he would decide to stay with his new unit.

About midnight he reached the estate near Walkowysk where the motor pool was quartered. In view of his deficient sense of direction he considered it well-nigh miraculous that he should have found his way home at all.

Kessler sent for him the next morning. "It's a wonder you ever came back from the depot," he snorted. "I really ought to take you in front of the security officer. You might be a spy for all I know, traipsing around without papers like that!"

Spies, Velten pointed out, were generally provided with first-class identity documents. Kessler growled something inaudible. At length, however, after a series of questions, he seemed satisfied. The unit moved off for Tykocyn near Bialystok.

From there the Chief sent Velten to Warsaw. In the office, they gave him a printed form headed *"In Lieu of Paybook,"* a belt that was too tight and had to be changed at the quartermaster's depot, and a captured Russian quick-firing rifle. He eyed the firearm with undisguised suspicion, not knowing whether it was loaded and, if so, whether the safety catch was on or not. He strapped it into the rifle rack next to the driving seat and hoped it would not go off on its own.

Thus Velten passed almost directly from the wilderness of Kuleni to a large European city. He did not go alone. The purpose of the trip was to pick up spare parts, and he was merely the driver. The main person was Lance-Corporal Fritz Erlenbach, a capable motor mechanic from Dresden who acted as the Pool's "procurement man" and knew all the answers. Velten's eyes had widened in surprise when Erlenbach stowed several bottles of schnapps, a few boxes of cigars and some bars of chocolate in the truck in addition to his kit.

"Don't go kidding yourself those are for us, my boy," grinned the wily Saxon. "You can't get anything for nothing these days, even in the Army. They're all little favors for the quartermaster and his friends. Grease well and you'll fare well!"

"Greasing" was a word Velten had only just begun to know in its proper sense. When he made this trip to Warsaw with Fritz Erlenbach, they got out in the Eisgrubenstrasse outside a building which had once been a factory and now accommodated a technical unit. The Eisgrubenstrasse lay in a busy quarter of the city, not far from the center. Velten, a city-dweller from birth, found his way about the streets of Warsaw as though it were his home town. There were shops, their windows bursting with goods. Underwear, dresses, shoes and stockings. Edibles from sausages and ham to the most enticing delicacies. Everything was off the ration, but at sky-high prices. Out in the streets snow-white bread, flaming red tomatoes,

265

black cherries, yellow plums and the first juicy peaches were on sale—but the prices chalked over them in zloty made it all seem quite unreal. Not to mention the fact that Velten didn't have a cent in his pocket.

In the center of the city a fashionable crowd filled the streets. There were beautiful women in exquisite clothes, escorted by smartly dressed men. The restaurants and coffee houses were filled to capacity.

Such was Warsaw in the days before August 1st, 1944. Naturally a critical eye perceived many signs of misery and want amid the bustling crowd. And there was one quarter, quite close to the Eisgrubenstrasse, of which the average German soldier preferred not to speak. It was surrounded by a high wall, but gaps had been blown in this affording glimpses of an atrocious labyrinth of earth and rubble. No one could guess that this zone of horror was merely a foretaste of what all Warsaw was to become.

As they left in their fully loaded truck a week later, Velten once more had that feeling of being on a holiday tour. No one knew where the headquarters was, for communications had not been properly established. But Fritz Erlenbach had the old soldier's instinct for his own outfit's whereabouts.

"Bet you anything you like," said the procurement man confidently, "that they're in Arys in East Prussia. That's where we were before the push started. And even if they aren't, East Prussia's got some fine countryside to drive through."

As it turned out, the unit was there. They arrived one evening. And because they had used the schnapps and cigars to such good effect, Kessler sent them straight back to Warsaw the very next day.

On their second journey back to Arys they swore to each other that they would extend the run through the East Prussian countryside into a full-scale holiday trip. But soldiers' schemes seldom work out: just behind Warsaw they ran into a column of vehicles bearing the tactical sign of Twenty-Ninth Army—an oak-leaf pierced by a sword. Army Headquarters was on the move to Komarow, a week-end resort outside the Polish capital.

From there Velten was sent to Brest. Not the Brest-Litowsk of that movement order with which he and Bernd Eichberg had failed

266

to comply—that had been occupied by the Russians long ago. This was Brest-Kujawski, a miserable hole near Leslau, as the Polish Wloclawec was now called. On this occasion Velten went with Max Seybold, a Sudeten German, and their job was to get two enormous balloon tires for the big breakdown wagon. They left one Thursday morning and were scheduled to be back on Saturday.

"It's only human nature to make mistakes," said Seybold. "We'll have so much trouble that they won't see us again until the middle of next week." He was considerably more venturesome than the persevering Erlenbach. Once they had put a few miles between themselves and the unit, they pulled up beside a wooded lake. Here they carefully camouflaged the vehicle against aircraft and the eyes of their own troops and slept blissfully until well into the afternoon.

While having supper in a tavern in Leslau they made the acquaintance of two enterprising Berlin girls. Both were evacuees who had been bombed out of their homes. Now, however, they felt a strong urge to return to the precarious existence of their home city. It would, they said, be better in the air-raid shelter than with Ivan!

The girls had a huge traveling basket filled with their worldly goods. As the railways would no longer accept luggage for shipment by civilians, the two soldiers got rid of it for them at the station in the little town of Brest. At the sight of the proffered cigars the official in charge beamed with delight and lost all his inhibitions. They had been able to acquire the tires without sacrificing much of their palm-grease, and even now there remained a bottle of schnapps for an evening celebration with the two girls from the banks of the Spree.

By way of return the girls provided a night's lodging in the broad beds of the chamber they jointly occupied. The mass-produced splendor of its three-compartment wardrobe and dressing-table marked it down as having once been the matrimonial arena of some Polish civil servant or merchant. The original occupants were now probably in some bug-ridden hovel in the Wolyń marshes—if they had not fallen victim to the colonial aspirations of one or the other of the partners of the Moscow Pact.

The sole reminder of the Polish owners was a breath-taking colored print over the marriage beds depicting the Adoration of the Shepherds. Its golden frame was black with fly-specks, and round its edge were stuck photos of handsome film-stars and scantily clad young women.

"Makes the whole place look a bit more human," explained the blonde-haired Erna, the proprietress of a sweetshop in Berlin-Lichtenberg. "Enough to make you feel like evacuated school kids, what with the stables and all that cattle!"

On the kitchen range a fat-chicken soup was simmering. "Organized specially for you two," the hostess proudly announced. In the kitchen stood a large tub which they now filled with hot water for the two privates to take a bath.

"After that," said Lucie from the Weissenburger Strasse in Berlin's North East, "we'll give your heads a good scrubbing. Otherwise you don't come into our chaste beds." She wore her smooth, black hair in a dainty fringe. "Being a ladies' hairdresser," she pointed out, "I should know how to get a pair of greasy old heads clean." With that she proceeded to massage their dubious scalps into a snowy lather.

When they arrived in Komarow on August 3rd, it was empty. They located the motor pool in Piastow, a workers' settlement outside Warsaw. In Komarow it had been attacked by partisans. A man had been killed: Biebel, a newcomer.

Over Warsaw there hung a thick black cloud, a dark symbol of destruction that was visible from afar. The howl of dive-bombers, the chatter of machine-guns, the thump of artillery and the boom of demolitions were all clearly audible. All the weapons of modern war hammered on the city in pitiless unison.

The Polish insurrection had broken out inside the capital. The approach of the Red Army had given courage to the Polish Resistance—but it was a doomed courage born of despair. The Polish bourgeoisie—or rather what vestiges of it had survived the extermination measures of the two hostile powers—had thought that the troops of Churchill's and Roosevelt's ally would come as liberators. It only remained for them to shake off the German yoke with one last, supreme effort—and then they could stick gay bouquets in the rifle-muzzles of the conquering Soviet heroes as the Red Army made its triumphal entry.

The calculation was false. The Lublin Committee, proclaimed as the legal Government of the Polish Republic, disapproved of the rising of the national intelligentsia. True to the precepts of its confederate in the Kremlin, Communist Poland refused to give the bourgeoisie armed support. Here on the Vistula the first cracks appeared in the forced alliance between Bolshevik dictatorship and Western democracy brought about by Hitler. Here on the Vistula there fell the first shadow of that ideological curtain whose fateful symbol was later to be the frontier on the German Elbe.

Up in the suburb of Praga, overlooking Warsaw from the eastern bank of the river, the men of the Red Army rested on their arms. The menacing barrels of the Stalin organs and self-propelled field batteries from the armament-factories of Detroit, Milwaukee and Minneapolis were trained on the raging hell of the city. But they were silent. They fired not a single round as the last bloom of the Polish nation set off on its Calvary into eternal extinction. So did the partners of the Moscow Pact unite once more as deadly enemies to efface their common adversary—the outpost of Western enlightenment in the approaches to the Eastern steppes.

In these days when the future of the world was being imperceptibly pre-ordained, a very personal breath of destiny was to mingle in the stench of fire and corruption that drifted towards Velten from the dying city.

CHAPTER III

PIASTOW had its own communal bath-house. For the men of the motor pool it was the height of luxury to douse themselves under its warm showers after a day's dirty work on the vehicles. In its primitive waiting-room Velten had an encounter which caused his own past to rise again before his eyes and brought home to him with pitiless clarity what havoc was being wrought in this century of hopelessness and woe.

The men were lining up in front of the shower-room, each with a towel and a piece of soap in his hand. There was no locker room: one simply hung one's things on a nail in the corner. Every five minutes five men were called in. They were allowed no longer, as the hot water was in short supply and had to be rationed.

Suddenly a whistle shrilled. The orderly corporal had entered unobserved.

"Finish bathing!" he yelled. "Clear the bath-house immediately!"

The German soldier was used to having his daily life disturbed by all sorts of untoward occurrences. Muttering and cursing, but quite obediently, the herd tramped outside.

There, on a species of village green bordered by the simple, red-brick houses of the settlement, they saw the cause of the trouble. Two army trucks and an ambulance were standing there. Soldiers were piling rowdily over the sides of the former, machine-pistols and respirators swinging from their necks. The eagle and swastika on their left arms identified them as Waffen-SS. They were a wild-looking crowd. Dirty, perspiring and weary, they had clearly come from the inferno of Warsaw. At a command from an enormous sergeant, they formed up in front of the bath-house and filed in five at a time as the men of the motor pool had done. Velten, who had been watching the scene, had just noticed that one or two of them were talking a foreign tongue when a fresh development caught his attention.

From the ambulance medical orderlies lifted two stretchers, which they bore through the crowd into the bath-house. The face of one of the wounded men struck a faint chord in Velten's memory. Quickly making up his mind, he slipped round to the side and, in the crush, succeeded in re-entering the building. He found the two stretcher cases lying unattended in the waiting-room, the orderlies having evidently gone through for a shower. The wounded men were conversing in an undertone. The line of SS men paid no attention to them.

Velten paused at the door to appraise that long, narrow face beneath the cropped, neutral-colored hair. Despite its grime and several days' growth of beard, it seemed somehow austere, controlled and distinguished.

When the recumbent man raised his head for an instant and shot a keen look at the newcomer from a pair of gray-blue eyes,

Velten's suspicion became a certainty. He walked up to the stretcher.

"Hello, Cismar," he said with forced calm, seating himself on the window-sill near the head end.

Georg von Cismar's head jerked round. He examined Velten closely. Then he smiled his wary smile and stretched out a bony, wasted right hand from the gray sleeve of his army shirt.

"Mr. Victor Velten," he observed in his cool, phlegmatic way. "On a holiday tour in uniform, I see—still drifting unscathed through the hazards of the Second World War."

Slightly mockingly, he wrinkled his brow.

"But how do you come to be here as a member of the common soldiery right on the brink of hell? Has God the Father already pitched you out of your comfortable interpreter's job with some town-major in France?"

"Never got there," said Velten. "I was pushed off to the Rokitno Marshes when General von Unruh decided I was 'only to be employed with a combat unit in the East.' "

Cismar grinned. "Don't seem to have come to any harm, though, have you, my little hero?"

"And what about you?" Velten asked. "Damn it, Cismar, not one of us would have given a cent for your life when they came to drag you away from Hacketanz's crowd of intellectuals."

The other's face darkened.

"For God's sake—you don't think one of us. . . ."

Cismar dismissed the notion with a tired wave of the hand.

"Hell, no. I had more on my conscience than that bit of chitchat about Portugal which our lance-corporal friend found so dangerous."

He looked around him. "Got a cigarette, Victor?"

Velten took out a package, held it out to Cismar and then, without giving the man a glance, handed it on to the other stretcher case.

Cismar inhaled deeply. "Yes," he said, blowing the smoke out in front of him, "first it was the death sentence for undermining Army morale: then they commuted it to life imprisonment. Then came Mauthausen concentration camp. After that, as a further act of clemency for"—here he grinned faintly—"exemplary conduct in the recovery of unexploded bombs, I was reclassified worthy for

271

military service and sent off to redeem myself with the Dirlewanger mob." He broke off. Velten, too, pricked up his ears: from behind the closed door of the shower-room they could hear raucous singing. Velten caught a few words of French:

"Et ils s'en foutent de la vérole . . ."

"Pour vite tirer un coup . . ."

"God Almighty!" he ejaculated. "Who the hell's in there?"

Cismar gave him a grim smile. "Stragglers from the Charlemagne Division—undergraduates who've ploughed their exams, soldiers of fortune and convicted foreign workers. All of whom have now volunteered to help the Führer fight his European crusade against atheistic Bolshevism! I wonder if Duke Heinrich the Good had rehabilitation units like that in his ranks when he saved Christendom from the Mongolian hordes."

" 'The flower of the Silesian knighthood threw itself against the Mongolian hordes on the battlefield of Liegnitz,' " recited Velten solemnly, quoting from the history lessons of his schooldays.

"Oh well," said Cismar, "in seven hundred years from now even the Dirlewanger mob and Kaminski's troops will have advanced to the status of European chivalry—if there are still any school-books in existence, that is!"

Velten had already heard about the SS unit Dirlewanger and the Cossacks of the Soviet deserter Kaminski being sent into action in Warsaw.

"Cismar," he asked, stammering at the horror of it, "is it true that both those packs of hell-hounds have been given a free hand with the Poles in Warsaw?"

Cismar curled his lip. "I'm one of the Dirlewanger crowd myself, my diligent little historian. I must maintain the esprit de corps, you know."

He plucked nervously at the blanket which covered him from his neck to his feet.

"Give me another cigarette," he said. Catching Velten's glance at the stretcher, he added: "Both calves smashed up when the dive-bombers hit a building. I'm afraid you'll have to count me out of your Final Victory celebrations. If I don't croak from this, I'll short-circuit it myself."

Then he took up the thread again.

272

"Naturally there's been no specific divisional order permitting three days' looting, murder and rape—but, as future reports will put it, 'the bitterness of the troops at the treacherous attacks of the indigenous population knew no bounds.' All the same, there are still the limits set by human compassion. Didn't we see Kaminski in person shoot down two Cossacks in front of a whimpering little Polish wench who was just about to be raped for the fiftieth time?"

The question was addressed to the man on the other stretcher, who until that moment had lain indifferently beside them.

Velten turned his head to take his first real look at him. Then his eyes widened in fearful, abrupt recognition. He knew this face with the dark, questioning eyes and energetic chin—however grubby and unshaven it might be now!

"Ja, Ja," said the man deliberately, extending his right hand. "I'm him all right. But you can still shake hands with me, Kamerad."

Hesitantly Velten accepted it.

"You've got two proofs that I'm not one of the very worst," the other began again. "First: I let you go that day in the rue des Saussaies, although—oh, well, let it pass! And secondly: I've landed in the Dirlcwanger mob, too—without my epaulettes or sword belt!"

He was silent. Velten sensed that he wanted a cigarette and dumbly held out the opened pack. The other took a few pulls and began to talk. Slowly and with studied calm the story came over the lips of that stubbly face.

"If you want to know what became of your silent sweetheart . . ." He broke off and looked straight into Velten's face. "Don't expect any touching little story from me, though. I've seen a lot more killing than that small-time stuff in France since then. I've probably got a harder shell to my soul than you. . . ."

"Get on with it," said Velten curtly. His voice sounded harsh.

"She was shot," said the SS man, drawing at his cigarette. "Without ever opening her mouth. That girl was made of the right stuff —genuine, stainless steel!"

" 'You don't use good iron for making nails,' " muttered Velten absently.

Cismar, obviously remembering the Chinese interpreter in Hacketanz's company, broke in.

273

"But soldiers today are made from every kind of metal—and I won't pretend you've become a useful nail either, Victor."

Velten waved the remark impatiently aside. "Go on!" he told the SS man. The other continued.

"She hadn't been sentenced, incidentally. The investigation was still going on. They wanted to make her talk whatever happened. She was to give information about the others—including you—but she didn't budge an inch. God alone knows what they didn't do to her: but she wouldn't breathe a word. Then there was an assassination in Paris—I think they killed some big shot from the Labor Front who'd come to get skilled workers for Germany. Naturally that meant shooting a few hostages. Round about fifty or a hundred, I should think. Through some stupid mistake she was stuck on the list.

"It should never have been allowed to happen," the SS man added in some vexation. "She was under the SD's protection as long as the investigation was . . ."

Something contracted in Velten's inside: "Under the SD's protection!"

The other went on talking. "There was more trouble after that. I had to bullshit them with several great long reports before the case was finally closed because of insufficient evidence—and that went for you, too."

Velten sat like a block of wood on the window-sill, gripping the ledge in his hands and staring dumbly at the SS man. The latter started speaking again.

"That isn't why I was degraded and stuck in this hell-crew, though. That was because of that red-headed sow, Cilly. You saw her at the interrogation. The bitch spied on me—and ratted. It was a political charge, as a matter of fact . . ."

Velten made an impatient gesture.

"You're quite right, Kamerad," said the other soothingly. "You couldn't care less. Well, yours didn't rat on you. She was the right kind. You can cheerfully wait for Final Victory while the rest of us are on our way to Kingdom Come. I've got a chunk of something stuck in my spine. If that's not the finish of me, I'll eat my paybook in mayonnaise."

274

The medical orderlies, fresh from their shower-bath, came back in with shining red faces and hair plastered flat.

"Give us a little longer," said Cismar. "I've met an old buddy of mine. You'll have to wait till the rest are through, anyway."

The orderlies withdrew contentedly enough.

"They shot her out in Vincennes," the SS man began once more. "At the butts of the École Militaire, if you know it."

Velten shook his head.

"There's an underground range there," explained the ex-captain of SS with an over-nice attention to detail. "At one end there's a table with rests for the execution squad's rifles. We often did target practice there. At the bottom end there's a stop-plate and straw mats we used to hang the targets on. In front there are two wooden posts—all hollowed out and splintered up at the top where the head comes . . ."

Velten buried his face in his hands.

"I've seen them all red with blood," the pitiless voice went on, "when we've been there for practice. I was never at any of the executions, but a chap I knew was in charge of the firing-squad and told me all about it. She stayed mum till the last, her face as white as chalk. Her body wasn't any wider than the post they tied her to. She was dead after the very first volley. The *coup de grâce* was only a formality."

"All execution regulations correctly observed," added Cismar in a voice like ice. "What more do you want?"

Velten did not move.

"Take hold of yourself, Velten," said Cismar. "You seem to forget the gravity of the times! I think you lack the ruthlessness befitting a soldier! Quite apart from that, my dear fellow: she didn't rat on you. The case—your case—was closed, even if only from want of proof. She died through an oversight—and she died for you!"

Velten pressed his face deeper into his own shielding hands. But Cismar did not relent.

"But for that convenient screw-up, the investigation would have gone on. In the end she'd probably have talked—and then both of you would have gone before the SS Court and both of you to the stake—the one that's so ominously hollowed out at the top. You

275

were born lucky, Velten. Europe's dying—in Vincennes and Warsaw. At the execution post and under the Cossack fists that clutch at tender women's throats. Europe's dying. Under the hail of bombs on Hamburg and Cassel. Under the crash of V-2s on the English coast. Europe's dying—and lucky Victor Velten goes on weaving through it all—from France to Wołyń, from the Rokitno Marshes to the Vistula, from the Vistula to the Spree and—unless I'm a very bad prophet—from there to the Elbe and perhaps even to the Rhine. . . ."

Velten lowered his hands from his face and looked at the speaker uncomprehendingly. Cismar smiled his enigmatical smile.

"I'm not trying to be unkind to you, Victor," he said with a quiet urgency. "I think I sized you up during our talks in Paris and Captain Hacketanz's barrack-room. You haven't the strength to make the big decision. You'll be among the survivors. Your case'll never be tried in court. It'll be dropped from want of evidence. Just as when they call off bankruptcy proceedings because there's no estate! I'm not familiar enough with all that legalistic jargon of yours. But I think I can read into your soul. You're too clever, Victor. First an interpreter, then a machine-gunner, then a driver— but always on the periphery of decision. What will you fellows do now, when we've all gone to the devil—you left-overs, you inconvertible assets from the estate of Europe's bankruptcy?"

He stopped. From outside, where the horde of SS were assembling, came more raucous singing. It was a students' song from the Quartier Latin, so shameless that even the proverbial innkeeper's wife of German university fame would have blushed like a maid at her first communion.

Cismar crooned the last line to himself:

"Les morpions rougeâtres sur les fumiers de leurs aïeux."

Then he began afresh in his soft, unsparing voice:

"Goddam red crabs on their ancestral dung-heap!—Do you see how Europe is dying, as surely as wherever else the hoof-beats of the Riders of the Apocalypse are heard? But," he went on almost tenderly, "have no fear, little bloodsucker at the shame-spots of our dying Europe: crabs don't get put on trial! There's a gray ointment against crabs! This time that gray ointment's wearing khaki uniform. . . ."

276

Only now did Velten realize that Cismar was delirious. Large beads of sweat stood out on his pale brow. His gray eyes were veiled and the pupils had narrowed down to pin-points. His breathing was irregular and barely stirred the brown blanket over his chest.

"The man's dying!" Velten yelled to the orderlies who were just coming in to fetch the stretchers.

"Not yet he isn't," grinned one of them. "We're taking him to the general hospital in Blonie. Plenty of room for dying there."

Velten walked beside the stretcher as it was carried outside.

"Listen to me, Victor," the dying man croaked. "Warsaw's dead. Europe's dying horribly—like me—Warsaw's—quite still—like a town of the dead. Up above is Ivan—not lifting a finger . . . Death is tired . . . or is he dead? . . . But I swear to you: he'll come back and sweep his scythe over all this ridiculous mechanical death . . . a proper scythe from God's own workshop . . . Death is dead . . . long live Death!"

Velten stood by the ambulance as they lifted the man up, raging in his fever. Raising himself as far as his crushed bones would permit, Cismar made a feeble gesture with his right hand.

"La mort est morte. Vive la mort!" he cried with all his remaining strength. Then his head fell back.

From the gloom inside the ambulance came a shrill peal of laughter.

"Just think, little crab," the SS man called, "this time the gray ointment's wearing khaki uniforms!"

One of the orderlies gave the door a violent slam, and the column lumbered slowly away into the fading evening.

CHAPTER IV

THE BULLION party reached Breslau in the afternoon. Having dragged the chests out of the station building into the square out in front, they found that the truck supposed to be meeting them had not arrived. In the end the lieutenant stopped an empty truck.

They took the chests straight to the Reichsbank. Though it was long past closing time, the staff was expecting them, and before long the lieutenant was able to dismiss them.

They separated at the station, since each man was going in a different direction. Velten took a slow train that traveled all night and stopped at every little station. But it got him to Berlin by morning.

This time his uniform flew down the cellar steps even faster than the last. With obvious gusto Janka, the Polish maid, pitched it into a corner from which Velten did not recover it till the end of his leave. Although the private soldier was not permitted to run around in civilian clothes while on furlough, Velten would rather have been arrested than show himself in the city in the garb of the *Barras*.

And Berlin, that rugged accumulation of stone and brick—she, too, was home! Not bedded in the creative environment of a colonized river bank like bitter-sweet Vienna, sad-rhapsodic Buda-pest, proud-playful Dresden or tender-doughty Paris, she drew her form and being from the masses which crowded into her from without. Just like the Madrid which self-willed monarchs had planted in the barren wastes of the Castilian plain, this city of Berlin had grown up quite inconsequently among the watercourses, marshes and forests of Brandenburg. Her real face had been molded not so much by the balmy charm of the surrounding lakes and woodlands as by the living will of her inhabitants, a vital race

278

of city-dwellers of broad-minded outlook and nervous drive. Theirs were the will and spirit which gave Berlin her life and color.

Such was the Berlin that Velten had known in his youth—and such was the Berlin whose magic he now sought once more in the days of that last, unexpected furlough. He sought in vain. With whole districts still untouched by the murderous war from the air, with factory chimneys and furnaces still breathing forth their smoke, and with the rustle of tree tops still audible in the Tiergarten, no one could foresee the agonizing death this city was fated to die. And yet the son who had now become her guest could sense the poison already in her veins. The people—those people without whom Berlin would not have been what she was—were changed: they went about their daily affairs like automatons harnessed to the burdens and drudgery of total war. They had become cogs and levers, driven by a gigantic, soulless motor which controlled their every movement. Hitler had slain the spirit and soul of this city long before the day when her twitching body was to perish in the flames of final ruin. Only at home did Velten catch a few sad vestiges of the abundant life of long ago.

Gaby was somehow dissatisfied that her husband should have become a driver. "What do you imagine a driver is then?" Velten asked in astonishment. "I'm in better company than I was with the Zorn mob."

And he went on to tell of the helpful good-natured men who had become his comrades—tough, rugged characters whose job in civil life was to drive trucks and trailers from Dresden to Munich and from Berlin to Cologne. They were the motor transport pool's main scroungers, and things would have had to reach a pretty pass for them not to have something drinkable to hand. In the Zyrardow school building where the pool was quartered their room was next to Velten's. Many was the nights' sleep lost through their noisy celebrations. The patronage of the sergeant prevented the orderly corporal from taking action, and no one could be cross with them when for the tenth time, to the accompaniment of Johann Kieswetter's accordion, they warbled through the refrain:

> Mamatschi, schenk' mir ein Pferdchen!
> Ein Pferdchen wär' mein Paradies!

279

Then there was Max Dotterweich, a fly Saxon from Chemnitz who had put up with much leg-pulling and mockery on account of his unusual name. Though probably a better scrounger than the men who drove the heavy trucks, he was too proud to give the sergeant and office staff a rake-off and had to suffer accordingly. He had a "Mule" to drive—the only one in the unit. A Mule was an Opel Blitz with caterpillar tracks, a constructional fiasco which was perpetually going wrong.

Another who had caught Velten's attention was a slim fellow with a mane of flowing blond hair, graceful wrists and well-kept hands who managed an enormous troop-transporter, a Kom. He spoke pure High German without the least trace of a local accent and was treated with a certain deference by the men.

"What are you in civil life?" Velten was once curious enough to ask.

"Bus-driver in Dresden," the other replied laconically.

Later Velten found that Lance-Corporal Kurt Kleinfeld had been an actor. In the hard times after the inflation he had left the stage and turned truck-driver, and now he and his pretty blonde wife lived a quiet, contented life in a delightful little cottage of which he would often hand round touching pictures. His motto was the concluding line of Voltaire's *Candide:* "Let us go into the garden to work and reap our happiness."

In his own introvert fashion Kleinfeld actually seemed to hate army life even more than Velten. If Kessler bellowed at him on a vehicle inspection, Kleinfeld would simply smile gently and reply: "When anyone shouts like that I can't understand a word." The captain's only reaction then would be to make a coarse joke and turn away in embarrassment.

"How the devil do you get away with it?" Velten asked in amazement.

"I've been in the game too long," Kleinfeld told him quietly. "One gets to see and hear too much for them to be able to do anything about it."

"And believe it or not," said Velten, "I've met Kracht. One Sunday morning they lined us up in a square to give the Chief-of-Staff a send-off. He'd been promoted and given a command. There was a speech for him and another for the new one—and a triple Sieg

Heil for the Führer. When we'd been dismissed I heard someone chatting with the Luftwaffe girls in broad Berlinerisch. I was sure I knew the voice and went through the crowd after it. And there he was—Kracht in the full splendor of a first-lieutenant!"

They had been undergraduates together and later colleagues at the Moabit criminal court. In 1933 their ways had parted sharply. Velten had moved to the other side of the fence. Kracht, a talented and extremely ambitious lawyer, had soon mounted the ladder to a senior ministerial post. The brown uniform, into which he had willingly flung himself, had been no hindrance to him in this respect. For all that, he had continued to show respect for his old colleague and sometimes even comradeship.

Now he greeted Velten, the private soldier, with boisterous delight and invited him to coffee that same afternoon. A telephone call to Kessler secured his release from duty.

"Well, Velten," said Kracht, when they were sitting in the office he occupied as a member of the intelligence branch, "do you realize we're done for?"

"Whom are you telling that to, Herr von Kracht?" Velten returned—he had dropped the Herr Oberleutnant from the start. "I knew that in 1933."

"Oh God," said Kracht in tormented tones. "We all worked for the best! When I and thousands like me went into it in thirty-three we all honestly believed we could guide the thing into decent channels. We were the famous second rank. We took over from the hooligans, the underworld toughs. At one time it really looked as if everything would turn out all right. You yourself know the sort of things I did."

He reminded Velten of one or two cases in which they had both been involved and he—from the other side of the fence—had shown courage and decency.

"It wasn't till this accursed war started that we saw we were ruled by a criminal lunatic!"

God, thought Velten, this was pretty strong talk! This had nothing to do with cheap opportunism of keeping in with a man from the other side when things went badly. This was honest-to-goodness, despairing repentance.

Kracht took him over to the wall-map, explained the course of

281

events over the last few months and showed how senseless orders from "that criminal lunatic" to stand and fight had again and again led to catastrophe and enormous losses in men and material.

"And if Rokossowski only had any drive," said Kracht, "he'd have gone straight through to Berlin in July. There wasn't a damn thing to stop him."

"What actually happened to the superior knowledge and courage of the generals," Velten asked, "when the madman gave his senseless orders? Did he give them to us privates or to you? Were you leading us or was it Herr Hitler in person?"

It was three weeks after July 20th. Kracht's reply came back pat: "But you've seen for yourself that nothing could be done! He's got the people behind him. You can't make a revolution when the enemy's on the threshold of the Fatherland."

The people, Velten thought. He had experienced July 20th under curious circumstances. On the way back from their first trip to Warsaw he and Fritz Erlenbach had come to an East Prussian village lying peacefully in the evening sunshine amid orchards and fields of harvest-ripe corn. The sign outside one farmhouse identified its occupier as the *Ortsbauernführer,* the head of the local farmers' league. On their request for a night's lodging the man had amicably taken them in and invited them to supper. His fair-haired daughter had served them with enormous rounds of home-baked bread covered with ham and sausage.

"Didn't you know," the man asked—and only now did they notice his feverish excitement—"didn't you know about the Führer? He's been assassinated! They've set up a military dictatorship in Berlin! The whole village is full of the news. It's a terrible pity my radio is out of order. No hope of getting a tube."

It surprised Velten how unmoved he was by the news. This seemed to him to be the natural outcome of the collapse he had witnessed.

"What will it mean?" asked the farmer.

"It'll mean," Velten replied slowly, as Erlenbach remained speechless with amazement, "that there'll be peace."

"Man of God," said the *Ortsbauernführer*, "that would be good!"

"Yes, it'd be good all right," said Velten.

"It certainly would," Fritz Erlenbach now agreed.

282

Velten remembered rumors that had gone around Paris in the late summer of 1943. Hitler was to be removed, people had said. Then the way would at least be open for a separate peace with one side or the other. Did this mean they had now reached that stage?

"I wonder how we're going to get home now, Fritz?"

"Ah! I was just wondering the same thing myself."

"Anyway, there are great things before us," the farmer averred as he conducted them to their barn. They bedded down in the soft straw, after promising not to strike any matches.

In the middle of the night the farmer woke them up. "I've been down the village," he reported eagerly. "The Führer's alive! I've heard him speaking on the radio myself! He was saved by a miracle. Now he'll give those traitors what they deserve and lead us to Final Victory! Thank God!"

"Thank God," said Fritz Erlenbach.

"Thank God," said Velten, if only to remain in the picture.

Then the *Ortsbauernführer* told them that the Special Court in Allenstein had sentenced a woman to nine months' imprisonment for the infamous assertion that the Russians would get into East Prussia.

When they drove into Arys they met Capt. Kessler coming along the village street. They stopped, jumped out and saluted by raising their hands to their caps. The sight of it drew a bellow of laughter from their commander.

"You louts don't know the right way to salute!"

What had happened? The Wehrmacht as proof of its bond with the Führer had put forward the fervent plea that it should in future be allowed to use the raised arm as its only form of salute. The Führer had been pleased to consent. Or so the Order of the Day put it.

"Yes, the people," said Velten to Kracht. "Propaganda and terror. Stupidity and fear."

Velten learned that officers on the staff of the Central Army Group had played a leading role in the events of July 20th. And this was none other than the staff with which he had blitzkrieged in France. Kracht put through a call for him to a lieutenant at Army Group who had still been a sergeant in those days. Part of the staff were no longer there—no longer officers either, for that matter.

What a far cry from the castle library at Serrant, over Russia's corpse-strewn fields into the cellars of the Prinz-Albrecht-Strasse! Couldn't you have made it cheaper than that, you clay-pigeon shooters of Serrant? You, the leaders, and we who were led?

"You can count on me, Velten," Kracht had told him as they said goodbye. "We must stick together when the end comes."

They had been in Zyrardow when the Western Front collapsed. Every day the troops discussed the impending end, forging thousands of plans for the journey home. Everyone saw what difficulties they must face when surrounded by Polish territory seething with insurrection. They talked of driving home in armed columns, of pitched battles and even of fraternization with the insurgents. But everything remained quiet. There was no collapse, and soon everything had resumed its daily course. They did vehicle maintenance, cleaned weapons, dug slit trenches and filled them in again—all the thinks covered by what the Army called the "occupation theory."

It was a bitter feeling for Velten to take leave of his home again. Every day of the rapidly expiring furlough had been spent in the irrational hope that the collapse would come while he was still there. It did not come. The war went on, and with it the despotic domination of every aspect of life.

So he hauled his uniform out of the cellar, climbed into a train amid the rubble of the Schlesischer Banhof and one wintry morning reported back in the office of the Army Headquarters Motor Transport Pool in Zyrardow's school building. The same evening Hans Arend arrived from Skierniewice on a bus.

CHAPTER V

IN MID-DECEMBER the headquarters moved from Zyrardow to Spala, the old hunting seat where Fat Boy Hermann had been the guest of Marshal Pilsudski. The pool did not, of course, move into the precincts of the castle but was quartered in a miserable nearby village, named Krolowska Wola.

The unit went by rail, which entailed the grim task of loading the vehicles onto flatcars. The men cursed as they worked in the icy cold to secure them with ropes and chocks—merely to save a few hundred gallons of gasoline! And all the time the pool had an unofficial stock of 4000 gallons, secretly "organized" and hoarded. It had to be hidden from the snooping noses of the commissariat, and every time the unit moved to a new location they buried the heavy drums in the ground and painstakingly camouflaged the spot by replacing the turf. Not one of them breathed a word, for each man recognized the fuel as a communal asset which would be their salvation when things became really bad. In addition to this, every driver had at least one jerry-can of "black" gas as well as his full tank and the prescribed number of reserve cans. He carefully concealed it in the bushes on every fuel inspection.

Officially, however, gasoline was short, and the unit duly moved by rail. Velten sat in his Mercedes 170 V, which he had now been driving for some time, on a flatcar. It was freezing hard, and although he wore felt boots and a lined overcoat he felt the cold dreadfully.

He was glad to have rid himself of his Kfz 11, in whose draughty cab he would have felt colder still. The pool had used the peaceful weeks in Zyrardow to switch the entire passenger vehicle park over to Mercedes 170 V's.

It was dark when they steamed into Spala station. The unloading operation was a long one, and by the time the last of them reached the village it was just on midnight. Once again their quarters was the school: an old building with cracking, whitewashed walls.

In face of what appeared to be a most precarious supply-situation, many people had worries which would have befitted more auspicious circumstances. One day Velten was summoned to the office. The chief clerk, Cpl. Weyermann, a manufacturer from a small town on the Sudetenland border of Saxony, received him with his usual smiling mixture of good humor and irony.

"You're a lucky fellow, Velten," he said patronizingly. "You're going to Cracow tomorrow to get some stuff."

285

"But I know nothing about spare parts," protested Velten in surprise.

"Nobody said anything about spares. You're to buy canvas and upholstery materials."

"For cars?" Velten asked.

"No," Weyermann grinned. "For a special train."

"What?" stuttered Velten completely dumbfounded.

"That's it. The Company's building the Army Commander a special train. Ivan bagged the other one at Bobruisk."

"A special train," Velten mused. "Apart from that you've no troubles, I suppose?"

The other declined to argue further. "Here are your papers. You're traveling by train. You and Krause. Gasoline is too short to go by road."

The next morning a dispatch-rider took them to Tomaszow railway station on his motorcycle combination. There they boarded an express which whisked them off to Cracow.

Lance-Corporal Krause was a quiet, friendly man. Like Velten he was looking forward to the strange city and a breather away from his unit. One more holiday trip, thought Velten guiltily.

At Cracow's main station a soldier on the rail transportation staff pressed a printed card into their hands. It bore various useful addresses—the enlisted men's recreation center, an army movie and transit accommodation for troops. On one side were the words "Officers' brothel: General-v.-Litzmannstr. 28." On the other "Soldier's brothel: Veilchenstr. 45."

"Must be a peak period for tourists," said Velten.

They found the way to the transit hotel and were given beds in the big barrack-room. After impressing on them what time soldiers were supposed to be off the streets, the reception clerk showed them the bell by which they could obtain admittance in the early hours.

"Quite a well-run hotel," Velten remarked. "And now let's eat."

They had already agreed not to eat in the recreation center. Near their lodging they found a good restaurant in a busy main street where, after handing the waiter a pack of cigarettes in lieu of ration cards, they each received a crisply fried pork chop.

Over the way, on the street corner, was the army movie. Outside was an enormous, iridescent poster depicting the film's seductive

286

leading lady and bearing the alluring title "Woman of My Dreams."

It turned out that before becoming a famous star and the owner of a fashionable villa and a high-powered car this goddess of the screen had been a poor flower-girl. Standing on a bridge at night-time with her basket by her side, dispensing oomph from denuded legs and swinging hips, she had sung a catchy little song in a hard foreign accent:

> There never was a girl
> On a cold, dark night
> Who liked to be alo-hone . . .

And after she had progressed to a world of glittering luxury, she crooned:

> Don't look to your right,
> Don't look to your left,
> Just look straight ahead:
> And whatever bad luck should come your way
> Never let a tear be shed. . . .

Astonishing fatalism after all that good fortune, Velten reflected.

"Well," he said to Krause when they had sat through this ersatz dream, "off we go to the Veilchenstrasse to seek the women of *our* dreams!"

The magical phrase "Soldier's brothel" had caught his fancy. He did not want to miss the chance of seeing something he knew only from the literature of the First World War.

Next day they were able to obtain their canvas and upholstery, and in due course, weighed down like mules, they arrived back in Krolowska Wola.

Velten's precaution of placing a second order proved superfluous, for only a few days later Kessler sent them both off again. This time it was the Commander-in-Chief of the Southern Army Group who wanted a special train.

On these two trips Velten earned a reputation as a "procurement man" almost as great as that of Erlenbach, the spare-parts specialist. What a difference from the first few weeks in Zyrardow, when he had gone in continuous fear of a transfer back to the Zorn mob!

287

His mind had finally been put at rest by an order that all personnel changes between units arising from the "troop movements of July/August 1944" were to be regarded as permanent. These troop movements, incidentally, had involved the loss of two armies in the central sector alone.

Velten would probably have gone to Cracow a third time, but this was not to be. After approximately half a year's breathing space, world history took a hand again. In doing so it showed so little respect as to prevent the completion of the Army and Army Group Commanders' special trains.

CHAPTER VI

As FAR BACK as summer 1944 Russia had forced two bridgeheads on the west bank of the Vistula. One lay between Warka and Gora Kalwarja, to the south of Warsaw. The other was even farther south, at Baranow. Nothing had been able to stop Ivan firmly digging himself in at these two spots—not even the hasty transfer of the Viking Division of Waffen-SS from Hungary. According to Kracht, the Germans' own intelligence reports showed the bridgeheads to be jammed full of men and equipment.

One of the greatest revelations of army mentality to Velten was the stupid indifference with which the daily round of military routine still went on—despite the ominous state of the war, despite the presence of the enemy on Germany's frontiers in East and West, despite the fatherland's progressive destruction under a ceaseless pounding from the air. Indeed, one gained the impression that the proximity of danger and the hopelessness of the overall situation had evoked a mood of defiance in which the broad mass of soldiery simply refused to believe their eyes or ears. They went about their duties and "organized" what there was to be had, completely absorbed in the futility of their day-to-day existence. All the talk of an imminent collapse at the time of the retreat from France had long given way to discussions on the supposedly precarious position of . . . the Russians. This "whisper-propaganda"—most of it skillfully projected by the National Socialist leadership officers—told of acute contradictions in the enemy camp and an impending rupture between the Soviet Union and the West. It pointed out, moreover, that with his supply lines now as long as Germany's had been, Ivan would henceforth be at the mercy of Polish and Ukrainian partisans. Even the special trains were regarded as a reassuring sign, the argument being that their construction would never have been ordered if the situation were really so hopeless.

What lay behind all this was quite simply fear—a titanic, all-pervading fear which robbed men of every sense of reason or proportion. It was no longer a matter of fighting for some strip of alien territory in Asia or Eastern Europe. It was no longer a case of retreating into the limitless expanses of the Russian hinterland. It was the German homeland that was threatened now—and with it one's family, possessions and existence. For every man harbored the gnawing dread that the enemy was going to fight this Total War to a total end.

It was the middle of January when it started. The pickets stood side by side that night, tensely listening to the endless thunder of enemy artillery borne to their ears on the clear, frosty air.

On January 14th the first truck-loads of wounded made a short halt in the Krolowska Wola school-building. They were tattered, emaciated figures, these men who came to warm themselves at the big barrack-room stove. Many of the first-aid dressings round their heads and limbs were saturated with blood.

"Will the front hold?" a member of the motor pool asked them.

"Front, front, front! I keep hearing the word 'front'!" grunted a haggard infantryman who was avidly gulping hot coffee. "Every hundred yards or so we've got a hole in the ground with three men and an LMG in it. That's the front! And Ivan's plastering it with his artillery!"

"See that you get to the rear as soon as you can," one of the casualties called back as they mounted the trucks again. "We've had it. We've had a bellyful."

On the 16th of the month the pool was warned to prepare to

move. The heavy column of workshop vehicles had left during the night. Velten was detailed to drive for staff intelligence branch.

By the time he reported to the staff in Spala there was hardly anyone left. Von Kracht was already away. In the intelligence office, where the clerks were packing up the last of the files, he learned he was to drive the G1(I) himself, who would be the last to leave.

Velten parked his vehicle under a wall and waited, watching the maze of buildings round the old castle slowly empty. Soon he was alone. By two o'clock he was ravenous with hunger. Going into the big, deserted cookhouse, he found there was still noodle soup steaming in the cauldrons and large chunks of cold beef on a table. He took out his knife and carefully sliced off strips of the fatty meat, which he then chopped up into little cubes. These he threw into his mess tin and covered over with boiling hot soup. After the meal he felt better fortified against the cold and the cutting wind from the east.

Gradually the fire of the guns and the Red tanks drew closer. Bombs dropped somewhere nearby, causing the ground to tremble beneath his feet. Only when things were becoming uncomfortably hot did the G1(I) appear—a youthful lieutenant-colonel with an Austrian accent. The only luggage he and the second-lieutenant behind him carried were dispatch-cases. They climbed in hurriedly.

"Off you go!" said the colonel. "Drive as fast as you can! I'll guide you—you obviously won't know the way."

The moment they reached the main road they found themselves inextricably jammed in a tangle of fleeing vehicles. Although the colonel got out and ran forward to make room for them, the drive to Tomaszow took them almost an hour.

As they drove through the streets of Tomaszow Velten's heart missed a beat: wounded troops lay in rows along the snow-heaped pavements. "Take us along! Take us along!" they cried beseechingly, raising the stumps of what had been arms and legs.

"Christ!" the colonel muttered. "The same damn shambles all over again. They've evacuated the field hospitals and put the casualties out on the streets!"

After Tomaszow the going was easier. As the colonel picked out the route along silent by-roads, it became dark and misty. Though

290

his headlights were correctly blacked out, Velten was not allowed to switch them on and had no choice but to crawl along in third gear.

At last they came to Litzmannstadt, as Lodz was called under the Government-General. It made an almost peacetime impression. There was plenty of traffic in the streets, including trams, as they drove through to the northerly suburb of Görnau. Its Polish name had been Zgierz.

A few hundred yards past the market place the colonel made Velten turn off to the left into a large group of buildings. It was a modern barracks.

On reporting to the headquarters orderly room, Velten found that the Pool was stationed in a small village four miles to the north. He arrived there about midnight. Pickets were tramping back and forth, Krause among them.

"Where's the office? Where are the quarters?" Velten demanded.

"Listen," Krause told him, "this isn't the same sort of hotel set-up as we had in Cracow. You'll have to find your own bunk. Just march into the first hut you come to and bog down as you are."

At this point they were joined by Gräfe, a rather uncouth fellow who spoke the appalling dialect of the Halle region. He had just trundled in with his charcoal-burner and was swearing luridly.

"I can't rake the sod out tonight," he announced crossly. "It'll be just too bad if I can't get it going again in the morning. Do you think we'll be here for the winter?"

Velten avoided answering the question. "Come on, let's find somewhere to shake down!" he said. He shook the door of one lowly dwelling: it was barred. Then he hammered on it with the butt of his carbine. At last shuffling steps approached and the bolts were pushed back. In the light of his flashlight he could see an old woman wearing a cloth round her head and wrapped in a shawl.

"We sleep here—sleep?" Velten asked her, raising one hand symbolically to his cheek. But she spoke German—remarkably purely, with the slightly sing-song intonation of the East.

"The parlor's full of soldiers," she said. "But if you're not afraid of us you can share the kitchen with my daughter and me."

In one corner was a wretched couch. The old girl huddled down on it with another female who was covered by a sheepskin but for

291

the tip of her nose. The two soldiers spread their thick driving coats out round the hearth and lay down.

"Oh dear, oh dear," the old woman wailed. "We're Bessarabian Germans they brought here in 1940. We had a lovely farm back at home. They threw the Poles out of here to make room for us. What will they do with us if the Russians come? Will you be able to hold them?"

They were silent. "Not by the look of it," said Velten at length.

Gräfe rounded on him then. "Don't talk such hogwash!" he growled in his boorish way. " 'Course we'll hold them. It'd be a fine mess if we couldn't!"

"Pray God you can!" sighed the old woman.

Velten preferred to say nothing. In Zyrardow Gräfe had lamented louder than anyone about what would happen to his wife and children and the little cottage he had built with the help of his comrades in the Party storm troops. Even then he had realized the war was lost. Today, with the icy hand of fear at his throat, he refused to believe that Ivan could not be held.

The next morning, while on his way to the office to see what he could find out about the battle, Velten ran into Cpl. Kratochvil.

"Just the man I want!" he cried. "You can come along to Litzmannstadt to haul a load of coal. We're going into winter quarters here."

"See?" said Gräfe. "Ivan's been stopped." He himself succeeded in evading the coal detail on the grounds that he must attend to his charcoal-burner.

Shortly afterward Velten was sitting in the back of the truck with five others, en route for the city. They shoveled the vehicle full of coal at a big dump by the station, taking their time about it after the usual fashion of soldiers. Then, having had a meal at the recreation center, they idled around the streets for a while. As they drove home in the early evening, they passed a jumbled heap of ruins.

"That was the ghetto," one man remarked. "There's still supposed to be a few Jews living under that lot, hiding in the cellars like rats."

Between Görnau and the village some of their own vehicles

292

flashed past them, heading in the direction from which they had just come.

"Step on it," Velten told their driver. "I don't like the look of this."

In the village pandemonium reigned. Most of the vehicles had their engines running, and others were driving off in wild haste. Amidst it all stood Cpl. Kratochvil.

"*Alarm!*" he yelled. "You can leave that goddam coal-cart where it is! Get into your own vehicles and push off right away to Görnau and report to the chief!"

In Görnau, too, Velten met motor pool vehicles coming out of the barracks gate. He found Capt. Kessler and Cpl. Weyermann in one of the offices, wearing equipment over their overcoats. There was a map on the table in front of them.

"Get along to staff," boomed Kessler, "and pick up as many men as you can carry. Here, take a look at the map. The headquarters rendezvous is in Lask. Turn right outside the barracks and drive straight to the market square. Follow the signposts from then on. Jesus, aren't you there yet?"

Outside the intelligence offices Velten found a *Sonderführer* and an ensign, surrounded by piles of luggage and supplies.

"Private Velten reporting as driver," he announced.

"All right, get the stuff in quickly," said the *Sonderführer*. "No lights, remember!"

"I know," Velten growled back.

He loathed the uncertainty of these night drives. Just as he came through the gates and was about to turn off to the right in accordance with instructions, he pressed hard on his brakes. The car skidded slightly on the slippery surface and came to a stop.

Sounds of battle were coming from the market place—tank guns and the chatter of automatic weapons. The grinding of caterpillar tracks, frenzied cries and the ugly crunch of splintering metal added to the uproar.

"That's him!" screamed the ensign. "He's already here! I goddam well knew it! He's cut straight across our convoy! Turn off to the left and drive like hell!"

Velten was already turning. Others were racing past them in

293

headlong flight. When they had put a few miles between themselves and the town he learned from his passengers that one of the enemy's armored spearheads had broken through. It would probably be wiped out, but the only thing the headquarters could do in the meantime was to beat it. But how were they to rendezvous at Lask?

It turned out to be an odd sort of journey that night. They never reached Lask. Now and again they would meet a vehicle from Army and pick up every conceivable rumor in the process. Some of the transport had gone straight through Kutno, heading for Poznań. Many maintained that the Red tanks in Görnau had put the main body of the headquarters in the bag. It was also claimed that the Russians had reached Lask. At length a pale moon rose, casting a weird, misty light over the landscape, and at about four in the morning they arrived in Turek, a neat-looking little country town. They rang the night bell of a modern hospital, and the sisters made up beds for them in an absent doctor's room. After a few wonderful hours of sleep they were served with rolls, honey and tea.

Then they drove to Sieradz. They found no trace of Army Headquarters. Sieradz, a large country town, had been completely cleared of civilians but was now teeming with stragglers. In the kitchen of the Hotel Posener Hof on the market square, officers and enlisted men crowded round a big pan full of hunks of meat. Irrespective of rank, each man piled in and stuffed what he could find into his mouth. Velten did not join them. He had plenty of food in the car —yet another advantage of a driver's life!

Nearby a mob of howling troops had gathered around the entrance to a big yard. The gate was barred by a second-lieutenant and two privates, their machine-pistols at the hip. "I'm warning you!" the officer shouted. "Any man who comes a step nearer will get a round in his belly!"

It was a schnapps factory. In the yard soldiers were busy tipping large barrels over and letting the coveted liquid flow away down the drains. Neither was this the only gratifying sign of order and discipline. At the station soldiers were distributing bread from a freight car to a line of troops. Velten stowed ten loaves into his luggage compartment and then filled up with gasoline at a pump. There, too, the vital fluid was being distributed in an orderly manner under the supervision of an officer. It was here they heard that elements of the headquarters were in Turek. They resolved to drive back. The countryside looked utterly lifeless under the white winding-sheet of snow. At intervals a headquarters vehicle would pass them. Of civil population there was not the slightest trace.

Towards evening, in a haze of drifting snowflakes, they overtook a group of Hitler Maidens trudging towards Warta in Indian file. They numbered perhaps a dozen in all, aged between eight and fourteen. The babies marched in front and the eldest brought up the rear, there being no grown-up leader in charge. With the rucksacks under their russet cloaks and the pointed hoods from which brown and blonde pigtails hung, they looked for all the world like little hunchbacked pixies. On they stumbled into the gathering evening—a brave, forlorn, heart-rending picture of the youth their Führer had betrayed.

In Turek they actually found a number of vehicles from the Motor Pool. Capt. Kessler was also there. Twenty-Ninth Army Headquarters seemed to have scattered like a flock of sheep struck by lightning. The losses on the Görnau market square had been slight, most of the headquarters personnel having been able to quit their vehicles when they saw the tanks coming. After that the T 34s had split the trucks and cars open like sardine-tins. As it later turned out, only one man—an Alsatian—had been lost.

At last the order was given to concentrate in Kalisz. They remained there for two or three days, sleeping in the town hall. Velten shook down under the grand piano in one corner. Gradually the headquarters came up to strength again, but the Army Commander did not return. The Führer had had him relieved because his staff had been out of action for several days after the hectic chase out of Görnau. The rank-and-file found it unfair that the Army Commander should have to take the rap, but lost no sleep over the change.

Shortly after the appointment of the new Army Commander, General Bessemer, the new chief paid them a pep visit. Toni Pfleiderer, one of the Army Commander's drivers, a friendly lad from Vienna, met him at the airfield. He came back badly shaken.

"God," he said, "that guy Bessemer's hot stuff! Jumps out of the car and sees two of the boys standing there with cigarettes in their faces. He goes across to them in one bound and then—whiz, bang —gives both of 'em a smack over the kisser that sends the cigarettes flying. Then he sees a young major standing there—a chap from the Signals, I think. 'What are you doing here?' he yells. 'You're posted to the front. Give your particulars to my Aide!' Then he turns round. 'Gentlemen,' he says, 'we're fighting an Asiatic war!'—Nice outlook, isn't it?" concluded Toni, with a sigh.

"And he's an Austrian like you, Toni," someone remarked. "What's it going to be like when the Prussians start on us?"

Velten himself had a nasty experience with the Austrians while they were in Kalisz. Being attached to staff intelligence as a driver, he would often fill in his time in the intelligence office and chat to a young corporal who was a draftsman there and—as Velten thought—an affable Viennese.

"I say, Wastler," Velten murmured confidentially, "how are we going to get home when the war's lost?"

Then he stood there, thunderstruck. The other had sprung up from his drawing-board with a face as red as a beet.

"Are you out of your mind, man? I won't hear that kind of talk! A remark like that can cost you your head!"

He became calmer. "If I didn't know you were friendly with Lieutenant von Kracht . . . You know perfectly well that this war will be won—it's *got* to be won, do you hear? We're making this stand for Europe. The war's going to be won! Not another word— or else . . . !"

Later the sergeant running the clerical side of the office, a quiet, prudent Saxon who was chief clerk to a Dresden lawyer in civil life, gave Velten a warning. "Watch your step with that guy Wastler. He's hot stuff. Hitler Youth leader and as fanatical as they make 'em. A terrific draftsman, all the same."

When they left Kalisz en route for Krotoszyn, Velten found that, together with a pile of files and maps, he had to drive, of all people, Sgt. Bärmann and Cpl. Wastler. They belonged to the rear party, and dusk was already falling by the time they left the town. They moved in convoy, the G1(I) leading in a *Kübelwagen*, then a string of trucks and staff cars, and finally Velten at the end.

The G1(I)'s car, a vehicle designed for cross-country work, led the way down side-roads and straight over fields that were frozen

296

hard. Time and again Velten was amazed to find what a performance a normal civilian vehicle like his own could put up.

Soon the pace increased. Through the misty night a dull rumble became audible from their rear and flanks. Tank guns.

"That's Ivan again," said Bärmann. "He doesn't give us a moment's break, does he?"

Suddenly Velten found that he had lost touch with the vehicle in front in the mist. He had missed it at some cross-roads or other.

"How damned silly to put a fast car like that in the lead!" he said. Privately he was aware that his lack of experience was partly to blame—though the speed had been pretty terrific, all the same. He was to learn later from the leading driver that the G1(I) had begun forcing the pace the moment the bombardment started.

"Well, Wastler," said the sergeant, "this is your chance to show us what you can do!"

The corporal took out a map and hung his flashlight on his overcoat. Then he opened the door and stepped out onto the running-board to give Velten instructions. His reputation as a first-class topographer proved fully justified. He was able to guide them so accurately by his map and compass that they reached Krotoszyn a quarter of an hour ahead of the column.

They found the vehicles of the Motor Pool strung out in a long row under the snow-laden trees of a boulevard, their engines droning noisily. But when Velten drew up and went over to one truck to inquire about quarters, the somnolent figure of the driver almost toppled from his seat as the door opened. His white face and sunken eyes showed he was sleeping the sleep of exhaustion. The few words he murmured were incomprehensible.

At length they found the quarters, and soon after that their lost column drove in.

When Velten reported to the Pool, Weyermann had a fresh job for him.

"Turn in as fast as you can," the corporal told him. "You're taking a courier to Breslau at six tomorrow morning."

"I like 'tomorrow morning,'" said Velten, "it's already half past three now!"

"Just thank your stars you're off to the rear," said Weyermann. "The devil alone knows how far Ivan will chase us yet. Collect your documents at 0600 and then report to the office. You're driving a Major Rassberg from the Staff. He's the G2(I) of 40 Panzer Corps. Landed with us as a straggler. He's getting map materials and situation reports from Army Group. No one here's got any idea what's going on."

Velten lay down to sleep on the floor of the Intelligence office. They were in a comfortable country residence, and the carpet was warm and soft.

CHAPTER VII

WHEN Velten reported himself ready to move off two hours later, the major was already waiting in the office. He was a callow, pasty-faced youth with a pointed nose, looking slightly ridiculous in riding-breeches with exaggerated wings and a broad crimson stripe. He might have been in his middle twenties.

"Do you know the route?" he asked Velten as he took his seat beside him.

"No idea," answered Velten curtly. His first look had told him he wasn't going to like this young man.

"That means I shall have to guide you," the major announced importantly. "There are Bolshevik tanks everywhere. There's no question of using the main roads. I'll take you across country."

Thereupon he brought out a map and a flashlight and started conning the route, compelling Velten to drive over bone-shaking causeways and farm tracks, across fields and through snowed-up villages.

"I only hope to God Ivan doesn't catch us," he said for the hundredth time. When at long last it dawned on Velten just how badly rattled this youngster was, he tried by dint of gentle persuasion to communicate to him some of the calm with which he, to his own surprise, was now filled.

298

"Oh, don't talk such poppycock," exclaimed the young man in irritated tones. "You haven't got the foggiest idea how dangerous the position is."

Finally he refused to let the driver talk at all. "Be quiet," he snapped, endeavoring to conceal his fear beneath a haughty accent. "I hope I can judge the situation better than you!"

No officer on Velten's own headquarters had ever spoken to him like that. He pressed his lips together and held his peace. After all, he hadn't been engaged as the brat's wet nurse.

About eleven o'clock they came out onto the main highway. Velten pulled up at the cross-roads and pointed to the signpost.

"Herr Major," he said, in as patient a tone as he could muster, "we've now been driving for five hours and we're seven miles away from Krotoszyn. Just when do you want to get to Breslau?"

A new development saved the youth in general-staff trousers the necessity of replying. Two soldiers suddenly appeared in front of the car. Each of them had a most unsoldierly looking leather dispatch-case in his hand, but otherwise they were properly equipped with carbine, bayonet and gas mask. One was a corporal and the other a lance-corporal.

"Two stragglers from 40 Panzer Corps," the senior announced militarily. Then came an exclamation of surprise. "Herr Major, it's you! Would Herr Major give us a lift?"

The youth perked up and became extremely friendly. "Jump in," he said. "You just caught us in time. Important mission to Breslau. Enemy tanks all over the place." Velten did not miss the looks of amusement which passed between the other two. The major stepped out to let them climb in behind.

"Now we'll stick to the main roads," he announced courageously, as they started off again. He even went so far as to give an explanation for Velten's benefit: "The lance-corporal is my draftsman. The other . . ."

"I'm the clerk, Herr Major," the corporal broke in.

"That's right," agreed the general staff know-it-all. "Now tell me, what's happened to our crowd?"

"Oh, yes, of course, Herr Major wasn't there when the trouble started," said the lance-corporal. Velten thought he caught an

299

inflection of irony in the words. "40 Corps has had it. Completely wiped out by enemy superiority."

"Where's the General?"

"Killed. They shot up his tank. His last signal was 'Farewell, comrades. Long live the Führer!' "

Once again Velten was conscious of the almost imperceptible, mocking undertone. The major seemed quite unaware of it. "Sounds just like the Brown Bomber," he remarked proudly, turning to Velten to add with remarkable affability: "Everybody knew General Borck as the Brown Bomber! One of the Führer's most faithful followers in this time of foul treachery."

The major fell silent now as they trundled along the smooth, icy road. Velten was doing a maximum of thirty-five miles per hour, despite the other's repeated efforts to goad him into increasing the speed.

"I'm driving as fast as I dare on this road," said Velten irritably.

The major turned round to the two soldiers. "Keep a sharp lookout for anything suspicious. There've been enemy spearheads reported everywhere."

"Good God, sir," said the lance-corporal impatiently. "We've tramped around this area all night without seeing anything. Where's Ivan supposed to be coming from?"

At that moment the general staff major gave a yell.

"*Halt!* Tank half-left!"

Velten took his foot off the accelerator and let the car slow down. From behind came a hoot of laughter.

"Haystack, Herr Major!"

The youth said nothing. It was not even clear whether he was ashamed.

"Now for God's sake get on a bit faster," he blustered at Velten. "I'm giving you an order. I've got an urgent mission to carry out!"

Then you shouldn't have traipsed me around for five hours, you idiot, thought Velten. But he made the mistake of complying, and put his foot down.

A truck came towards them, breaking all the rules by driving straight along the crown of the road. Suddenly it stopped and a man jumped out. He stood with his back towards them, directly in their

300

path and quite oblivious of their approach. Velten cursed wildly as the realization flashed upon him that he could not stop. Snatching his foot off the accelerator, he hooted like a man possessed and tried to describe a wary curve round the man as he stood there urinating. At the very last moment the man gave a foolish start and . . . the nearside wing had already caught him. His body thudded to the ground.

When Velten had brought the vehicle to a standstill the major ran back to the spot.

"You've picked yourself a fine passenger," the lance-corporal told Velten the moment the officer was out of the car. "The most cowardly swine in the whole Corps! A major on general staff at twenty-eight—and as dumb as they make 'em, for all that! Oh well, you've already had some experience with him. Just you wait and see what's still to come! You're going to have some fun with that boy!"

The major came back. "The man's unconscious," he reported. "He's got a gaping hole in his skull and seems to have broken his hip into the bargain. Give me your paybook so that I can let his sergeant have your particulars."

Velten tugged out his paybook. "Herr Major," he said reluctantly, "I've driven for fifteen years without giving anyone a scratch. This is my first accident. If you hadn't pushed me along like that . . ."

"It was the man's own fault!" the major interrupted. Pissing in the middle of the road!" Then he ran back with the paybook.

"You've got us as witnesses," said the lance-corporal soothingly. Velten was upset. "I wouldn't have hurt the poor devil if I'd been going at a reasonable speed. Now he may croak just before it all finishes!"

"Don't let the stupid fool push you along any more, whatever you do," the lance-corporal told him. "You watch me handle him. Main thing's to show him you don't stand any nonsense."

"That's settled," said the major abruptly, handing Velten his paybook. "The sergeant's reporting that it was the man's own negligence."

It was apparently the end of the affair as far as he was concerned. Nevertheless, he made no further attempt to force the pace.

Little by little the road began to show signs of life. Towns and villages through which they passed were more reminiscent of peace-time, and an increasing number of civil vehicles came into sight.

Suddenly the major gave an order to stop and climbed out.

"All right," he told his two subordinates in an imperious tone, "you can get out now. We'll manage by ourselves from now on."

The other two did not budge.

"I don't quite get it, Herr Major," said his draftsman. "Are you kicking us out because you don't see any more danger? You'll have to take us as far as Breslau now! I thought there was comrade-ship between officers and men!"

A slight flush rose in the youth's arrogant face. Without a word he got back into his seat and they drove on in silence.

In the early afternoon they entered snow-bound Breslau. Velten stopped in front of a bar in the suburbs. He knew now how to treat this whelp of a staff officer.

"I'm hungry," he announced briefly.

"But we haven't any ration coupons," the major told him in astonishment.

"Leave that to me!"

Velten got his knapsack out of the compartment and they went into the crowded tavern.

The friendly waitress stared in wonderment at the two slabs of chocolate which Velten handed her.

"Will that cover four lunches?"

They swiftly settled on four pea soups and four portions of the main dish—blood and liver sausage, with sauerkraut.

Then the major went to the toilet and did not return. At length they espied him in the background sitting with some officers at another table. He informed them through the waitress that these gentlemen and invited him over—a fact which did not deter him from accepting the lunch for which Velten had paid in kind.

"There you have him in his full stature," said Rudolf Herbrand, the draftsman. They had introduced themselves to each other in the meantime. "You saw how the pig wanted to dump us out on the road after he'd sweated out his fright. You haven't seen all of him yet by a long shot!"

Herbrand went on to tell how he had gone through the entire campaign in the East with this paragon of a neo-German officer.

Incompetent, arrogant, cowardly and uncomradely were only some of the epithets he used to characterize his superior. "I ask you! A general-staff officer at twenty-eight! Back at home you wouldn't trust him to take the dog out for a run!"

"Nothing surprises me any more," said Velten, who then went on to tell the story of Mortensohn and the hand-grenades.

"You seem to have got the right attitude," said Heinrich Keller, the corporal. Unlike Herbrand, a lively native of Cologne, he was a man of few words. He hailed from the Eifel and was a secondary-school teacher by profession. Herbrand had been a draftsman in the designing office of a Deutz engineering works.

"We two have had just as big a bellyful as you," Herbrand explained. "Just like anyone else who's still got his five senses about him. The only thing now is to get home in one piece. To hell with everything else!"

"For the time being you two are stragglers!" said Velten. "That's always a good thing to be. Perhaps we'll straggle ourselves all the way home yet!"

By this time they had polished off their meal. Velten handed round cigarettes.

"What made you keep offering them to Crimson Pants on the way here?" Herbrand inquired.

"Good Lord, he's cut off from his unit, too, you know!" said Velten. "He's got none of his own to smoke!"

"Let's hope you're not mistaken," replied the draftsman doubtfully.

Velten felt how comforting it was always to find congenial spirits amid this chaos of unreason and crudity. His mind went back gratefully to all those who had kept their individuality in the service of the *Barras*. He owed much to such encounters and had friendly memories of them all. Cismar and the Silver Stripe; Jack Hahn, the good-tempered cynic; Bernd Eichberg, the devout zealot; Kurt Kleinfeld, the quiet mechanic; Max Dotterweich, the slick "organizer."

"There's one good thing about the Army," he said aloud. "You do find real comradeship."

"As long as everyone's in the soup, anyway," grinned Herbrand, ever the cheerful sceptic.

303

When they called for the bill they found that the major's share was already paid. "I wouldn't have thought it possible," said the Rhinelander. "I was all ready to see him try to bum some cash off you."

"The Herr Captain with the mustache has paid for the Herr Major," said the waitress.

"See?" said Herbrand. "You'd have been caught all right!"

Then the major came over and gave an order to move.

"How are you going on from here?" he asked the other two. "You've got to report to the collecting point."

"We're staying with you for now, Herr Major," said Herbrand firmly. The youth made no reply.

They drove to the Command Headquarters, the location of which the major had learned from his lunchtime acquaintances. "Wait here!" he ordered curtly, very much the general-staff officer again. Then he strode into the building. The other three remained standing in the icy wind of the street.

Shortly afterwards an orderly appeared.

"Are you Major Rassberg's driver?"

"Yes, Corporal," said Velten. "I have that honor."

"Herr Major has forgotten his dispatch-case," said the man.

"You don't say!" cried Herbrand. "It'll be too bad if the louse locked it!"

The case opened easily enough. Without a word Herbrand held out the contents.

"Why, the measly little runt!" roared Velten, quite beside himself with indignation. "And he was smoking my cigarettes the whole way!"

Apart from a few papers and a rolled-up towel the case was full of cigarettes. There must have been several hundred.

"We'll soon fix that," said the Rhinelander, pressing two packs into Velten's hand. The latter accepted them without a twinge. Keller hesitated somewhat. "Come on, you're not a schoolteacher now!" Herbrand scoffed. Keller helped himself then. After providing for his own needs, Herbrand gave the orderly a pack.

"That's to remind you to keep your mouth shut! Anything that goes astray on the way back is your own business!"

304

"Never you worry," the man assured them. "I don't give my mates away!"

"And tell the Herr Major we're going for a spin round the town," Velten called after him. "We'll be back in one hour."

They drove to the station post office and sent postcards to their families. War in one's own country had its good points. During the summer retreat through the Polish wilderness there had been no postal communication whatever with home.

Already the war was casting thick shadows over the hitherto unbombed city. Few people were about, and there was stark fear in the emaciated faces of those who stopped to ask: "Do you know where the Russians are?" Posters on pillars and the walls of buildings affirmed that there would be no evacuation and warned the population under pain of death not to leave without official sanction. There was no danger yet. But should the military situation deteriorate, Breslau would defend herself to the victorious end. "Long live the Führer!"

It was an appeal from the Gauleiter.

They drove back to the Command Headquarters. It was past sunset and bitterly cold. From time to time Velten would start up the engine to generate a little warmth. In the intervals they would jump out and run around the car, beating their arms across their chests.

When it was midnight, Herbrand resolved to investigate. He was soon back. "He's in with Lieutenant Count Fartbelch," he said. "Least, that's what the name sounded like. They're having a very important conference. The orderly's just taken in the second bottle of brandy. The pig had a good feed in the mess before that. Never a thought for us, of course."

Velten was accustomed to officers from Army always arranging a meal for their drivers. Since Rassberg had instructed them to remain by the car in readiness to start, however, they had been unable to do anything about food. Not that they had gone hungry, in fact, as Velten had an abundant stock of tinned sausage meat, and there were still seven loaves from Sieradz.

Around four in the morning the major re-appeared. He smelled of liquor and was inclined to be talkative.

305

"All right, off you go," he said. "Long conference. Been trying to find out where Army is. Quite imposhible to get through. We'll have to drive farther west. They can't be in Krotoszyn any more. Russians have got it."

He turned to the two men from his own outfit.

"I'm taking you along. Better for us to stick together."

Aha, thought Velten. That meant he was getting windy again.

"Herr Major," he declared, "I've been standing about in the street all night. I must have a few hours' sleep. Otherwise I shan't be safe to drive."

It was a good point. "Safety's the main thing," the youth agreed.

Velten drove his car into the yard. The major obtained four mattresses and had them laid out on an office floor, his own at an appropriate distance from those of the men.

Herbrand poked Velten in the side. "Now you know how to handle him!"

They were off at eight next morning. A sudden change had come over the city since the previous evening. The streets swarmed with people—men unfit for military service, many of them on sticks and laboring under the weight of rucksacks and suitcases; wild-eyed women tugging terrified children along with one hand and lugging bags and baskets in the other. Many pulled loaded sleds behind them. Others were pushing hand-carts. Weeping women carried babies on their arms, the thongs of their makeshift rucksacks cutting into their flesh.

Overnight the heroic Gauleiter had changed his mind. The order now was that "those members of the civil population with no official commitments are at liberty to leave the city." Transport would not be provided.

And so the people of Breslau marched out of their city—a city they were never to see again. They did not look back. With fear and despair in their hearts, they pressed numbly on through the snow.

Just as Velten and his passengers were out of the city, the engine stalled. He stepped on the starter, once, twice, a third time.

"She isn't firing," he remarked equably. "The line is stopped up. The gas is full of muck."

While he was sorting out his tools the major stamped around like an ill-bred child. "Come on, come on, hurry up! I'm always getting landed with these blasted breakdowns! God knows what you'll mess up next!"

"I haven't botched anything," Velten told him as he dismantled the carburetor. "There you are." He showed the major the float needle. "Bung full of dirt!"

"You could have cleaned it before this," said the major.

"You try cleaning anything when Ivan's after you!" retorted Velten, angry with himself for not thinking of it while kicking his heels in the early hours. By way of precaution, he carefully cleaned the pump as well. The engine fired immediately. Thank God, he told himself. He had not been at all certain whether that was really the trouble. If it had been the ignition he would probably have been stymied.

"I'll be interested to see what it is next time," the major sneered as they drove on again. "I've had just about enough of you drivers!"

He did not have to wait very long. As they were passing through the friendly little town of Neumarkt there was a rending clatter under the hood and the engine faded out. Velten de-clutched and let the vehicle coast to a standstill. As he climbed out he glanced back and saw a black trail of oil behind them. He lifted the hood. Oil was seeping out of a crack down one side of the block.

"This is where we fall out, Herr Major," said Velten almost cheerfully. "Your presentiments have proved correct. Damaged engine. I can't get you any farther."

The young man was livid with rage. "This always has to happen to me!" he screeched. "It's always me! If you hadn't . . ."

"Hadn't what?" demanded Velten without the slightest respect.

"Perhaps you think I could have motorized the Wehrmacht with something better than vehicles pinched from the civil economy? This car's all right! The only trouble is that Daimler-Benz didn't build it for the Russian campaign!"

Any further dispute was obviated by a friendly character emerging from a grocer's on the other side of the road. He had seen the misfortune from his shop, he explained. Would the gentlemen care to come in and take some nourishment?

Soon they were seated in the parlor in front of a mountain of sandwiches and a steaming jug of tea. The major piled in manfully,

307

his ire abating somewhat. The proximity of danger made the grocer's family lively and communicative. They inquired after the state of the front.

"We don't know that ourselves," said the major. "As a matter of fact"—here the gallant fellow's breast rose under its Iron Cross First Class—"we're on our way there now." As it happened, Velten had learned from the mischievous Herbrand that the decoration was not for prowess at the front but "meritorious assistance of a senior commander."

The major withdrew after they had eaten. "I'm going to find some transportation," he told them. "Wait for me by the car."

They stood out there for a good half-hour. The street presented a familiar picture of retreat—army convoys, horses and carts, and people fleeing on foot. Among it all they saw the first signs of the Great Trek of rural population—covered ox-wagons with frightened children's faces peeping out, men and boys driving jaded cattle. There were even communities from Hungary among them. Long-horned oxen drew wagons whose name-plates showed their passengers to be ethnic Germans from Transylvania and the Banat.

"The whole pride of France," someone had once told Velten, "is perishing in the glowing dust of these roads." How long ago had that been? No longer than the road from a carefree blitzkrieg to Stalingrad and back—into the misery of defeat.

"You can take it from me," said Herbrand. "We've seen the last of the little bastard!"

"He'll have to come along this street, I bet."

At last a private car pulled up close by. Next to the driver, incredibly enough, was the major himself. The back seats were loaded with suitcases and hampers.

"I've got a car from the forester," the major told them. "Must carry out my mission. Sorry to have to leave you here. You'll manage somehow. Best of luck! Heil Hitler!"

"Wait a minute!" Velten called. "Here's my work-ticket, Herr Major. Fill in the names of my two comrades here, so that they've at least got a proper authority to stay with me."

"All right," Rassberg agreed, doing as he was told.

"And then you'll let my unit know I've broken down?"

308

Hastily the major promised to do what Velten required of him. Then the car drove off.

Velten glanced round at his two campanions. "Well, here we are again. Three leaderless mercenaries, thrown on our own resources."

"Could be a lot worse!" Herbrand reminded him.

"If only this car weren't busted," said Velten anxiously.

He went off alone to the market place, where the stream of traffic was moving a little more slowly. After several attempts he managed to stop a Luftwaffe truck.

"Can you give me a tow, chum?" he asked the driver.

"Where to?"

"My unit."

"You're crazy. Give you a tow to Berlin, if you like! We're heading for home!"

The truck was already gone. The mood of *sauve qui peut* seemed to be setting in.

A military policeman wearing the regulation silver gorget was on point-duty at the cross-roads. Velten stepped up to him and produced his paybook and work-ticket.

"I've had a breakdown and have got to get an officer courier with important orders to Army," he lied. "Will you make some vehicle take me in tow?"

The German redcap examined the document bearing the inscription "Special courier" and "Major General Staff."

"I'll see."

For several minutes he tried in vain to stop a military vehicle. Finally a weird-looking caravan chugged into sight, setting up a terrific din as it came. It was a farm tractor pulling two open trailers tightly packed with people in civilian clothes, most of them women. The driver stopped in obedience to the MP's signal. A youngish man clad in Tyrolean hat and raglan coat jumped down. As he came closer Velten saw that under his coat he wore a brown uniform with a great deal of gold braid.

"Heil Hitler!" he greeted the MP with raised hand. "What is it? My papers are in order." He fumbled in his breast-pocket. "Authorized transport of National Socialist Welfare personnel from Party Headquarters in Breslau. I've only members of the staff office with me."

309

Well, well, thought Velten. And the ordinary folk of Breslau had to walk it.

The MP waved the papers aside. "I don't want to see those. Where are you heading for?"

"Our emergency headquarters in Liegnitz to put my staff back on an operational footing," came the glib reply from under a blond toothbrush mustache.

"Will Liegnitz do you?" the MP asked Velten.

"Yes, I can probably find a field workshop there."

"You're taking this driver's vehicle in tow," said the MP peremptorily.

The golden popinjay did not dare object. Having already hooked the tow-rope onto their own car, Velten's two companions swiftly secured it to the second Welfare trailer. Then they trundled slowly off in the wake of the Party bandwagon.

Soon after Neumarkt the tractor had a puncture. It took an unconscionable time to repair, partly because a jack had be be borrowed from the next village. Herbrand and Keller lent the driver a hand. The popinjay assisted in a purely supervisory capacity.

Velten took three completely frozen Welfare ladies into his car while the two non-coms moved over onto the open trailer. They were elderly and gray-haired, with washed-out faces and gloomy eyes. Now, thoroughly terrified, they squatted in their seats and gazed in silence at the multitude stumbling past them through the snow.

"That'll give the Party Welfare something to think about," remarked Velten, nodding at the endless flow of refugees disappearing into the driving snow ahead of them. The three females shivered. Never before had they come so close to real physical distress. They seemed utterly at sea in the face of such intense misery.

At length they felt impelled to make some fundamental comments on the situation. "If only everyone would trust the Führer," sighed the big-boned one next to Velten. "He's always tried to do his best by us. It's just that there are traitors all around him."

"Like 1918," the little fat one piped up from behind. "Only five minutes before Victory—and they can't hold out."

"We Germans," said the red-haired one with pince-nez who occupied the other back seat and had said nothing till now, "simply

310

aren't hard enough. War is war! Sacrifices must be made—for Germany!"

Dear God, thought Velten, I wouldn't care to have you looking after my welfare! As the three prattled on for a while longer, he was able to sense their dreadful fear and perplexity. There was something parrot-like about the claptrap phrases with which they sought to comfort themselves and to persuade each other to accept the official view of the war.

Another incident put an end to their chatter. Two second-lieutenants came up with a couple of utterly exhausted women hanging in their arms. "They're going along with you," one of them announced.

The official in charge of the group intervened.

"Very sorry, gentlemen," he announced, casually loosening his coat to reveal his gold-braided brown uniform, "but this is a special detachment from Party Headquarters in Breslau! Can't give rides to strangers, I'm afraid. Strict order from the Gauleiter!"

"One more squeak out of you, you conceited little turkey-cock," growled one of the officers, moving his hand towards his pistol, "and we'll give you such a pasting that you'll never fit into a uniform again!"

In an instant the two women were up on the trailer. The young man turned hastily away and began taking a sudden interest in watching the nuts being tightened on the tractor wheel.

At last the caravan was able to resume its journey. By the time they reached the outskirts of Liegnitz it was almost nightfall, and Velten kept a sharp lookout for a favorable place to stay. He was in luck. As the tractor croaked to a standstill on a hairpin bend, he was able, in the uncertain light of the snow, to pick out a rustic inn with a big courtyard in front.

Quickly making up his mind, he jumped out. "There you are, ladies," he said, motioning to them to descend. "This is my destination. Would you be good enough to move over onto the Party transport again?"

At a shout from Velten the two soldiers sprang off the trailer and released the tow-rope. The same moment the tractor started off again. They pushed their car into the yard.

"Three soldiers and a broken-down car would like quarters for the night," said Velten when the door opened. A young girl was standing there in the light of the kitchen lamp.

"Mother's in hospital and father's been killed in the war," she said. "I'm doing everything by myself. Our rooms are full of evacuees. Two attics are still empty," she added hesitantly. "But they're unheated."

"Unheated!" Velten laughed. "No hot and cold running water either, I suppose?"

At length the girl let them into the kitchen, directing searching looks into their faces as she did so. Perhaps it was just as well to have three men under one's roof in these unsettled times, she remarked.

The two stragglers took the larger attic, in which there were two beds. Velten took the other.

Down in the kitchen again, he planked two tins of beef on the table. "Stew and fried spuds this evening," he decided, his experienced eye having already spotted a bowl of cold boiled potatoes. Herbrand was elected to look after all the culinary arrangements while Velten and Keller went into the town.

They soon found a large Luftwaffe headquarters, the command post of a fighter formation. Velten produced his papers for the orderly sergeant's inspector.

"Have you got a telephone line to Twenty-Ninth Army?" he asked.

"We've no longer any contact at all with the forward areas. Everything's in a hell of a mess. You can write down a message if you like. We may get through on the air during the night, when things are a bit quieter."

Velten scribbled a few words on a message form: MT POOL TWENTY-NINTH ARMY FOR ATTENTION CPL WEYERMANN STOP STRANDED IN LIEGNITZ WITH DAMAGED ENGINE STOP PLEASE HELP STOP VELTEN.

When they got back, a dish of golden-brown *sauté* potatoes stood on the kitchen table. Two more guests had attached themselves to the party in the meantime: a thin quiet little girl of about fourteen and a plump serving-girl of rustic mien.

Velten augmented the stew with a third tin of beef, and the girls

312

set to with appetites that put even the ravenous hunger of the soldiers in the shade.

As they were sitting with a bottle of Kümmel on the table and nibbling chocolate amid cries of delight from the female guests, the mother of the fourteen-year-old joined them—a slim woman of youthful appearance.

It wasn't long before Herbrand, the easy-going Rhinelander, was doing his level best to flirt with her. She proved icily unco-operative. "My husband's on active service," was her curt explanation. "In Crete."

"The Russians won't ask about that when they get here," Herbrand parried cynically.

The young woman's face went hard. The others gazed numbly in front of them. A blanket of paralyzing horror had descended on the little gathering.

This was the one point on which the propaganda of the Third Reich had pounded unsparingly ever since the collapse of the central front in the East. It seized hold of a man's most deep-rooted emotions and turned a woman's face white with primitive dread. Everyone sensed that there was nothing here of the limping demon's customary exaggeration.

On the morning when the Motor Pool had moved from Wolkowysk to Bialystok, Velten had taken on a load of telephone cable. While the people from the signal section wound up the drums, he had read a leaflet distributed by the Propaganda Company at Army Headquarters. With a view to inflaming a will to supreme resistance, it carried quotations from the enemy's own propaganda. "Seek out the fascist beast in his lair!" was the keynote of this hate. Then there followed translation of some verse. The verse of a man whose books one had read in a bourgeois world long sunk into oblivion.

> Take their blonde women as your booty,
> And smash these fascist Teutons' pride!

That was not poetic word-power. It was a literal exhortation to unimaginable wantonness. What now came welling over from the plains and primeval forests of the East was not an advancing army. It was an alien world rising against a doomed era. How frivolously he had toyed with the safeguards of our old world—the Man from Braunau who had embarked on a war of conquest and finished by opening the way to terrible forces that were to alter the course of human destiny! He had torn down the dams, and now the flood was surging closer and closer. Everything was fused in that mighty inundation: the primitive strength of an inexhaustible continent; the compelling might of a political idea which held the heart and spirit in its thrall; the vital energies of a young race bent on procreation.

"If the Russians come," said the blonde woman, slowly stubbing out her half-smoked cigarette, "that's one of the things we can expect. It'll be the same sort of peril as fire or high water. Until then I have my own will. Say thank you," she admonished her daughter, who had been listening mute and hot-cheeked. "We're going to bed. My day begins early."

After the mother and daughter had gone the party was unable to recapture its previous good cheer. Even Herbrand felt the time inopportune for jest and dalliance, and they too decided to retire.

Half way up the dark staircase something white and barefooted slipped up to Velten. For one brief instant he felt the throb of heartbeats through a thin nightdress and the firm touch of two hard, small breasts. A pair of thin, girlish arms entwined his neck, and a brief kiss burned on his lips. A hasty whisper: "I just wanted to say thank you for the chocolate!" And then she was gone.

The next morning Velten found an answer to his message at the Luftwaffe headquarters. "Get tow to nearest workshop" was Weyermann's solution.

"Very smart," said Velten. "I didn't need Mr. Weyermann's help to find that out."

Nothing precise was known about the location of Army Head-quarters. At the collection point for stragglers someone thought it might be in Oppeln.

"We certainly aren't going there," Velten told Keller. "Anyway, I don't believe they've gone so far forward. They were already nicely settled on the withdrawal axis, heading west!"

They decided to move off to avoid the risk of being impressed into some *ad hoc* unit. They left the daughter of the house a tin of meat and a few bars of chocolate, for which she mutely thanked

314

them with a handshake. Looking downcast and scared, she watched them push their vehicle out of the courtyard.

Out in the road they took up a position some distance away from the car, knowing that it would be easier to stop another vehicle if the driver did not immediately realize that they wanted a tow. After they had made one or two vain attempts, an empty Luftwaffe truck drew up.

"Can't give you a lift," said the driver. "I'm only going as far as the Army Motor Pool depot."

"Bad luck," laughed Velten. "That's just where we want to go."

The man relented, and they quickly coupled their Mercedes to his vehicle.

"Big end gone," was the verdict of the sergeant-mechanic at the depot after he had examined the engine. "We can't do anything for you here. That kind of repair is out of the question now."

Velten pointed to the rows of vehicles out in the compound.

"Do you intend leaving all that lot to the Russians? You could surely give me a replacement for the old one."

"It's not quite as simple as that," said the sergeant. "You'd have to produce a release certificate first."

Velten had not gone through Fritz Erlenbach's school for nothing. He took two cartons out of his knapsack.

"Hundred cigarettes and one expended car for a usable one," he said, holding them out to the sergeant. "All right?"

It was all right. In very short order they transferred their belongings from the old car into a reconditioned 170 V. While the papers were being made out for Headquarters Twenty-Ninth Army they inquired about its location. Army was in Glogau.

The new car was a joy to drive, and they reached Glogau without any further incidents. A vehicle from the Motor Pool was just pulling up in front of the town-major's office.

"You'd better get out of here as fast as you can, chum," the driver told Velten as they greeted each other. "They're picking up everyone they can find here for a defense force. Get back to our outfit quick or they'll make a hero of you yet! You can't risk being seen here without an officer." He named a village in the vicinity where the Pool was quartered.

315

Weyermann stared in amazement when Velten drove in with his new car.

"I'd never have thought you could do it! We'd given you up. Brought us a new car, too! Seems we've taught you something after all!"

Velten experienced the pride of being no longer "one of the new ones." He was part of the unit from now on.

"What made you send me such a bright answer to my SOS?" he asked the corporal.

"Good God, man," the other laughed, "there was nothing I could do for you! I just banked on you realizing you'd have to fend for yourself!"

CHAPTER VIII

FROM NOW ON the retreat continued unremittingly as far as the Oder line. The next morning Velten drove with the advance party to Crossen. They were only there for twenty-four hours. They left again the very next day, just after the main body had moved up. This time their departure was so precipitate that Velten was not even allocated his own vehicle. He drove alone to the new destination: Manschnow, a village on the southern bank of the Oderbruch, near Küstrin.

Only a few days later it was time to decamp afresh. Velten was on the rear party on this occasion. The evening sky around the hamlet glowed red from numerous conflagrations as the enemy artillery hammered incessantly on the Oderbruch. This time they were German towns and villages that were being consumed by the fire of war—the flames of frenzy which were driving this land into the abyss. How long would it go on? Stronger and stronger grew the hope that something or other would intervene to save the fatherland from the last, bitter cup. But nothing happened. The madman gave his orders. And unmurmuringly, unflinchingly, men went the way they believed to be the path of duty.

Velten had long to wait before Corporal Berner, the non-com in charge of the rear party, gave the signal to move off. In the little village church the Luftwaffe had had an equipment dump, and this was now thrown open on account of the lack of transportation. While the guns all around thundered out the death-knell of the German lands, the villagers and troops jostled into the church to pick up what they could from the coveted air-crew kits. Every item was brand-new—fleece-lined waistcoats and jackets, fur-lined boots, all with a soft, gray-blue leather on their outer sides. Velten helped himself to an armful of woolen socks and one of the sheepskins.

Double-decker omnibuses from Berlin lurched through the crisp snow into the village and began taking refugees on board. For Velten the sight of these yellow monsters with the Berlin Bear and the letters BVG on their sides was a grim reminder of the war's proximity to his home town. They were the same vehicles which had once taken Berliners out to the lakes and other Sunday-afternoon resorts west of the city. Now, as part of the Total War, they were conveying total misery to doubtful safety.

When the buses left, there was still a pathetic little cluster of weeping women and children at the roadside. Helplessly they let their pitiful bundles and parcels of belongings fall into the snow.

An officer stopped a Luftwaffe car.

"What are you carrying?"

"Blankets."

"Off with them! Use the space for these women and children!"

The men pitched the bulky woolen bundles onto the road. Simultaneously Velten threw his own shabby gray ones out and helped himself to five soft, warm air force blankets. The Luftwaffe always had had the best equipment!

At last they moved off. During the night it began to thaw, and as they drove into Fürstenwalde in the early morning of the first day of February there was the merest touch of spring in the air. They took over quarters in a large barrack area of the old garrison town.

Now came the war's last breathing space. The improbable happened. Just as before on the Bug and Vistula, Ivan came to a halt on the Oder. Once again time stood still while Germany hoped and

317

feared and buzzed with rumors and contradictory reports. The ordinary soldier again relapsed into a deceptive, almost peacetime, routine of motor transport inspections and weapon-cleaning.

Velten remained more or less unscathed by this barrack existence.

Like Fritz Erlenbach, who was now with a field workshop somewhere in the Brandenburg March, he became the unit's "procurement man." By February 3rd he was already off on a trip to Berlin with Hans Arend as his driver. They went in a big Horch with a long list of requirements, neatly typed out in three copies, one white, one red and one green, together with the appropriate stock of "lubricants"—schnapps, chocolate and cigarettes.

It was the mildest of early spring days, with a sky of the softest blue. They had still not reached the junction with Berlin's circular highway when Hans Arend slammed on the brakes. Before them, directly above the jumbled rooftops of the metropolis, a drama of such appalling immensity was in progress that their breasts contracted at the sight.

Squadron after squadron of aircraft, their metal bodies blinking in the early-morning sun, were curving in from the west in perfect line, filling the spring sky as they came. One formation was already disappearing over the horizon; a second was banking away again; the third was hovering over the defenseless city; and the fourth was just going down onto its target. And far behind, flashing out of the mists of the morning, radiant, overpowering and ominous, came still more aircraft—and more, and still more! For one hour, two hours, they attacked the capital with the unrelenting precision of an air exercise. Of anti-aircraft guns or fighters there was no sign. The air vibrated with the thunder of the detonations. The city lay prone under the angels of death. Thus did the air force of the West batter the capital of the Reich into readiness for the final assault from the East.

At last the procession of mechanical death had passed. The two men breathed again. Velten forced the pace from now on. What would they find in the martyred city which had once been his home?

As they drove into the southeast suburbs the sirens had only just begun to howl the all-clear. Fire engines were racing through the streets. Streams of tormented beings, eyes wide with horror in their blackened faces, staggered out of shelters and cellars into the mangled streets. Gigantic fires, gaping craters and piles of masonry barred the way and compelled the vehicle to follow time-robbing diversions. At long last, Velten, the man born lucky, found his house undamaged and his wife and child unharmed.

"Here I am again. But not on leave. In fact we've brought the war with us."

Not until weeks later would Gaby be persuaded to move to a little town on the river Saale where Velten had relations. Thereafter he had to listen to Wehrmacht communiqués for week after week before hearing, to his immense relief, that the Americans had occupied the little place.

Meanwhile he busied himself procuring spare parts and became a highly respected client at the depot in Charlottenburg's boulevard Empress Augusta.

"What've you brought us today?" the distributors would ask whenever he called. He obtained the rarest and most coveted items, and the Pool was able to bring its vehicles up to a peacetime standard in readiness for the last great race with captivity and death.

Max Dotterweich's fate seemed sealed, however. Kessler put his name in for a posting to the Small Arms School prior to a transfer to the infantry. Max had to pull every string he knew before finally getting himself sent to a corps staff as a driver. From there he safely wangled himself through the ultimate collapse.

At the beginning of March Army Headquarters moved to Saarow-Pieskow, the twin hamlets on the tapering Scharmützelsee, a health resort full of sanatoria, white villas and comfortable hotels.

The staff took over the big sanatorium on the narrow peninsula, and the senior officers quartered themselves out in the villas. The Motor Pool was quartered in wooden huts near a wood which afforded cover for the vehicles. It shared the accommodation with an SS fire-fighting platoon. Capt. Kessler lived out in a detached house on the far side of the road.

On March 9th, 1945, Velten was promoted lance-corporal. With something of a jolt he found that it gave him a certain pride to sew the new chevron on his sleeve. And still the war went on and on—as if it simply could not bear to end. Not content with the terrain it had swallowed in the north, south, east and west of the continent and on the borders of Africa and Asia, it ate deeper and deeper into Germany with fiery breath and greedy, licking tongue. For generations, for hundreds of years, no Germans had met this scorching, violent, merciless monster in their own land. Wherever they were mauled by its pitiless claws they became numb with fear and sick with horror; while those in the daily diminishing areas where the old tyranny still prevailed were goaded on by terrorism and propaganda to further senseless resistance.

"Our Front is the Oder!" the ubiquitous posters screamed. If a soldier was found more that three miles west of the river without proper authority, his life was forfeit. Squads of military police and storm troopers patrolled the prohibited zone, hanging out of hand all suspicious characters who fell into their clutches.

One day Florian, the Viennese, returned wild-eyed from a trip to the front. He had been driving the Army Commander in an open staff car.

"You know how regimental he is," Flori told them. "Well, he'd been sitting next to me reading the map with his glasses on his forehead, when suddenly he looks up and—shortsighted like—spots some uniforms. 'Can't you louts salute?' he shouts across the road. The Aide leans over from behind. 'Herr General,' he says, 'Herr General, they've been hanged. They can't salute any more!' Gave me the creeps, I can tell you," said Flori with a shudder. "Imagine —they'd strung six of 'em up on trees by the roadside. Hanging all in a row they were, feet in the ditch and heads kind of wobbling from side to side in the wind. The General didn't say a word. That took his breath away for him, I thought to myself. But not a bit of it. After a while we meet three more boys coming along the road. He stops the car and shouts to them to show their authority. They stutter out some sort of excuse—naturally they were on the run. 'Into the back with you!' he bawls. They climb in, pale as death. A few miles farther on we meet a provost patrol car, and he hands the poor guys over, all three of 'em shaking like leaves. 'By this evening,' he says, 'I want a report that you've hung the scum up!' This is a savage war, by God," Flori concluded with a sigh.

There were still glimpses of reason through the murk of barbarity, nevertheless. On yet another occasion the beery-voiced Kessler was to win Velten's heart. A clerk from the Quartermaster-General's branch, a pigeon-chested, bespectacled creature, had put in a charge against two members of the Motor Pool. They had been heard to declare that the war was lost and that even if the country were stiff with Werewolves nothing would stop them from driving home in their own trucks.

Forthwith Kessler and Capt. Bendewitt from Q branch set to work on the denunciator. So baffling was the line of cross-talk to which they subjected him—Kessler in his hoarse bass and the ever spick-and-span Bendewitt in a shrill falsetto—that the unhappy wretch had finished up without the remotest idea of what he had really heard. Gazing unsteadily through the lenses of his steel-rimmed army spectacles, he had perused a deposition admitting that he was mistaken and hastily signed it with a trembling hand. "They're only getting windy now the end's in sight," one or two of the men maintained. "A year ago they'd had both of them court-martialed like a shot."

"Oh, come," Velten remonstrated. "A year ago neither man would have indulged in defeatist talk. Let's give them their due! If they'd brought both men to the gallows, no one would have given a rap. When this lot cracks open, you won't be able to trace anyone, guilty or innocent."

Yes, but when would the crack come? Again and again the same idle chatter went the rounds—stories of the wonder-weapon that was to turn the war, of discord in the enemy camp which would bring Final Victory at Five Minutes to Twelve.

Indeed, it really began to look as if uniforms would be in demand for some time to come. The staff's National Socialist Leadership Officer, NSFO for short, made a special trip to Berlin in this very connection. Having just been promoted major, he deemed it quite natural to call on his tailor in the Kurfürstendamm and have a new uniform fitted. Velten, who had various errands to do for the pool, traveled in the same vehicle. Behind the wheel, next to Major Wirth, sat Alfred Henseler, a taxi-driver from Breslau. Henseler, as Velten well knew, had "had" the war in a big way.

"Did you hear my lecture the day before yesterday?" asked the major. Velten replied in the negative, having been away on a duty trip. But he was aware of what the NSFO had said. He had spoken of the Führer whom he had recently seen at a meeting of political offi-

321

cers. And how aged the Führer had looked—quite gray and bent. But in his eyes the same old fire had glowed. "Just like the Emperor Friedrich! Think of Old Fritz and the way he led Prussia from darkest defeat back into the light! The Russians were outside Berlin then, too. Aye, they'd even broken in at some places. And still Old Fritz beat 'em!"

Then the major had spoken of Western Culture, whose salvation was now their task. "The threat comes from the East! The others are already beginning to see what we mean to them." And with that drastic vulgarity which NSFOs were wont to affect, he had concluded: "And so we shall stand here and face the Red Flood from the East! We shall stand here till the American panzers drive up our arses!"

When the major embarked on an informal recapitulation of his discourse for the benefit of the two enlisted men, something snapped in Alfred Henseler.

"Herr Major," he said with suppressed fury in his voice, "I can't stand listening to that any longer. Not any longer I can't."

Completely disconcerted, the major shot his driver a look from the side. But he uttered not a word.

"Nee," said Alfred from Breslau. "I've lost my home and the few belongings we'd taken so long to collect. Where the wife and kids are, God alone knows. And now I'm supposed to let the American tanks drive up my arse?"

After a pause, he added: "You know just as well as me we're in a spot, Herr Major. Every one of us!"

The major still said nothing. Sitting in the back, Velten sweated blood. That the NSFO would report Alfred seemed absolutely certain. Frantically he tried to make up his mind how he would word his statement. Could he and Henseler flatly deny a charge by a field officer? Hopeless—particularly when the man was an NSFO!

"Yes, Herr Major," the Silesian continued, "I'm just telling you the way things are. It's a crying shame to let even one more man bite the dust from now on. Let's give up, I says. The war's lost. Lost, I tell you. It's the truth."

The miracle happened. The major did not explode. He did not say to Velten: "Pass me your paybook! I need you as a witness!"

322

He went quite still and gazed out at the ruins of the Frankfurter Allee.

"You're a little mixed up, my good man," he remarked at length, in a tone that was patronizing but propitiatory. "It's hardly surprising, after all you've been through. You'll come round all right after you've seen how . . ."

He broke off at this point. What Alfred was to experience was never explained.

The NSFO did not raise the matter again. Somehow the gentlemen of the staff were no longer quite so sure of themselves, as a similar experience some days later was to confirm.

Velten was returning from Berlin with Major Herzlieb, whom he often had to drive nowadays. Even when he was not driving the Herr Major he had to make all kinds of peculiar journeys on his behalf. Herzlieb was the camp commandant and reputedly the biggest racketeer in the formation. He stood a good six feet five in his socks and measured half that round the middle. In his fleshy, bloated face he wore a rimless monocle like a frozen puddle in the mire of a wintry farmyard.

Though gross and stupid, Herzlieb had a certain rustic cunning which always stood him in good stead as far as the pursuit of gluttony, booze, women or rackets was concerned. He was the fruit of a union between a well-known scientist and a Portuguese lady of great erotic fire. Though he had inherited none of his father's intellect or his mother's physical attraction, the combination was a success inasmuch as his ignorance was concealed beneath a certain charm and his greed toned down by his stupidity.

The camp commandant lodged with his driver, batman and other appurtenances in a well-appointed lakeside villa. One of the appurtenances was Black Lola—a piece of booty he had brought back from the Caucasus. She was a tall, majestic figure, with big, blue eyes, jet-black hair, smooth creamy skin, well-rounded breasts and comely hips.

One day, either because Herzlieb had jibbed at the usual postprandial gymnastics or because his hot-blooded Lola was not in the mood, they had gone out for a row. Lola steered while the shirt-sleeved Herzlieb sweated away at the oars. Acting on some wicked impulse, Lola made for the land. Hardly had the craft grated onto the gravely beach when a brown-uniformed apparition wreathed in gold braid rose before them. His glance took in the major's gray-green trousers, but he could find no indication of rank on the open-necked shirt. Neither were there any high boots to betray Herzlieb's officer-status: he was wearing carpet slippers. A soldier with a tart, the Party bigwig decided.

"Hey, you!" he bawled at the flabbergasted Herzlieb. "Don't you know there's a total war on? We're fighting for the Fatherland! While scum like you fool around with women, you, you. . . ."

The gentleman in brown foamed with indignation.

The major gaped back at him in speechless fury. Before he could find a suitable rejoinder the tempestuous Lola let fly.

"Chort palassaty! Svinya chornaya! Go, galupchik, poke heem in chops viz oarrr!"

She shook her fist menacingly and tossed her fine head so violently that her black locks flew loose.

"Davai, you peeg, idi i yub tvoya mat."

At this Slavonic invitation to commit incest with his own mother, the peacock's words stuck in his throat. A spy! A spy! A spy with a Russian woman agent, beautiful as sin and wild as a tigress! His knees shook. He threw another look at the ferocious creature with the open blouse and impressive bosom. But no knife snapped open in his pocket. On the contrary, his underclothes became clammy with sweat.

Then, with a frantic wrench, he whipped out his pistol. "Halt or I shoot!" he called, his voice shrill with agitation. But Herzlieb had already shoved the boat off the beach and was backing it away through a high clump of bulrushes. At the same time he finally found a retort to the brown interloper.

"You can kiss my——, do you hear?" he yelled in the direction where he knew the peacock to be. Then he rowed swiftly away along the screen of giant rushes. Black Lola allowed her hands to drift through the water and contemplated her lord and master from under lazy, drooping eyelids.

The peacock, having neither the courage nor the opportunity to fire his pistol, put it back in his holster and went home to pen a report to the Army Commander. Although the peacock gave an exact description of the suspects, they were never found.

This, then, was the Major Herzlieb whom Velten had to drive from time to time. According to Kessler, his reason for using Velten instead of his own driver was to enable him, Velten, to attend to his own domestic affairs. Velten did not believe a word of it. Obviously the major feared his driver's gossip and had more confidence in Velten's discretion.

"Why aren't you an officer?" Henzlieb inquired from out of the darkness. They had not left Berlin till late, and now, well after midnight, theirs was the only vehicle moving along the white ribbon of the autobahn.

Oh, not that again, Velten groaned to himself. He resolved to be circumspect.

"My profession left me little spare time before the war," he said. "That's why I couldn't go on maneuvers. And I wasn't called up till late."

"Na, you can become an officer any time!" the major snapped. "A chap of your class is expected to, damn it all! You only need to give your consent and I'll put you in for a commission straight away."

Velten did not like the sound of this. He decided to speak quite frankly. Knowing that the major worked for a firm of wholesalers in peacetime, he felt it would be apt to frame his reply in analogous terms.

"Herr Major," he said slowly and emphatically to the lump of flesh beside him, "would you ask your chief for a directorship when you knew the firm was going smash?"

Involuntarily he drew in his head in anticipation of the storm which must now burst about his ears. But no sound came.

The major said nothing more for the rest of the journey. Velten was plagued by uncertainty. Would the man get him into trouble? Or would he realize that Velten knew too much and was liable to open his mouth?

If only Velten could have guessed the identity of the friendly gentleman to whose Dahlem home he drove the major almost every Sunday, he need not have worried his head. According to the metal plate over the buzzer on the white-painted garden gate, his name was Emil S. Pifremont. He was a pot-bellied man in his sixties with an artful smile and graying hair of inordinate length which receded from a friendly forehead. Emil S. Pifremont invariably made a point of inviting Velten in for coffee whenever he brought the major. At the table there would usually be two or three middle-aged ladies, one of whom appeared to be on most intimate terms with Black Lola's master.

On one occasion Velten had been detailed to accompany a truck —"some fiddle or other for that clapped-out old pig Herzlieb," Weyermann had explained—with a load of cement, bricks, girders and other building materials. Their trip took them out to the Glienicke Lake, that idyllic spot between Kladow and Potsdam, west of the river Havel, where only a few years before the war the Berliners had begun to lay out a delightful little week-end colony.

At their destination, a fenced-in building site, they found Emil S. Pifremont and two of his ladies. Nine or ten soldiers were busy building a cottage under the direction of a man from the headquarters' defense company who was an architect by profession.

"Just imagine it," this worthy told Velten. "At the very time when the rot's setting in, that fellow Herzlieb starts building himself a summer house. Has us detached to do the job for him. That's corruption, if you like! Sabotage, I call it!"

"I don't know what you're worrying about," Velten reported. "Wish I could spend the rest of the war like that! Out here you can just wait for your chance to fade quietly away!"

In addition to the building materials, the truck had picked up rations for the bricklayers and a few crates of wine for Emil S. Pifremont. Today the latter was cheerfully talkative.

"Just you wait and see," he told Velten in a confidential undertone. "I've got my own sources of information. The Russians will never get as far as this. I'm hanging on here with a good bottle of wine till the Americans turn up."

"May God bless your information, Herr Pifremont," said Velten. "I only hope my comrades profit from it, too."

"You can depend on that." Pifremont slapped him paternally on the shoulder. "The boys will be well looked after along with me. They will be well wined and dined till the time comes for the Americans to take them over."

Let it be said here that Emil S. Pifremont's information was not so good as he thought. Instead of the Americans, the Russians came. This failed to disturb the good fellow, however. He adapted himself very rapidly. Before long one saw that jovial, artful face of his on banners and placards which showed him exchanging symbolic handshakes of proletarian unity. Emil S. Pifremont had gone into politics. When this particular line no longer seemed profitable, he discreetly disappeared, in due course to turn up in Frankfurt-on-Main—at long last in the company of the Americans for whom he had waited in Glienicke.

The assumption that the Russians would advance only as far as the eastern outskirts of Berlin and that the Western Allies would occupy the city itself was widely current. Clearly people had misunderstood the Allied radio reports on the outcome of the Teheran and Yalta conferences. It was to such a misapprehension that Velten and several members of the Motor Pool owed a delightful binge.

Herr Otto Wendeborn was the owner of a liqueur factory in Berlin-Schöneberg and a villa in the eastern suburb of Saarow-Pieskow. In the cellar of his villa he had snugly stored away seventeen wickerwork-enclosed balloon flasks, each containing twenty-five gallons of pure Jamaica rum.

"Dear, oh dear," Wendeborn moaned to Major Herzlieb after making his acquaintance over a convivial game of skat, "just think of it—it's a capital asset! I would have shifted it out of Berlin because of the air raids, and now the infernal Russians are going to come and swill all that wonderful rum of mine!"

It was agreed that the civilized Americans would never dream of looting and that Herr Wendeborn's rum should be moved accordingly. A deal was speedily clinched. The major was to provide the transportation to West Berlin next morning, and in return Otto Wendeborn would supply schnapps for the canteen and officers' mess.

Velten went straight back to the office.

"Listen," he said to Weyermann, "you've got to find me an unused gasoline syphon and as many clean bottles as you can manage."

"The good soldier always helps himself . . ." Weyermann began reprovingly.

"Stuff it," Velten interrupted. "I'm off to Berlin with Erwin

327

Schöttler. That old crook Herzlieb's on to a new racket. Over four hundred gallons of pure Jamaica rum! If you boys aren't interested you only have to say so. I've bottles enough for myself."

Inside half an hour he was in possession of twenty empty bottles and an unused length of red rubber tubing.

When they had loaded the wickerwork baskets, Otto Wendeborn started to climb up.

"For God's sake, Herr Wendeborn!" said Velten. "You're endangering the success of the operation! There's a strict order against carrying civilians in army vehicles. I shall be having quite enough trouble getting the stuff through the check-points as it is."

The schnapps manufacturer allowed himself to be talked round and begged them to proceed with the utmost care.

"Right, Erwin," said Velten as soon as they were out of sight, "into the woods with her for a start!"

Erwin turned down a leafy lane, and as soon as they were well under cover Velten went to work on the balloons. "Let's have your bottles, Erwin," he said. "I'm not giving you a drop till you've finished driving, you poor bugger!"

Then, with great care, he tapped each of the seventeen flasks in turn to make the overall deficit imperceptible. Because he had to take a suck at the tube with every new balloon flask and could not bring himself to spit out the precious fluid, he was tight by the time he arrived back at his unit.

He shot into the office like a rocket. "Out you go!" he yelled. "Every man collect his share!"

The clerks piled outside as one man, leaving him alone with Weyermann. Velten looked into the corporal's eyes.

"Rudi," he said thickly. "Rudi, who would have thought it of me? Who'd have believed that I'd pinch a liquor-dealer's schnapps off him? Do you know what I am, Rudi? I'm a thief, that's what I am, a booze thief!"

"Rot," said Weyermann. "There's no such thing as thieving in the army—leastways, not unless it's from a comrade. All you've done is a bit of honest organizing. That's part of your job as a member of the Pool!"

But Velten was not to be comforted. "To think I've come as low

328

as that in this God-damned army! Pinching on the sly from my own load. With a mis'rable piece of tubing. . . ."

All at once his unsteady gaze focused on a framed, half-length portrait on the wall. The face peering down at him through pince-nez was mawkish and repellent with its receding chin and trim little toothbrush mustache. It was none other than Heinrich Himmler— the "Reichsheini," as Herr Schmidt had called him on that trip to Paris.

With a rush everything came to the surface in Velten's inebriated brain. He saw the polite, dispassionate young man who had called on him in his office, holding out the metal badge on his palm. He saw the guards in the Prinz-Albrecht-Strasse, the colorless autom-aton in the interview-room, the sedulous Herr Schmidt with his stupid smile—"it's the idea as a whole that we're concerned with, Herr Doktor." He saw the interrogation office in the rue des Saussaies. The chestnut-haired jade smiled at him mockingly and snapped her crimson-tipped fingers. "That red-headed sow Cilly— she bitched me," the Hauptsturmführer told him. "But yours is all right!" The good old Silver Stripe was there, too. "You don't make good iron into nails," he smiled, raising one finger admonishingly.

And she was standing at the stake. The stock was broader than her trunk. The dark wood surrounded her like a shadowy frame. She was quite naked. Cruelly naked—as white as chalk. Was this the body which had once quivered and flared in his arms? There was no flame in her now, this silent corpse at the martyr's stake. But from the black cavities of her eyes came a smoldering fire. Those eyes, those eyes, they bore straight through him! Oh, those merciless eyes, that icy, speechless mouth!

"She didn't betray you, you poor little crab!" came the mocking voice of Cismar. "You won't go before a court. You're already sentenced. . . ."

The bespectacled eyes still peered down at Velten from the black frame. Before Weyermann could stop him, he tore the picture from the wall and, raising it above his head in both hands, smashed it with one frenzied blow against the sharp corner of the writing table.

"Are you crazy, Victor?" gasped Weyermann. "The SS are next door. One of them might come in any minute!"

329

Sobering up with a jerk, Velten watched the corporal hastily sweep the fragments of picture, glass and frame under a cupboard. Then he drove to Berlin with Erwin to deliver the rum.

CHAPTER IX

WHILE Army Headquarters and its Motor Pool thus whiled away the days before the final decision, much was happening in the outside world. Dresden, the lovely rococo city on the Elbe, met a frightful death from the skies. The baroque buildings of Würzburg and the Gothic antiquities of Nuremberg crumbled into débris. On the heights of the Brilon Forest the corpses of the fallen heaped steadily up. Field-Marshal Model was encircled in the Ruhr. The Americans stormed through Thuringia and Saxony, leaving the boundaries demarcated at Yalta far behind them. In the East the hosts of refugees wandered hopelessly along the roads. In the West swarms of liberated slave-laborers fell on defenseless towns and villages on their way back home, burning, pillaging and destroying as they took their long pent-up revenge. Children, unscrupulously incited to commit futile acts of sabotage against the advancing armies, died pitiful deaths before they had begun to live. Isolated voices of reason were choked into silence by the hangmen's halters of summary courts where the old tyranny still raged. German soldiers hung from wayside trees and lamp-posts. "I was too great a coward to fight for my homeland!" said the placards on their breasts.

To Velten it was almost a merciful release when, towards the middle of April, Russian artillery on the Oder front opened the last act of the tragedy with a thunder that carried for dozens of miles. From that morning on there was to be no more "idling." The Motor Pool was on one hour's notice to move. The Army lay in the Spree Forest around Halbe, southeast of the capital it was committed to defend.

The Russians broke straight through the ludicrous defenses on the Oder and the Red tanks moved in on Berlin from the east and northeast. Eberswalde, Freienwalde, Strausberg fell one after the other. At Erkner the Russians crossed the Spree and prepared to launch a pincer movement on the capital. They ignored Twenty-Ninth Army, still lying idle in the Spree Forest.

Velten met Kracht. He was fuming. "The same old story! The Army's supposed to defend Berlin, instead of which it's lying here useless in the southeast. The Führer won't give the order to retire."

"And the generals?" Velten asked.

"They obey, as always!"

"Your lunatic?"

"And he *is* a lunatic!" Kracht cried. "The Americans were going to cross the Elbe at Barby. So he withdrew the assault-gun training brigade from the Eastern front. Élite troops, if you please! They've knocked off a dozen of the Yankee's tanks, as a result of which he's pinned down behind the Elbe. He could have been in Berlin by tomorrow!"

"The Führer," said Velten, "is fighting for his life. It'll mean death to him whichever of them gets to Berlin first!"

"It makes a hell of a difference to our wives and children, though," said Kracht bitterly.

"The Führer is fighting for his life," Velten repeated. "Let the generals fight for their homeland!"

"They obey the Führer," said Kracht.

April 20th came round. The Führer celebrated his birthday and issued an Order of the Day: "Berlin remains German. Vienna will be German again. Europe shall never be Bolshevized!"

The Motor Pool left its quarters and concentrated its vehicles in a nearby woods. The entire headquarters had assembled in a glade there to mark the occasion.

The chief-of-staff stepped forward. That day he had been promoted major-general, and there were now brand-new, broad red stripes running down his trouser-legs. He delivered an address in which he spoke of the difficult situation, of the way fortunes of war could change, however late the hour. Had not Providence worked a similar miracle in the case of Frederick the Great? "But if it is not to be, then let us do our duty as free Germans and die honorable deaths. Our Leader Adolf Hitler: Sieg Heil! Sieg Heil! Sieg Heil!"

I'm damned well not going to die, thought Velten. Neither are you, for all your red stripes!

Then every man received a hundred cigarettes. Because it was the Führer's birthday.

After the ceremony the heavy vehicles rumbled off, reportedly heading for the Olympic Village at Döberitz. Velten was detailed to drive for General Staff Intelligence. They left their cars standing under cover of the thicket and gathered in the bowling alley of an inn right at the base of the narrow peninsula from which the staff issued its orders to the army lying isolated and idle in the Spree Forest.

Gradually the men in the alley slipped into that mood of indifference and passive expectancy which fortunately always seems to overtake soldiers condemned to inaction in the face of dire events. So far the staff had never failed to decamp at the appropriate moments, and the rank and file of the headquarters could not see their officers paying any serious heed to the heroic death-vow of the newly baked major-general. Now and again Velten went over to the staff building to ask the intelligence clerks or Kracht about the situation. It was hopeless, they told him, and growing increasingly desperate from hour to hour. The Russians were coming in from the south now and had already entered Teltow rural district. In other words, the time limit for withdrawing the army on to Berlin had finally run out.

"The Headquarters can't move," Kracht told him, "because the Führer can't be contacted. He's having a birthday party. Without orders from the Führer we just daren't pull out."

And so they waited. The hours went by. About four in the morning the rumor went round that Ivan had crossed the Spree at Fürstenwalde and was already in Petersdorf, four miles east of Saarow. No sound of battle, not so much as a single shot, could be heard. Obviously there was not a single German soldier out in front of them. Were it not for the Russians' slowness and caution they would have already been in the bag.

Shortly afterward Corporal Berner appeared. "Get ready to move off!" he said, involuntarily lowering his voice. "No lights and no unnecessary noise! And don't race your engines. Drive at a walking pace, and keep well closed up. Where we're going to, God alone knows!"

Velten took three clerks and orderlies from intelligence on board, together with a load of files and maps. Then the column slipped quietly away down forest tracks and across the fields. Like links in a chain they stuck close behind each other, automatically following the movements of the man in front. Guides standing at road junctions called out directions in lowered voices. Once they passed over a bridge.

It was already gray morning when they were flagged into a large courtyard. In the background rose the stony façade of a château-like building.

Berner arranged the vehicles out in the park so that they were partially camouflaged and not standing too close together. Velten found himself next to Hans Arend with his Horch.

"No quarters for drivers this time either," said Berner after the last clerk had disappeared into the château. "You will have to make do in your vehicles."

Hans Arend had a brain wave. "Listen," he said, "we'll make a better sleeper out of your crate than you've ever seen on the Mitropa!"

They dismantled the front seats of Velten's 170-V and put the leather-covered cushions from Arend's *Kübelwagen* inside. Then Velten hauled out one of his warm Luftwaffe blankets and spread it over the upholstered base. In due course the two of them were reclining at full length, their feet in a warm blanket and their heads on one of Arend's cushions.

They slept till after midday. No one bothered them. There was no reveille, no mustering out, no shouting or cursing.

After breakfasting on smoked ham, sausage, cheese and bread, they fitted up the insides of their vehicles again. Then they went out to reconnoiter the area. Most of the drivers were at work on the vehicles, the remainder asleep. It did not seem as if any immediate alarms were expected.

They came to a cross-roads. There was actually an MP on point duty. But no traffic for him to direct. A signpost showed that the road led to Storkow.

"What château is that back there where we're bivouacked?" Velten asked the MP.

"That's Hubertushöhe hunting lodge in Beeskow-Storkow rural district," the man told him with a slight reproach in his voice, as if disapproving of such ignorance in one directly involved in the current operations.

They returned to the park. Velten brought out a map.

"There, just see what a God-forsaken tract of country they've dumped us in. We're stuck between the lakes and the forest."

"It's certainly an out-of-the-way spot," said Hans Arend pensively. Suddenly he gave a start. "Lord, surely they're not going to carry out their old threat and make a stand?"

There had often been talk of the headquarters taking up a "hedgehog" position when there was no way out. Then, when Ivan came, everyone was to sell his life as dearly as he was capable.

"Anything's possible," said Velten. "Perhaps that's why they issued us those hand-grenades and panzerfausts a few days ago."

They spent the whole afternoon in deliberation. One thing was clear: whoever stayed where they were now was trapped. There would be nothing else to do but to sit and wait for Ivan to show up.

"That is, if we're allowed to surrender!" Velten pointed out. "They're quite capable of making us fight for it first."

"Ach, don't kid yourself," said Arend. "They've got just as big a shake on as we have!"

Next morning there was even warm soup for breakfast. Apart from a field-kitchen, only the operations staff appeared to be in the bivouac area. The quartermaster-general's branch and the main body of the headquarters had gone to the Olympic Village. Most of the Motor Pool was also there, including Kessler and the clerical staff. The only full-rank non-com in the trap was Berner.

After dinner the two men built up their "sleeper" again. "Let's get in a stock of sleep," said Velten. "Who knows what the next few nights will bring?"

The sky above them was blue and remote. Lazily stretching out their limbs, they slid gently into the cushiony billows of slumber.

A violent thumping on the windshield brought Velten up with a start. An orderly was standing outside.

"You're to come straight to the office! Lieutenant von Kracht wants you!"

Hurriedly Velten laced his boots, wound on his ankle puttees, smoothed back his hair and, pulling on his cap as he went, doubled off towards the hunting lodge.

He ran into Kracht in the corridor outside the Intelligence offices. He had his cap and belt on, and caught Velten by the sleeves to draw him close.

"I've got a duty trip to the Supreme Command of the Army at Eiche near Potsdam. I specially chose you as my driver. We must leave immediately, or we shan't get through. Get ready as fast as you can!"

Velten noticed that the other was all keyed up. The sight made him completely calm.

"Papers?" he asked briefly.

"Collect them from the orderly room sergeant. But do get a move on! You must pick me up in front in five minutes from now!"

Velten now felt entirely sure of himself. He really was born lucky, he reflected. Every time there had ever been any sign of heroics starting, he'd always got away just in time. This latest turn of events so emboldened him that he never considered the possibility of anything going wrong.

He found the orderly room. The young sergeant was holding a weapon inspection.

"My God, sergeant," said Velten, "I've never seen you doing anything as warlike as that before."

"You may well talk," the other replied. His voice sounded quite friendly—it had an almost civilian mildness, Velten thought. Normally this youthful bureau warrior had adopted a much more regimental tone. "I don't half envy you, believe me! What a stroke of luck to get out of this rat-trap!"

He gave Velten the work ticket.

"It says 'and back to unit,' sergeant," said Velten after a glance at the document.

"Lieutenant von Kracht's meant to collect situation reports and maps. You're supposed to get back today. But you know perfectly well you won't. You probably wouldn't get through again, even if you wanted to."

"I shall do my very best at all events," Velten replied with the utmost solemnity.

"I bet you will!" The sergeant twisted his face into a somewhat painful smile. Then he held out his hand. "All the best to you!"

"You too, sergeant," said Velten, squeezing the slightly damp hand. "I hope we'll meet again, safe and sound."

Then he went into the Intelligence office to ask whether there was any gear to load for Kracht.

"Gear? Bags?" barked Wastler, the Party-minded draftsman. "What do you think he wants that for? You're coming back today."

Velten bit his lip. "I thought he might be taking a bag along for his maps and things."

"All that will go in his dispatch-case. He's got that with him. Now buzz off!"

"All very chummy in here, isn't it?" Velten could not resist the gibe.

The draftsman flushed. "You expect a man to be chummy in the middle of all this?" he cried. "You ought to see the situation we're just marking up—as far as we've got any situation reports to do it from."

He brandished his drawing-pen at Velten. "You don't seem to know the war's lost!"

Velten pricked up his ears. He was unable to suppress his grin. Taken you long enough to see the light, he thought. Then he said, as gently as possible: "When I was bold enough to say as much back in Kalisz, one gentleman in particular was terribly indignant."

"Man alive!" yelled the Viennese. "I never suspected then that we were ruled by such criminals!"

He stared fixedly at the situation map pinned to his board. "I'm a good twelve or fifteen years younger than you," he continued in a calmer voice. "My generation believed! We were offered something full of power and drive! We were full of trust and hope! Who could know they'd drag us through the muck like this?"

Velten was silent. I'd have liked to see you seven years ago, he thought. Anschluss! Union with a Greater Germany! Hullabaloo and flag-waving! Out with the Jews! To hell with reason!

"Listen to me," said the draftsman in tormented tones. "I'm from Vienna. Have you any idea what's going on in Vienna now?

336

That's where my wife is—and she's only eighteen! We've only been married a year. Think of it—eighteen! And the Russians are there!"

He began marking the map up with data from a situation report.

"I could have got her out to relatives in Vorarlberg," he muttered. "But who thought they'd ever reach Vienna?"

"I got my wife away long ago," said Velten. "But then, I was inferior enough to realize long ago that the war was lost. . . ."

"Where have you taken her to?" the man asked, as if absentmindedly.

"To a place the Americans reached long ago," said Velten in quiet triumph.

"The Americans! The *Americans*!" the draftsman mimicked. He raised his head from the drawing-board, his face red again.

"Americans *or* Russians!" he spat. "It's all the same in the end. Do you think the Americans stick it between the door?"

Velten strode out, slamming the door violently behind him.

When he got back to the car he found Hans Arend busy restoring their sleeper to its normal status.

"You knew?" asked Velten in surprise.

"I guessed you'd be leaving."

"Take a couple of those good blankets," said Velten. "Three will be plenty for me."

"You are a lucky dog," said Arend, without the least trace of envy. "Not one man in the pool gets a trip. We all go on sitting in the trap. And you get out!"

"I'm supposed to be back today," Velten interposed lightly.

"Sez you!" said Hans Arend with a knowing grimace. Then they shook hands.

"Take care of yourself, you old rogue," said Velten. "Don't keep the little girls back home waiting too long!"

"Get along with you . . . Give my regards to Ivan if he catches you!"

Velten started up his engine and drove cautiously out of his vehicle emplacement. He had only dug it that morning. Some other driver could have it now! He drove round to the broad flight of steps leading up to the terrace.

Kracht was standing on the terrace, his black dispatch-case in his hand. Velten could tell from a distance how restless he was. He

337

was moving from one foot to the other, like a child wanting to relieve itself. As he pulled up in front of him, Velten noticed that there were sweat beads on his temples as well as his upper lip.

"At last!" roared Kracht. "I thought you must be taking a bath!"

Then he turned to the doorway and called to someone inside. The next instant an officer in Luftwaffe uniform hastened out. He had his belt and cap on but carried no luggage of any kind. With a bound he reached the car, tore open the door Velten had already unfastened, and threw himself into the back. Kracht followed suit and took his seat next to Velten.

"Off you go," he said, "beat it!"

Velten drove off unhurriedly in first gear and leisurely changed into second.

"Come on, come on, step on it!" cried the Luftwaffe officer.

The car rumbled slowly down the broad, poplar-lined avenue.

CHAPTER X

As THEY EMERGED from the avenue onto the main road, Kracht turned to Velten.

"You realize we're not coming back?"

Velten decided to act dumb to begin with.

"How come?" he asked. "I thought we had to return today."

"Yeah?" Kracht gulped. Then he recovered from his astonishment. "What the hell do you think I specially chose you for?" he asked in his hasty way. "For God's sake, man, think of our talk in Zyrardow. It's now or never! Our lives are at stake!"

Look now, thought Velten, the MP was no longer at the crossroads. No more traffic control being done, apparently. No traffic either, if it came to that. The road was lonely and entirely devoid of life. Then it occurred to him that Kracht was waiting for an answer to his reminder of Zyrardow and their promise to stick

338

together when things became really grave. However, he wanted to harass the other's nerves a little more. Apart from that, the air-force officer interested him. He wasn't on the work ticket. There was something blatantly phony about him. Velten meant to let the two of them see that they needed him at least as urgently as he needed them.

So, as he turned off in the direction of Storkow, he remarked to Kracht in a confidential undertone that was just loud enough for the Luftwaffe captain to hear:

"Yes, Herr von Kracht, you and I should always manage all right together. But I don't know what the Herr captain's mission is. For all I know he's got to return to army by tonight."

He could feel the embarrassment which spread through the car.

"Oh, no," said the captain at last. "I don't have to return as fast as that. This mission's going to take some time."

That's why you haven't any luggage with you, I suppose, thought Velten. Not even a dispatch-case for your toothbrush.

"By the way," the airman went on, "I gather from Herr von Kracht that you two are friends. You're a colleague of his and a university man. I think we might drop the 'sirs' from now on. My name's Marschner."

Velten was aware of a hand being proffered from behind. He stretched his own right one over his shoulder and felt a firm grip. Not a bad sort of chap after all, he decided.

"Captain Marschner is the air liaison officer at army," Kracht explained. "He's going to look for the two Fieseler-Storchs belonging to our staff that have been missing for the last few days."

"Air LO, is he?" said Velten. "He's certainly the right man to go looking for spotter aircraft."

Neither of the passengers made any reply. The matter seemed already settled as far as they were concerned.

Kracht brought out a map. "It's a mystery to me just now," he said, "how we're going to get into Berlin at all."

"Are we bound to go there, then?"

"Listen," Kracht told him uneasily. "The Russians are driving on Potsdam from the south. There's only a narrow corridor left to us to get into the city. It may be possible to nose along the southern edge of the city and over Glienicke Bridge."

339

They had just passed through Storkow when they ran into their first road-block. It was manned by old men and thirteen- to fifteen-year-old boys. All of them, young and old, had fire-arms slung over their shoulders. Out of their pockets peeped the handles of hand-grenades.

As they swung across the fields to avoid the road-block, Kracht said with despair in his voice: "So those are the defenders of Berlin! And the Army's stuck in the Spree Forest! and Headquarters is forming a hedgehog!"

"And we," added Velten, "are on the run because that's the only thing left for a sane man to do."

". . . If he has the opportunity," Marschner interposed.

"And if he can get away with it," said Velten, slowing up before yet another road-block.

From now on they kept exclusively to lanes and farm tracks or even went straight across country. The 170-V behaved wonderfully, just as though she had been built for rough-riding. Now and again the figure of a Home Guard would bob up behind a tree or hedge. They were mostly elderly men who gazed gravely after the car, rifles across their shoulders and hands deep in coat pockets.

"What I don't understand," said Velten, "is why the Russians haven't already got Berlin in their pocket. Faced with these poor unfortunates, they ought to do it in no time."

"One thing you mustn't forget," said the airman, "is the relative length of the final battles. When a war's drawing to its end and everyone knows it'll all soon be over, both sides fight with the utmost caution. Everyone, irrespective of whether he's an attacker or defender, tells himself he mustn't get wounded just before the final whistle. That's what gives us a chance of reaching Berlin before Ivan."

And reach Berlin they did. How, remained a mystery to Velten. But by devious routes they gradually found their way from the fields onto asphalted streets, and all of a sudden they were in Rudow, just before Neukölln. Velten knew a seldom-used string of side-streets running from Neukölln to the Tempelhof airfield. From there he turned south to get on to the main circular road going west.

They had not realized how utterly deserted the neighborhood

was when suddenly, fifty yards ahead of them, a figure sprang out of a camouflaged slit-trench. It wore a steel helmet and gas mask and had binoculars slung round its neck.

"Well, well, a soldier!" said Velten. "The first we've set eyes on in Berlin."

The man planted himself in the middle of the street with outstretched arms and stopped the car. Velten saw that he was a second-lieutenant.

"Halt!" he yelled. "Don't go any farther! There's a Russian armored spearhead a mile and a half from here, at the Lankwitz Church!"

Thereupon he vanished into his hole again. All around him it was now possible to discern riflemen dug in among the foliage of the front gardens.

Velten had already turned the car and started off the way they had come.

"There's nothing for it now but to push straight through," he said. "Sachsendamm, Schöneberger Strasse, Kaiserallee and the Zoo. Then over to the Heerstrasse and down to Kladow—if they haven't blown the Havel bridges!"

"My God," said Kracht, utterly horror-stricken. "Russians at the Lankwitz Church!"

Despite the gravity of the situation, Velten could not suppress a grin.

"Yes, Herr von Kracht, if only that could have been prophesied on the Day of Potsdam in 'thirty-three!"

They drove swiftly through the late afternoon. She was a heart-rending sight, Berlin in her hour of agony. As the car raced along the long line of streets, they might have been passing through ravines of death. It was almost more bearable to look at ruins than the undamaged districts, for only here did the emptiness make itself fully felt, emphasized by the occasional human beings who showed themselves in the streets. None of them walked with a normal gait. They ran like hunted animals, flitting along the shadows of the house-fronts to disappear into some doorway or other.

Over the city circled a few Rata machines, their engines grinding away discordantly. They dropped no bombs, however, nor did they fire a single shot. They seemed entirely sure of what they were about

—like vultures hovering over a prey which they know must soon be lifeless carrion.

"It smells of death and destruction," Velten murmured. "They talk of men being marked down by death. This is a whole city with the mark of death on it . . . You can see it, feel it and taste it! You can smell it with every breath you draw!"

They finally saw a policeman.

"Are the Havel bridges still free?" asked Kracht.

"No news of demolitions or barricades so far," the man told him, raising his hand to his helmet in the pre-20th July salute.

Velten stepped on the gas, and they whizzed down the east-west axis at fifty miles an hour. After passing the Reichskanzlerplatz he put his foot down still farther, bringing their speed up to almost sixty-five.

True enough, the bridge over the Stössensee was intact, and so was Havel bridge with its iron arch. Best of all, there were no check-points anywhere. No provost or SS patrols to stop the car and ask for papers. What a stroke of luck for the Storch-seeker!

As they reached Eiche in the gathering dusk, the Air LO suggested they should turn into a side-street and wait for nightfall. He was feeling unsure of himself.

Hardly had Velten brought his car to a standstill in an avenue of fruit trees when they noticed a military vehicle tailing them.

"There's nothing for it," said Velten. "We'll have to bluff it out."

He climbed down, pulled up the hood and began fiddling at the carburetor with a screwdriver.

The strange vehicle stopped immediately behind them. A second-lieutenant got out and came over to the door, saluting politely. Had the gentlemen lost their way, he inquired? He had better warn them in case they were making for Potsdam. The Russians had already occupied the eastern part of the town.

Kracht, quickly pulling himself together, was fulsomely grateful. No, they weren't going to Potsdam—nor had they missed their way. They were carrying messages to the Supreme Command of the Army. Yes, they knew the route, thank you very much. Their driver simply wanted to cope with some engine trouble in this side-street where he wouldn't be disturbed.

342

This seemed to satisfy the zealous lieutenant. Taking his leave as courteously as he had come, he wished them *bon voyage*, climbed back into his car and drove off.

So that was how they treated you when you deserted with officers, thought Velten. He resolved there and then to spend the rest of the war in Kracht's company and continued to toy with the carburetor until the other two thought the evening dark enough.

"I say," said Velten as they drove into Eiche's maze of barracks. "There's not a single sentry! Looks too damned quiet to me."

In one courtyard two big trucks were standing with their engines running. Soldiers were busy loading office furniture and packing-cases.

The two officers disappeared into one of the long white buildings, the Luftwaffe LO obviously considering it safer to entrust himself to Kracht's company than to stay in the car and risk some sudden encounter. Velten, for his own part, preferred to remain behind the wheel. He wanted to avoid any conversation with the troops by the trucks.

The two officers were soon back. "The place is as good as empty," Kracht told him. "There's only a small rear party left. No one knows where the main body's gone. Pulled out in a hell of a hurry. The General's with the Führer in the Chancellery fixing a new location."

"Suits us just nicely, if you ask me," commented Velten.

"I'm not so sure about that. My job's to find Supreme Head-quarters. We'd better go on looking for it!"

They drove off and sought all night long—naturally without success. They began by trying to reach the Olympic Village, but did not get that far. Half way there they ran into an endless flow of military and civilian vehicles racing from the direction of Döberitz. Even one or two red monsters of the fire service were to be seen weaving in and out of the confusion.

With some difficulty they turned and drove to Nauen. The usually dull little town was in a tumult as columns of refugees, some in cars, some on foot, converged on it from all sides. In spite of reports that the Russians were outside Kremmen, they took a chance and drove through Fehrbellin and Neuruppin. On this route the roads were reasonably free. Just before Neuruppin they pulled into a lane, camouflaged the vehicle behind a hedge and slept for a few hours, sitting upright in the car.

Neuruppin was fairly quiet, and in the early-morning light it still had the look of the peaceful country town one knew from Sunday-afternoon excursions. Kracht was in a hurry to move on, for although there was no trace of Supreme Headquarters, they could not exclude the possibility of its passing that way. And for their particular purpose it was infinitely better to be looking for headquarters than to find it.

All this time the Luftwaffe officer was—or claimed to be—on the lookout for his Fieseler-Storchs. But he had no success.

And so they cruised around for a while in the northern March of Brandenburg, passing through Pritzwalk and then turning south again to Kyritz. Suddenly Velten waved vigorously out of the window: there were actually vehicles from the Motor Pool coming towards them. They found that the part of the headquarters which had left Saarow on April 20th was now in Segeletz, a hamlet between Wusterhausen and Friesack.

Dropping his passengers off in the village, Velten located the transport office in a farm on the floor of a wooded valley. Opening the first door he came to, he found himself in a large, gloomy kitchen full of soldiers. At a small table by one wall sat Weyermann, filling in work tickets. Opposite was an enormous range from which came a delightful aroma of bacon and eggs. And who was this bending over the fire with poker in hand, busy stirring up a crackling blaze? As dainty as ever in well-creased slacks and a blouse plunging low between two pouting breasts, with her honey-colored hair upswept and her willful mouth a strawberry red? It was none other than Puttylein! Or so the men called her. As he stood there watching her wield a frying pan as big as a cart-wheel, Velten marveled for the umpteenth time at the contrast between this fragile figure and the hulking Kessler.

Puttylein was a not unknown star of the stage and screen. Finding herself stranded by events in that Brandenburg spa, she had, like any native of Berlin, taken opportunity by the forelock. In her case opportunity had been Wehrmacht transport and the forelock Kessler's rather bristly scalp. She thus succeeded in dispatching her most

344

valued possessions to Western Germany on the Motor Pool's trucks. Kessler acted as any other man would have done in his position: he made the most impossible things possible. In view of the splendid example set by Major Herzlieb, he was running no great risk.

"I'd have felt there was something really wrong if you'd no longer been here," was Velten's comment as his eye fell upon her now. "Your presence gives the finishing touch to the picture of demoralization and final collapse."

"Why, our defeatist is back again!" she piped delightedly, turning round with the sleek grace of a she-cat. "We might have known that hedgehog game wouldn't suit you! Smelled unhealthy, didn't it, mein Kleiner? I wouldn't mind knowing how you wangled it this time!"

At that moment Velten heard a boom of familiar laughter behind him. Turning round, he found Kessler's massive frame filling in the doorway.

"There's the runaway!" he cried. "Don't you know they're looking for you?"

"Are they?" replied Velten evenly. "We've been told to find Supreme Headquarters. Well, we haven't so far—for all the trouble we've taken."

Then he remembered the military proprieties. Stepping up to the bulky captain, he shot his right arm up in the air, let it fall again, clamped his hands along the seams of his trousers and bawled:

"Lance-Corporal Velten reporting back to the Pool! Impossible to comply with order to rejoin operations staff owing to present state of the front!"

"Don't be so sure of that," said Kessler nastily. "We've had a message from the Army Commander today. Major Herzlieb and several others have orders to report to Hubertushöhe."

"Herr Hauptmann, if Major Herzlieb's under orders to join a hedgehog position, my mind's at rest. That makes it quite definite that no one can get through!"

"No need to get fresh," Kessler rumbled. Velten was right, nevertheless. Another radio message was received ordering Kracht and Capt. Speer of GSI to return to Hubertushöhe. They replied that it was no longer possible.

The Luftwaffe LO was the subject of a particularly malevolent order. Capt. Marschner, it stated, was to be placed under arrest and brought before a military court. It seemed that he had left the hedgehog position without any kind of authority.

Marschner was never court-martialed. Before they could lay hands on him, he had disappeared without trace. He had actually run the aircraft to ground in a wood and, by ordering them back to Hubertushöhe, fulfilled his self-appointed mission.

The tactical headquarters joined up with the main body of Twenty-Ninth Army in the Spree Forest. Part went to Kingdom Come, the rest into captivity. Only a very small force succeeded in breaking through to the Elbe. This was the army which was to have defended Berlin. Now Home Guard, Hitler Youth and SS were trying their hand at the task pending the arrival of the mythical Wenck Army which was supposed to be advancing from the West.

Velten spent only one night in Segeletz. Next morning the mob moved. By now they were more like a band of marauders than the Main Headquarters of a military formation. What now wended its way through the Prignitz under the command of Major Herzlieb was but a miscellaneous residue of the headquarters' various branches. There were remnants of the defense company and the signals, clerks and draftsmen from various bureaux, and, last but not least, the drivers. The defense company was still employed to the extent of providing guards and manning the cookhouses. The signals staff did a certain amount of work. And the drivers had to lift the headquarters personnel from one stopping-place to the next and maintain their vehicles in the intervals. Apart from that, however, this accumulation of men—and women, if one counted the black Lola and the blonde Puttylein—simply lazed around.

From Segeletz they moved to a wood not far from the town of Pritzwalk. April had brought an almost June-like warmth, and Velten scorned the idea of sleeping in the car. He got an enormous bale of straw from a nearby barn, and in this he camped with Kracht.

Little by little the unoccupied unit sensed the imminence of collapse. No one knew how it would come. But all of them had one wish—not to be caught by the Russians!

Members of the Motor Pool brought back odd items of intelligence from their occasional reconnaissance trips. It was reported

346

that the Americans had opened up a crossing over the Elbe for German casualties and were holding Swedish Red Cross ambulances ready on the far bank. Before a man was let across, the SS checked up to make sure that he was incapable of further deeds of heroism. What about wrapping an arm or leg in an enormous bandage? Velten put the thought straight out of his mind. *His* neck was not itching for the noose! None of the others tried either.

In the anxiety of suspense between Russians on one hand and SS and provost on the other, the best thing seemed to be to stick to Kracht. In the company of an officer one always had the possibility of absconding under a cloak of legality.

For the time being Kracht was still undecided. "Would you come in on something?" he asked. "The driver of an officer on the Artillery Commander's staff has his home in these parts. He can get hold of a boat. We could get across the Elbe by night."

"Good enough," said Velten. "When do we start?"

Kracht, however, had all sorts of qualms. How would one be able to detach oneself unobserved? How did one get to the river? And what if they were caught?

A fresh stir arose in the meantime. Major Zwiesel, the DAAG, had an attack of acute heroism. At an officers' conference—the details of which Velten heard from Kracht—he declared that "the men" must be formed into an alarm unit and committed to battle. One or two people objected, but none very vigorously. It still seemed dangerous to oppose a heroic plan in public. Only Kessler came out energetically on behalf of his enlisted men and attained their collective release from the undertaking.

Quite pitilessly the clerks and draftsmen—none of this category being indispensable to their superiors' personal safety—were drummed together and made to exchange pens and chinagraph pencils for rifles and carbines. They set off under the leadership of Corporal Feuerhard of A Branch.

Two clerks returned that evening. One had a bandaged head, the other his right arm in a sling. The pathetic crowd of pen-pushers, it appeared, had been wiped out by enemy gun-fire on a knoll near Döberitz. They were the only survivors.

That, Major Herzlieb decided, was more than enough. To every man on the headquarters, irrespective of rank, he issued a pass signed by him personally and stamped with the Army Headquarters seal. Velten's was worded thus:

> Lance-Corporal Velten is a member of HQ Twenty-Ninth Army. Any attempt to detach him for other employment will be interpreted as interference in the competence of this Headquarters and will render the offender liable to court-martial.
>
> (Signed) HERZLIEB
Major and Camp Commandant

In the Field
April 26th, 1945

Fortunately no one ever found himself in a situation where he needed to test the efficacy of this document. They remained tightly packed together in their little wood, counting the hours till the time would be ripe to go over to the Americans or bolt for home.

They were better supplied with news now than at any time in the whole war. With a loudspeaker provided by the Signal Corps in constant use, officers and men listened jointly to the bulletins of German and Allied transmitters.

In this way one learned that the generals, too, were now beginning to run for it. And then things began to crumble around the Führer himself. From the bomb-proof shelter of his Chancellery he thundered out anathema on the heads of Fat Boy Hermann and Heinrich, the chief of his Black Guard. Both of them—quite independently of one another—had suffered sudden attacks of rationality. They were, it seemed, just as keen to cut loose as those common soldiers had been who now adorned trees at the roadsides.

Velten began pressing Kracht to act. But the lieutenant still hesitated.

On April 30th they moved to Crivitz in Mecklenburg. It was here that they heard the news of Hitler's demise. First the official version telling of a hero's death. Then the ignominious truth.

"Now there's nothing to stop me," said Kracht. "I've sworn no oath to Mr. Dönitz."

That's rich, thought Velten. As if you'd have thought twice about bolting in Hitler's lifetime if only it had been as safe as a train ride from Berlin to Munich! Aloud he said: "Speaking as a lawyer, Herr von Kracht, I'm inclined to take you up on that. The military oath

348

isn't the decisive factor in determining a case of desertion. Besides, before he deserted himself, Mr. Hitler was good enough to safeguard our allegiance by transferring his rights to Mr. Dönitz."

Kracht stared at him in astonishment. "Are you backing out all of a sudden?"

Velten laughed. "Who said anything about backing out? I'm as game as ever. But I'm all against rushing it. Let's carry on as before —with a work ticket and a special mission! Long live legal desertion!"

Velten was right. Militarism was stronger than Adolf. Each unit crouched woodenly next to its neighbor. Everyone driven to desertion by anxiety for his wife and children, aged parents or widowed mother came before a tribunal. And the insensate vassals of that pagan deity, the *Barras,* obediently shot his breast full of holes or laid the hempen cord around his sweating neck.

CHAPTER XI

LATE that afternoon, April 30th Velten was standing by his car, which he had carefully camouflaged in a sunken road. He was considering whether he should prepare it for bedding-down when Kracht approached at the double.

"Here," he cried, "you can read for yourself—a movement order signed by Major Herzlieb! I'm to drive on ahead with Captain Speer to reconnoiter the route. Admittedly Herzlieb's as drunk as a pig, but there's no sign of that in his signature."

"Excellent," said Velten. "Get the captain and try to stay within hailing distance." He was already behind the wheel. "I'll get the work ticket from the office."

Kessler was among those in the office, in a forester's house. He winked broadly when Velten announced that he was to drive west with Capt. Speer and Lieut. von Kracht on reconnaissance.

As Velten took his leave, the captain held out his hand. "I'd like to thank you for everything—since Wolkowysk!" said Velten.

"Here, what's all this about?" demanded Weyermann from his corner.

"You can shake hands with me, too. I'm doing a bunk—legal desertion!"

With that Velten was gone.

They drove well into the night, zigzagging through eastern and northern Mecklenburg. The roads were crammed with the familiar whirl of hurrying convoys and fleeing civilians.

Capt. Speer sat next to Velten, and the jumpy, restless Kracht behind. Speer was quiet and composed.

"I've only one interest," he said, "and that's to go into captivity on four wheels."

He was the eldest of the three. With embonpoint such as his, it was an understandable wish.

On the morning of May 1st Velten stopped in front of the post office in the little Mecklenburg town of Wittenburg. It was here that they were supposed to be meeting Herzlieb at 8 a.m. They waited for two hours, but no one came. Then they moved into the parlor of a small hotel on the market square. At some time past noon Kracht sprang to his feet and plunged to the window. A car from Army was outside, its driver having obviously spotted Velten's vehicle. Then Lieut. von Schliephaacke sailed in, accompanied by his driver. He was in charge of the interpreter's pool at Twenty-Ninth Army, just as Hegestein had once been at the Army Group.

"How's the old firm doing?" Kracht inquired.

"Gentlemen," said the interpreter, "a nice thing happened yesterday evening. A General Kunze suddenly turned up, furnished with special powers. He ordered Herzlieb to make the whole outfit dig in and prepare to fight a defensive action against the Russians."

"Good God, it seems that we got away just in time again!"

"Oh, Herzlieb's skedaddled as well in the meantime," said Schliephaacke in his broad Baltic accent. "He gave orders to move off the moment that windbag of a general had made himself scarce. I've driven on ahead. Damned if I'm going to let the Russians catch me."

They conjectured for a while regarding the probable whereabouts of the headquarters. But it was perfectly clear that none of them really cared a rap about Headquarters of Twenty-Ninth Army.

An uproar out in the market place interrupted the conversation. A man wearing a blue peaked cap came past swinging a big brass bell. Then, at the top of his voice, he proclaimed that the Americans were about to enter Vellahn, eleven miles away, and could be expected to shell Wittenburg. The burgomaster advised the population to take to the woods. Fortunately this fatuous suggestion had not the least effect. People stayed where they were.

Schliephaacke took his leave, intending to get as far west as possible. Hardly was he gone when another headquarters vehicle showed up—a Volkswagen this time. Two officers got out.

"Now the fun's really starting," murmured Kracht to Velten. "Those are Messrs. Schwede and Birkhahn from the Artillery Commander's staff. The same two who wanted to clear out back in Pritzwalk."

The newcomers, a lieutenant and a second-lieutenant, were in the best of spirits. As they themselves blithely announced, they no longer regarded themselves as members of the Wehrmacht. They had put their entire unit on a self-supporting basis and were now established in an ideal hiding-place in a wood outside the town.

It was decided that they should all stay together. This meant their final break with the Wehrmacht. Henceforth they would go it alone.

CHAPTER XII

THE VOLKSWAGEN led: Velten followed. Just outside the town it turned off from the main road and drove a few hundred yards down a wooded track. Then it disappeared behind some rising ground. As Velten followed up he found that behind the hump the track dropped sharply into a marshy glen. This damp hollow was thickly overgrown with a confusion of intertwining brushwood over which towered the massive tree-trunks of the forest. It was certainly an ideal place of concealment. Neither provost nor SS, to say nothing of Gen. Kunze, would ever find their way in here!

A number of vehicles, including a troop-transporter, were skillfully camouflaged among the bushes along the edge of the glen. The place was plunged in an indefinite twilight, the last rays of the sinking sun not penetrating thus far.

The men of the unit were in a cheerful frame of mind. They had just slaughtered a pig, the gift of a fleeing estate-owner from Pomerania who had attached himself to their convoy, and for supper everyone received a large hunk of boiled pork. The men obviously placed great trust in the two officers who had brought them as far as this and were counting on their being able to get them into Western captivity and, if possible, all the way home.

Velten had just finished re-arranging his car for the night when Kracht appeared. Once again something was exercising him.

"Hurry up," he whispered, "I've fixed a place for the lot of us."

They drove out of the hiding-place and left the car behind the rise by the fork. Kracht led them the rest of the way down to the main road on foot. They came to a village standing on its own. "Dr. Johannes Kagelwitt" was the name on the door. "A lawyer in Wittenburg," Kracht explained. "We can spend the night here."

He concluded by warning Velten to be ready to start at four next morning.

Velten slept wonderfully in a bed with sheets. The master of the house did not show up. He was said to be ill. With a soldier's indifference Velten did not ask many questions. He enjoyed the bed.

The next morning Lieut. Schwede showed him the map. "We're the advance party. The Volkswagen will lead and you'll follow us. We're taking the smaller side-roads." He traced out the route with his finger. "Here, through Karft, Neuhof, Zarrentin. Then along the Ratzeburger Chaussee for a bit. Behind Seedorf we turn off to Sterley, where we'll stop for breakfast and wait for the main body to come up with my staff-sergeant."

The two artillery officers climbed into the Volkswagen, which was driven by a reliable-looking blond giant. He drove off immediately, and Velten had some difficulty in keeping up. Once again Speer sat

352

next to him, exuding confidence and calm. The nervous Kracht fidgeted in the back seat.

Kracht chattered away excitedly in the back. "One thing we do know from intelligence reports on Yalta," he said, more to himself than to the two men in front, "is that the Elbe will be the demarcation line between East and West."

"That means we must get right past Hamburg," Velten exclaimed.

"We shall, if we can. But we don't think—do we, Speer?—that the Allies will let the Russians have Hamburg. They simply can't afford to! Just imagine it, Velten! They can't possibly let the Russians come near the Elbe estuary. . . ."

Speer's quiet voice interrupted the flow of words.

"Neither are they going to let them near it. We've pretty reliable information that the demarcation line is to run along the Elbe. But northwards from Lauenburg the boundary will be the Elbe-Lübeck Canal. It's reasonable to suppose that the British aren't going to hand over Schleswig-Holstein and the Kaiser Wilhelm Canal to the Russians."

"All right, we've got to get over the Elbe-Lübeck Canal any way," said Kracht eagerly. "Then we're safe."

"I wouldn't be in favor of going as far as Hamburg, in any case," said Velten. "It's a dead certainty that those lunatics will make a second Berlin out of it. Am I to get myself stuck in an alarm unit to help defend the city after all the trouble I've taken to get out of defending Berlin?"

Then something else occurred to him. "But if the Elbe's really the boundary—how did the Americans come to be outside Vellahn yesterday? And it's quite definite that they were there. We saw the searchlights ourselves last night when they were calmly sailing over the Elbe! They might have been on maneuvers!"

"Naturally they can't keep to the agreed areas of interest as long as they're operational," said Kracht impatiently. "Saxony and Thuringia are two other cases where they're well into territory that's officially Russian."

"But," persisted Velten, who was in a contrary frame of mind that day, "it doesn't matter a damn where the Americans pick us up —this or the other side of the demarcation line!"

"That's just the point," the other retorted heatedly. "In the mo-

353

ment of capitulation we must expect all members of the Wehrmacht to have to stay put. When the enemy starts dividing up the territory, everyone east of the demarcation line will probably land in Russian captivity. Now perhaps you understand why we're so set on getting across the canal."

Kracht sighed impatiently as he finished speaking.

"My God!" cried Velten. "This is Sterley—and they're not stopping!"

The Volkswagen was indeed roaring straight through the silent village. They had already passed a signpost marked "Nach Mölln."

The two officers said nothing. "That was where we were going to stop for breakfast," Velten continued obstinately.

"Are you so hungry?" asked Speer.

"No," said Velten, now genuinely angry, "but you know we were supposed to wait here for the rest of the party."

"Oh, forget it, Velten," said Kracht. "Apparently Schwede's changed his mind. The main thing is that we get across the canal!"

"Those fellows had such faith in their officers," Velten began anew. "They said such nice things about them yesterday evening."

"Good God, Velten, I've never seen this side of you before!" Kracht sounded thoroughly cross now. "Haven't you ever heard of bridges being blown? Our only interest now is to get over the canal bridge at Mölln as fast as we can move. The thing can go sky-high any moment. And that won't help Mr. Schwede's mob any, however attached they are to him!"

Velten realized this. They were, he felt, doing a double desertion, one from the Army and the other from their comrades. But if it was a matter of the bridges—in God's name!

At high speed they drove through the idyllic little town of Mölln. As the Volkswagen swung right, in the direction of the canal, all three involuntarily craned their necks.

The bridge was intact. What was more, it was unguarded. At all events, there was no check-point in evidence. A little group of men were standing at the far end, some of them carrying rifles. They were Home Guards. None of them made any move to stop the cars.

"Right," said Velten when they were across, "now the Yanks can come."

"I'd prefer to go into British captivity," said Kracht. "I'm con-

354

vinced that's where one'll get the most decent treatment. After all, they've got the best human material. And then there's their conception of fairness."

"I'm afraid we can't co-ordinate our capture to that extent," said the portly Speer. "The main thing as far as I'm concerned is to get to the prison camp in a car."

The Volkswagen in front was now following a somewhat tortuous route along country roads and through little villages. In a place called Siebenbäumen Velten's engine petered out. The men in the Volkswagen noticed him stop and pulled up, too.

"Feed line is blocked," said Velten, after several times whirring vainly with the self-starter.

He dismantled the carburetor, with Kracht breathing nervously down his neck. Then Schwede came over and showed Velten the map. "Look, we're making for Sandesneben. It's a little wood right out of the Sleeping Beauty. We'll lie up there and let things take their course. The nearest place is Steinhorst."

They were just driving out of Siebenbäumen, up a slight slope, when Velten had a puncture. Kracht fumed. The other driver helped, and within a few minutes the wheel was changed.

Soon they were bowling along the metaled highway towards Steinhorst. On both sides stretched the thick undergrowth of a wood. No vehicle was visible in either direction, and the road was bare of humanity.

A booming and crashing to their front brought them up with a jerk.

The Volkswagen was already swerving off to the right into the woods. Velten followed suit. The metallic din drew closer and closer. There was no possible doubt—these were advancing tanks. Between the bark of guns they clearly heard the grating screech of caterpillar tracks.

"You can thank your stars for those two breakdowns, Herr von Kracht," said Velten. "But for the loss of time we'd now be bang in the middle of that."

They steered their cars into a broad clearing behind which lay a pine plantation. There they decided to dig in.

Kracht, who had crawled up to the road, returned to inform them that a build-up of incredible size was rolling past in the direction

355

they had come. He had been unable to ascertain whether the force was British or American, since the vehicles of both armies bore the same white star and the troops wore a similar shade of khaki.

The two drivers settled down some distance away from the officers, on the edge of the clearing. Kracht suggested they should do a bit of guard duty.

The driver of the Volkswagen was called Wilhelm Meier. In civil life he was a tram-driver in Bremen. A pleasant face, Velten decided. Calm, reliable and forceful.

"What was the idea of driving straight through like that?" Velten asked. "After all, it was agreed that we'd wait for your outfit in that little place."

"Didn't like it at all," said Wilhelm Meier pensively. "We've done them dirt."

Velten explained to him why in the officer's view it had been necessary to cross the bridge with the least possible delay.

"That's a lot of crap," said Meier with a calm that carried conviction. "They kept pushing on because they wanted to get into safety. What do they know about Americans and Russians?"

Even Velten now found something rather far-fetched in all the talk about demarcation lines and the disturbance of German prisoners. But none of this could disturb him any more as he lay on his back squinting into the sun. Meier's deep, regular breathing told he was already asleep.

It was a most comforting feeling to know that one was behind the enemy's lines. SS, provost and Ivan were far away. The whole business was faintly reminiscent of Cowboys and Indians. Sleepily Velten watched a gold and brown mottled beetle trying to transport a withered flower-stalk crosswise through the grass. Now and again it was partially successful and managed to bend a few weaker blades aside. Ultimately, however, it did not progress a single inch. The possibility of simply tugging the load longways through the grass obviously did not occur to it.

Was this some kind of sport? Velten wondered. Perhaps it was one of the rules for champion beetles to push their loads sideways through the grassy forest. He himself had always gone the easy way. From his Army Group job under the cynical and nonchalant Mattersen, through the rue des Saussaies, the "undisciplined pack of intellectuals," Jack Hahn's corruption syndicate to the despair of the Zorn mob; and finally from the firm of Herzlieb & Co., as far as this Red Indian forest. Was it really a matter of being born lucky? Or was not this luck of his more of a personal characteristic? That is, a refusal to take the whole ghoulish foolery of this or any other war seriously? A defeatist was what the shapely lady of the screen had called him. Well, if he was, it was certainly not from conviction. Admittedly it would have been a particularly cruel joke to die for Hitler of all people! But had he been a Frenchman, would he have wanted to die for Danzig? Or, as an Anglo-Saxon, to make the world safe for democracy? Not even as a Bolshevik, to free the home of the working class from the fascist yoke.

What a lot of claptrap all those phrases were! No man had ever gone off to war with any thought of dying. Although everyone knew a high percentage would inevitably do so. Indeed, war subsisted on man's readiness to believe that others would do the dying. I, thought Velten, am against war because I am not convinced that only the others will die. Death is admittedly the only certainty in human life. But why the devil should I seek to influence the When and How of this inescapable event just because a handful of rulers are too unintelligent and too malevolent to settle their differences in a decent manner? I want to die my own death, not that prescribed by my Government irrespective of whether this Government pursues a fascist, democratic or bolshevist mode of behavior.

And, when all's said and done, you people want exactly the same. One man hastily commits suicide before he can die the death he had prescribed for others. The second clears off in a Fieseler-Storch and the third gets across the Elbe in a skiff. And the only reason why those on the victorious side don't experience the embarrassment of exposing themselves in a similar way is that they were smarter and stronger!

At all events, Velten told himself, I've pulled a fast one on them. I've cheated them out of my death. Just as they meant to cheat me into it.

Even as, with a sigh of relief, he was about to turn over onto his side, however, he was no longer so sure about these beliefs of his. Was there not, beyond all the slogans, a something which called for and rewarded the supreme decision? As from afar he again saw

357

Corinne's dying eyes fixed on him, resolute, ready—and challenging. She, Corinne, had not been a futile sacrifice to brute force. Corinne had died her own death.

And, very gradually, there dawned on Velten, the wanderer on the periphery of decision, the knowledge of the things which are greater than our lives. The perception of good and evil, readiness to act, and obligation. With painful clarity, and yet with a profound sense of release, his heart realized that the march through the jungle of war had not ended in a cheap let-out. He knew that he, too, would be ready . . .

He fell sound asleep, a man at peace with the knowledge that he has his affairs in order.

"You've put us in a fine fix," said Kracht querulously. "Did you both have to sleep? You could at least have taken turns!"

"My God," yawned Velten, still drunk with slumber, "they'd have found us whether we'd have slept or not! Those guys come creeping up like Indians and scent anything unusual a mile off."

They were all sitting under cover in their hiding place looking thoroughly sheepish. They had been taken by surprise in the middle of their afternoon nap. Two soldiers had suddenly been standing there as if they had sprung out of the earth. They wore the black uniform of the *panzer* troops, but it was stained and tattered. In their thin tanned faces had shone the joy of secret adventure. Standing rigidly to attention before Speer, whom they had immediately picked out as the senior officer, they had reported that they belonged to a band that was engineering disorder behind the lines by small-scale raids and acts of sabotage. They had their camp in the depths of the forest, no great distance away. At present they were away notifying their officers, delighted with this prospect of reinforcements.

"Anything can happen now," said Schwede. "To think that those crazy little bastards can ruin everything for us after we've wangled through this far!"

"It's all your fault!" Kracht burst out, glaring from Velten to the meditative Meier and back again. "Now we shall either get killed or be forced to crawl around on our hands and knees with that band of idiots till the Yanks finish us off!"

358

"Who was to know that even back here there'd be lunatics haunting the woods?" asked Velten. Inwardly he found the affair intensely funny. With what pains and cunning they had escaped everything—Russians, SS, provost, Herr General Kunze, and so far British and Americans—only to fall victim to a handful of adolescents playing at soldiers!

"Leave it to me," said Speer in his quiet way. "Perhaps I can make them see reason."

Before very long there was a crackling in the undergrowth. Like braves on the warpath they came crawling through the woods in single file. A second-lieutenant in the armored corps led the way. After him came about twenty youths, some in *panzer* and others in infantry uniform. The rear was brought up by another second-lieutenant. The officers were in their early twenties. Not one of the boys could have been more than eighteen.

They settled down in a circle round the six runaways. One or two lay down some distance away, gazing into the surrounding forest. These were the guards. *They* certainly wouldn't fall asleep, Velten reflected.

The officers introduced themselves and began to palaver. Velten spoke to the infant soldiers, of whom there were always at least two talking simultaneously. Their eyes radiated boyish enthusiasm. They were, they told him, stragglers from various units who had been fortunate enough to elude capture. And now they were running their own private war in the Holstein forests, under the leadership of the two lieutenants. The latter were "first-rate."

"There's another operation coming off tonight," one of them proclaimed importantly. "We're going to call on the burgomaster of Siebenbäumen."

"How's that?" asked Velten. "What do you want with him?"

"He's getting a little call from the Holy Ghost," said a freckled young infantryman with several front teeth missing. "We're going to finish him off, the dog!"

"For God's sake!" said Velten. "What's he done to you?"

"Nothing to us—but to Germany!" replied a tanned little tankman pompously. "The swine told the farmers to hang out white flags. This morning, when the Tommies came."

Velten began to feel uneasy. Darting a look over to the officers,

359

he saw they were shaking hands as they took leave of each other. After that the little band crawled away as it had come, the last man soon being swallowed up in the gloom of the pine trees.

"Everything nicely fixed up again," Kracht announced with renewed optimism. Speer had told the two officers some cock-and-bull story about his party being on a special mission from Army to deliver secret orders for the defense of Hamburg. The youngsters had believed it and appreciated the "Speer Group's" inability to join in their guerrilla war. One of them had actually given Speer a piece of advice. Since the enemy still moved without lights at night on account of the continuing possibility of air attacks, he said, all one need do was to smuggle one's vehicle into an enemy convoy. Provided that they pulled out before the others stopped, nothing could go wrong.

"Thank you very much," said Velten when Speer passed this on to him. "I'm not that much in need of excitement."

The interlude had deprived them all of any desire to remain in the hide-out. As dusk began to fall they broke camp and loaded the vehicles. Then they drove very slowly through the clearing, the officers walking in front. By now it was dark. The road was quite empty and strangely still.

Velten climbed into the front passenger seat of the Volkswagen. Lieutenant Schwede drove. Meier took over the 170-V Mercedes. The purpose of this arrangement was that the English-speaking Velten should interpret when they came in contact with the enemy. A large white cloth, providently brought along by Schwede, lay on his knees.

"Wave it whenever you see any troops," Schwede whispered.

Unhurriedly they cruised through the sleeping village of Steinhorst. The houses and streets were in darkness, and not a soul was about. White sheets hung from windows.

"Perhaps the place isn't occupied at all," Velten murmured.

"It is, you know," Schwede told him, pointing to a dimly lit sign over a doorway. It was rectangular and divided diagonally into two fields, one red and the other yellow. Superimposed on this was the word REAR, followed by a number.

This, Velten deduced, meant that a rear headquarters was located here. So they were where they belonged—well behind the front.

Leaving the village behind them, they drove on through the darkness of the country road. At the next junction they found a signpost pointing off to the right: Bad Oldesloe.

"Are we going there?" Velten whispered.

"No, it's too far north. We'll try to get to Sandesneben," Schwede replied.

They accordingly turned off to the left. They had hardly driven a hundred yards when a sharp command rang out of the darkness.

"Halt!"

Schwede stepped so hard on the brakes that Velten almost flew over the windshield.

"The white cloth!" cried the lieutenant. Velten waved it about in the air and then jumped out of the car. By now the other four had pulled up behind them in the Mercedes.

The six of them stood round one small khaki-clad soldier. He was carrying a Sten gun and wore a flat steel helmet above his clean-shaven features. He gazed at the excited travelers with the utmost composure.

"Ask him whether he's American or British," said Kracht.

Velten translated the question into English.

The sentry's mouth broadened into a grin.

"British!" he replied. He sounded half-proud and half-surprised.

"Good! Very good!" cried Kracht, actually attempting to slap the fellow on the shoulder in commendation of his nationality. The Tommy stepped back a pace and took a firmer grip on his weapon. Then, recollecting that he had a small gathering of continentals before him, he grinned again with his broad mouth and tiny eyes.

Behind him, meanwhile, a gate had opened in a barbed-wire fence that was more than man-high. Out of it came some British soldiers.

"What's up?" one of them asked the sentry.

"Four German officers and two men want to give themselves up," said Velten, relieving their friend of the need to reply.

"That so?" growled the Englishman. "Well, you've come to just the right place. This is the division prison cage."

No, Velten told him, they didn't want to go inside at this juncture. His companions were officers from a senior staff and had important information to impart. They wished to be handed over to a formation headquarters.

361

This was what they had arranged beforehand. As intelligence experts, Speer and Kracht were all against getting involved with the lower units. Their view was that one must put on a bold front and get at least up to a corps staff. At that level one could expect the best of treatment. The important thing was to bamboozle the lower orders into passing them higher up.

It did not look as though this British corporal intended to be bamboozled. He quietly waited for Velten's blather to finish. Then he said evenly:

"I don't give a damn for your officers. I've been given orders to slap every goddam Jerry into the bleeding cage. That's all I'm worryin' about."

In the end Velten managed to mollify him. He sent one of the men to get the officer.

A short, powerfully built man in peaked cap and overcoat appeared. He wore the two pips of a first-lieutenant. The four German officers greeted him in the old military style by raising their hands to their cap peaks. He returned the salutes with polite dignity and listened patiently to Velten's story about the important information the German officer had to impart at a higher level.

"Yes," he said, without moving a muscle of his smooth, slightly plump face with its fair toothbrush mustache. "We'll see about that tomorrow. It's too late today."

It was evident from his tone that the whole affair left him completely cold and that his only interest was to be bothered as little as possible.

Velten explained to his officers that the Englishman had said he would certainly bring them to a senior staff on the morrow. This was the simplest way of keeping them quiet. Kracht instructed him to thank the Englishman and to tell him how delighted they were that the British were occupying this particular sector.

"Yes," the Englishman replied, apropos of nothing in particular, "we took Lübeck today."

Velten translated.

"Tell him how glad we are that this war is over at last. And most of all that the Russians haven't got this far."

The Englishman livened up slightly. With a pedantic inflection in his voice, and looking Velten firmly in the eye, he said:

362

"War is a terrible thing."

"He says war's a terrible thing," Velten informed his superiors. "But he says it as if we were to blame."

The Germans all hastened to agree that they too, thought war quite frightful.

"Yes," said the Englishman once again, "war's a terrible thing."

Then he gave the corporal a brief order and disappeared with a cursory salute.

They drove the cars into the barbed-wire enclosure. The British impressed on them not to show lights under any circumstances, as German aircraft were still coming over nightly. At first they were going to separate the officers from the enlisted men, and then the corporal decided they could spend that night together in the cars.

"I've made it!" said Speer. "Into captivity by car, just as I planned!"

Early next morning all officer prisoners were called together and loaded onto trucks, which left immediately.

"I can't see them getting near any higher echelons," Velten murmured. "The British will hardly be very worried about intelligence from now on."

CHAPTER XIII

THE CAMP was constructed round a sort of barn—a roof on four poles as high as well-grown trees with merely a wall of boarding over one of its narrow ends. The other three sides were open, but this mattered little in view of the early and unusually dry summer. The whole arrangement was surrounded by a low paling, the only actual barbed-wire fence running along the side nearest the street. At the corners facing into open country tanks were posted with their guns trained on the camp.

Inside the rectangle of wire the German soldiery swarmed round and over each other like a hopeless tangle of weeds. Though there was hardly anywhere to put one's feet, a group of British soldiers succeeded in finding a way along the rows. Stepping from man to man, they made everyone open up his kit and hold out his hands. Anything they considered worth having vanished into their pockets —watches, rings, cameras, cigarette cases. Velten, who wore no rings, quickly stuck his wrist-watch into the turn-up of his cap, only to lose it soon afterwards while sleeping.

When the frisking squad reached him, he refused to open his pack. "I've already been searched," he announced in English.

"When?" demanded a brutal-looking Englishman with a blue tattoo on the inside of his hairy forearm.

"Yesterday," Velten lied. "When I was captured."

The Tommy looked at him mistrustfully and without a word turned his attention to the next man.

Velten inferred from his manner that, while the man did not believe him, he had been frightened off by Velten's use of the English language. Probably he expected a complaint.

Velten noticed that the majority of the Tommies took no part in the plunder of the prisoners. At the same time they did nothing to stop it. They stood there with expressionless faces, endeavoring to overlook the whole affair.

At one spot in the wire a group of Germans were crowding round a British soldier. Out of curiosity, Velten stepped over. The Englishman was a good-looking youngster of about twenty with a bronzed face, an ample nose, wavy fair hair, full red lips and dark, somewhat melancholy eyes. The reason for the crowd was that he spoke fluent German. He had a slight Viennese accent.

The Germans showered him with their various laments. One was hungry. Another had no blanket. The third needed a drinking cup. The boy's readiness to help was touching. He was constantly on the run between the wire and the separate compound where the British had their tents, and on almost every occasion brought something back with him.

"How do you come to speak such good German?" Velten asked him in English at the first favorable opportunity.

The lad looked at him hard for a moment.

364

"I was born in Budapest and grew up in Vienna," he replied, also in English.

Velten attached himself to a soldier who had just received a blanket from the Englishman. He was a tall, flaxen-haired fellow of a particular type. Velten needed only a quick glance to see that there was no eagle on the breast of his tunic. On his left sleeve there was a broad smudge.

"I say," said Velten, "do you know the chap who's just given you that blanket is a Jew?"

The SS man stared at him in astonishment. "That would be a disgrace to accept help from a Jew!"

The words came out with open hostility.

Velten held the other's gaze. "Well, he can't have been a Jew after all then, can he?" he said and turned away.

A group of RAF officers appeared by the barbed wire. They had a somewhat scruffy look about them, and were wearing neither belts nor arms. Beckoning one prisoner over to them, they shook him by the hand, slapped him on the shoulder and gave him cigarettes. He was an elderly sergeant with a plump, good-humored face. Velten soon caught on: they were liberated prisoners from a neighboring *Oflag* and the sergeant must have been one of their guards.

"Oskar was always decent to us," one of them told the sentry. "Treat our Oskar properly!"

Otherwise the Britons regarded the Germans like a menagerie of strange animals. A young, bareheaded Englishman sprang over the wire into the cage. He ran a critical eye along a row of prisoners until he had found several with headgear in good condition. Then he relieved two or three of their caps and tried them on in turn until he found one that fitted. Those which did not fit he threw carelessly to the ground. No one moved. No one uttered a word or made a gesture of objection. There was infinite contempt in the Englishman's movements and facial expression.

Velten was even more incensed by this pantomime than by the systematic robbery.

"It all makes me so damn sick," he told Wilhelm Meier, who was lying peacefully beside him, "that I could break out and go back to the *Barras* again!"

"Oh, go on with you," was all Meier said, half in wonder, half-soothingly.

"I don't know whether you understand me," said Velten. "I'll tell you what I mean." He patted his pack into a pillow and stretched himself out as far as was possible in that confined space. "Now look," he began, "when I was a child, I lived in the assumption that the adult world was a decent, well-ordered affair. Quarrels, strife and physical violence were just childish naughtiness to me. I took it for granted that I should dispense with them once I grew up. It may be that my parents had brought me up wrongly. As I grew older, I found it terribly hard to grasp that this world of adults is built on nothing but oppression and force. Even today it's like a blow between the eyes for me to see Man using force against Man. It upsets me terribly—whether it's actual war or just the things which go with it, like plunder and imprisonment behind barbed wire. Yes, even when it means taking away people's caps!"

Velten had not noticed that another soldier had been listening attentively.

"What a benighted imbecile you are!" said a deep voice behind him. Velten swung round and found himself looking into an extraordinary face that was at once attractive and repugnant. The man's brow, though not high, was forceful. From under his dark, receding hair a deep scar ran almost all the way across his forehead. From under his bushy eyebrows gazed a pair of penetrating, mocking gray eyes in which green lights played. Goat's eyes, Velten thought.

"I see," he said, straight into the derisive face, "so it's weak to abhor violence!"

"It's certainly weak to try to deny its reality," the quiet voice replied.

"It isn't a denial of the reality of violence to oppose it with the reality of the idea," said Velten, somewhat taken aback.

"Speak a little more intelligibly, you apostle of weakness," said the unknown soldier disdainfully. "Your comrade there wants to understand you, too."

"I mean," said Velten, "that the idea of non-violence does exist and is effective. Does Gandhi live in vain, you think?"

"Yes, of course he lives in vain. The English will never leave India because of him."

366

"It has nothing to do with whether they go or not," Velten declared. "It's entirely beside the point whether an idea has any practical success. The important thing is that there is such a thing as spiritual life alongside all this senseless, rabid violence."

"That sort of philosophy will do all right for Sunday afternoons," laughed the stranger. "But things aren't done that way on weekdays."

"The question is whether the true life is lived on Sundays or during the week."

"I'd better put it to you plainly," said the unknown soldier. "Listen. You're bound to be against Hitler—or 'always were' is what we've got to say now, isn't it?"

"Do I look as if I stood for Nazism?"

"All right. You were against it. Because you rejected the principle of the thing or because you thought you'd never get anything out of it?"

"I feel I've long answered that question. You heard what I said about Gandhi, didn't you?"

"Good enough. So you hated the Nazis and their Hitler. They were absolute evil in your eyes. They were violence—something from the other side of the world of morality. Fine. That was your standpoint—and you've done well if you were able to sustain it without too many compromises! Though I doubt it. After all, the non-compromisers ended in the concentration camp or on the gallows, didn't they? And you're alive and kicking—wearing the uniform with that infamous swastika on it."

He grinned. It was a satyric grin. The tip of his nose wrinkled: the bushy eyebrows slid up: the hircine look about him became even more pronounced. He felt in the knapsack he had lying between his crossed legs and brought out a metal jar that was shiny with age. Removing the lid, he shook some tobacco into the palm of his hand. From the hollow in the lid he took a small paper. Then, with considerable skill, he rolled himself a cigarette, moistened the adhesive edge with his tongue and lit the final product with a lighter which was shaped like a cartridge and gave off a great, smoky flame.

"Where were we?" he asked.

"Talking about the uniform with a swastika on it," said Velten.

"Yes. I was about to point out one or two adjustments vital to the further existence of the Idea, but we'll pass over that. Let's

367

start from your rejection of the Nazis. Right. Now, I think you'll agree they were pretty damned successful, weren't they? There was no unemployment. Everyone had enough to eat. They broke the Versailles Treaty like a monthly subscription to a paper banned for carrying immoral advertisements. And foreign Powers still came cringing up to them to conclude new treaties. Haven't there been times when you've secretly wondered who was right—you or the others? What is it that makes them right? Why, success! And didn't Might cast its spell on you, too, when it was successful in the first two years of this war?"

"I'm not denying for a moment," said Velten, "that the big successes of this system had a corrupting, seductive effect on people, including myself. But right deep down the old sense of justice remained. Success does not justify the means."

"What *is* justice?" asked Goatface cynically.

"If you yourself have no sense of it. . . ."

"Piffle! Justice is the formal expression of the existing conditions of power! There's nothing there to be sensed!"

"I don't think we've anything more to say to each other."

"Oh, yes, we have. I've something to say to you." The stranger shifted closer to Velten. In a softer tone he continued:

"It's a small grain of truth—and it'll hurt! You've got through this war safe and sound in that lance-corporal's uniform. You've found your way into the somewhat inhospitable squalor of a British prison camp. Tell me, though: how did you wangle it so successfully? By the purity of your ideas or by subtlety and cunning? Cunning and craftiness are forms of force, too, you know! With your ideas you should have ended on a wayside tree, you living confutation of your own sermons."

Involuntarily Velten looked away. He liked neither the man nor his talk, although there was something fascinating about his face and mannerisms. His gaze fell on Wilhelm Meier. He had fallen asleep with a contented smile playing around his lips. His chest rose and fell evenly.

The stranger had followed Velten's eyes.

"You see," he said, pointing at the sleeper. "They're the ones it depends on. As long as they're digesting their food properly, sleeping well and procreating, I'm not worried about the continued existence of this world—for all the moonstruck notions of people like yourself!"

"It depends which is worth more," said Velten, "a world intent on digestion and procreation or . . ."

But the stranger had turned away and was no longer listening. Soon afterwards sleep descended on the camp.

The next morning a number of trucks appeared. The prisoners were lined up in threes—what had been called order-of-march in the German Army. Then came the wait. They had been used to that in their own army, too.

"First they've got to swill their tea," one soldier remarked.

"Must be around ten," said another voice.

"This is the time they get tea with milk or cream in it. You should see their rations! Ever known anything like it? Imagine having the troops in for tea."

"That's nothing. You want to see their chow!" It was unmistakably a Berliner's voice. "Did you know those boys get warm food four times a day? First thing there's tea and something warm. Baked beans and tomato sauce. *And* a piece of fried sausage or bacon. Ten o'clock or half past there's more tea and a piece of cake!"

"Cake!" someone interrupted incredulously.

"Perhaps they get whipped cream with it!" suggested another.

"If you know better than me," said the Berliner calmly, "you'd better tell the story. I know what I've seen. I've seen them guzzling cake with big currants in it. One of them chucked a piece away, and when one of our boys—you know, one of those they took over for fatigues—bends down to pick it up, a bastard of a Tommy goes an' tramples on it. . . ."

"Did you think they'd come here to ask us to tea or something?" Velten inquired over the speaker's shoulder.

"None of your lip," said the Berliner. "This is a matter of human decency. I ask you: is it human to trample on a lousy piece of cake in front of a man's very eyes?"

"That's the way they want it," another put in. "Don't you understand? It's their policy to rub our noses in the dirt! That's why they give us damn-all to eat! Five men to a tin of beef and a package of biscuits!"

The prisoners' rations were certainly inadequate. The young Jew

369

with the Austrian accent had put it down to supply difficulties. The British had not been prepared for such a number of captives.

"Now just stop interrupting," said the Berliner. "At noon there's something warm. Not enough for the likes of us to eat our fill. They get their real dinner around five or half past. And in the evening they get tea again and biscuits."

"Anyway," another man said thoughtfully, "men pampered like that can't be soldiers. Just imagine what it would have been like if we'd only had them to deal with! We'd have sent them scuttling home so fast they wouldn't even have had time to drink their tea!"

"Yes," someone else agreed, "superior numbers is what did it. No wonder—the whole world against us alone for the second time!"

"We really are a funny people," said Velten to Wilhelm Meier. "First we start on the whole world—and when we get a good hiding we reproach it for fighting us!"

Velten had spoken quietly, but loud enough for others to hear him. He heard a peal of laughter. Then came the deep yet incisive voice which had interrupted his talk with Meier the day before. He shivered at the sound of it and turned sharply round. True enough, the goat-faced apparition of yesterday was in the row behind.

"So you think it's a bad thing that we should have involved so many others in this war?" he said. "You're a dolt, my poor fellow. You're showing the same stupidity as yesterday evening. The more people that have been dragged into this war, the more have lost it. They've lost merely through having to wage it! And the winner is the side that made them fight. Ourselves, in other words. Always assuming that there is such a thing as 'we'—that there is a common interest between dolts like you and those who've grasped the meaning of the era. So the winner is the suicide in the Reichskanzlei. *He* saw the meaning of his era . . . And he won. . . ."

An outcry from several hundred German throats interrupted the speaker. The loading of the prisoners had started. Shirt-sleeved Tommies with short canes in their hands had taken up positions from which they could every so often separate off a group of Germans from the waiting columns and hound them into one of the canvas-covered trucks. As there were obviously far too few vehicles for the number of prisoners to be transported, the guards strove to cram as many as possible into each one. Whenever the utmost

370

limit had been reached, five or six Englishmen had to use all their might to crush the tailboard against the human freight to get the vehicle closed.

The Tommies thoroughly enjoyed themselves. They accompanied their labors with a great deal of laughter and talk. "Bastard" was the most frequent imprecation, though by no means the most obscene.

"I can't face that," said Velten to Meier in disgusted tones. "Let's try staying behind. All of us can't go in any case. Perhaps the next move will be better. I'm not going to let myself be beaten!"

"Naturally," came the voice of Goatface from behind them. "Violence gives them belly-pains, these disciples of the spirit! It makes them want to faint away. Look, there are the fruits of our victory —there—!"

He pointed to a knot of Germans in the act of lurching forward into the next truck propelled by blows and kicks from the bawling Tommies. The latter were beginning to warm up, spurred on by pleasure in their own performance, the intoxication of power and the delight of raining oaths and blows on defenseless human bodies. From time to time they would reach for their hip pockets and bring forth a flat bottle. This they raised reverently to their lips, throwing back their heads so that their Adam's apples bobbed up and down with each swallow. Thereupon they would return to work with fresh enthusiasm. "Come on, you blasted Jerry, up you get! Jump to it, you dirty Nazi bastard!"

"And take a look at that, too," said the stranger, pointing to another scene. "Not bad either, eh?"

A row of civilians was standing at the wire—Polish land-workers, to judge by their excited chatter. They were thoroughly enjoying the drama from their ringside seats. Now and again one of them would point to a German wearing some garment or other which had caught his fancy. Thereupon a Tommy would march over, compel the German to take off the boots or jacket, and sling the coveted object over the wire to the Poles. Velten had to smile when the blond SS man thereby lost the blanket with which he had only recently been presented by the Jewish Tommy.

"It's even worse than this in Berlin," said the stranger. He spoke as though he had the most gratifying news in the world to impart.

371

"I was there until the very last days of April. They've properly shat on the place, as a soldier would say. Rings and watches—well, that wasn't much different from here. But how they went for the women. Pounced on them like parish poor on almshouse soup! Round about twelve was the qualifying age. 'Tsitska yest!' they'd say. 'If she's got a breast, good enough!' "

He mused on the memory with a smile that had actually a touch of relish about it.

"Mind you," he went on, "our Adolf didn't lag behind either. As Ivan got near the city center he had the subway flooded from the Landwehr Canal. There were thousands of wounded and women and children down there. They drowned like rats.

"The leader of our party ward was out on Havel Bridge in Spandau with a thousand Hitler Youth. None of them was more than twelve—same age as the girls. After all, what Ivan thought old enough to rape was old enough for Hitler to slaughter! When he'd used up all the kids in the enemy's MG fire, my party leader left his command post and made for home to slip away with his whole family. When he got there he found them all lying around in the kitchen—mother, two sons, a daughter and the aunt and uncle. The uncle still had a pistol in his hand. He'd taken the whole lot to Hades with him! Our friend never stopped running after seeing that shambles!" Goatface laughed his penetrating laugh.

Meanwhile the last truckload of prisoners had rolled away. The Tommies packed the rest back into camp, where they once more established themselves under the enormous roof of the open barn. There was more room this time, and one could stretch out one's legs without running the risk of kicking in the next man's skull.

CHAPTER XIV

THE NEXT DAY the trucks returned to load up the remaining prisoners. There were further curses but no more swipes or kicks. After only a short run they were deposited in mid-country on the main road between Hamburg and Lübeck and marched off down a track leading to the village of Rathbeek.

On a large meadow they found vast members of prisoners being herded together. This was where they spent the night, crouching next to one another like crows on a stubble-field. Anyone possessing a blanket or ground-sheet pulled it over his head, for a steady, penetrating drizzle had begun to fall. There they squatted with hardly a face showing, nothing but gray humps on the damp carpet of the meadow. The British had brought up a few tanks, and the whole scene was floodlit by enormous searchlights. It looked as if a whole multitude of wild beasts had been rounded up and were now cowering against each other in a paralysis of fear. The guards plodded mutely back and forth, camouflaged waterproofs draped round their shoulders. Rain and cold had killed their urge to curse.

"I'd give a lot to know," said Velten, "what put it into their heads to bring us those extra ten miles. They might just as well have left us under the barn where there was a bit of cover. What utter stupidity! Just like our own army!"

"But I've already told you," said Goatface perversely, "that it's we who've won the war."

He was sitting next to Velten. On the far side of him crouched Wilhelm Meier on his pack, already fast asleep.

They were all stiff, soaked and frozen through when they lined up in threes next morning. Slowly the long column moved off on its march.

Before long they found themselves on the Hamburg-Lübeck

autobahn. Like a repulsive gray blind-worm their column moved slowly south along the broad ribbon of concrete.

The British escorted the procession in small tracked vehicles mounted with light machine-guns and equipped with radio. One drove on ahead and others covered the flanks at intervals of several hundred yards. Another brought up the rear.

The pace was unconscionably slow. Every two or three miles a halt was ordered and they rested on the grassy banks beside the highway. On each occasion rations were issued: a tin of corned beef and one or two biscuits to every five men.

From time to time Tommies would appear from across the fields or down from the bridges, those with cameras loudly drawing each other's attention to what they considered the more picturesque types of prisoner. Velten found himself frequently honored in this respect. He was marching in the same file as Wilhelm Meier and Goatface. The latter was in the middle.

"Look at 'em, Alec!" Velten heard a tall Tommy yell. He was sprucely turned out, with a knife-edge crease in his trousers. A cigarette drooped from one corner of his mouth and a camera dangled on his chest. "Just look at 'em! To think we had to fight this dirty crowd all the way from Normandy to the Elbe!"

Goatface gave Velten a nudge.

"He doesn't yet know who's won the war," he leered.

He began to hum to himself. Little by little a tune emerged. A few others furtively joined in. Then Velten realized the stranger was singing some words. He sang them softly, through his teeth. But Velten could pick them out, nonetheless:

> We shall still be marching
> When all other flags are furl'd
> For Germany belongs to us today—
> Tomorrow it'll be the world!

He sang it hoarsely, to the dragging rhythm of their marching feet.

As he sang, he grinned slyly at Velten from the side.

374

DATE DUE